Contents

SECOND EDITION

Teaching REAL WRITING

Additional Resources

Susan Anker

Eddye S. Gallagher
Tarrant County College

BEDFORD/ST. MARTIN'S   *Boston ♦ New York*

For information, write: Bedford/St. Martin's
75 Arlington Street, Boston, MA 02116
(617-399-4000)

ISBN: 0-312-25814-3

Preface for Instructors

TEACHING REAL WRITING: *Additional Resources* is designed with your needs in mind. This handy collection of materials for classroom use supplements the materials in *Real Writing* itself.

We have reproduced key pages from the book so that you can use them as handouts or make transparencies.

- Checklists, provided for each of the writing chapters, help students keep track of the smaller steps in the writing process. (See p. 117.)

- Chapter Summaries define key concepts covered in each chapter. (See p. 423.)

- Quick Review Charts provide a visual summary of chapter content. (See p. 423.)

We have supplemented the text to provide more step-by-step support for developmental writers.

- Guided Practices for Paragraphs or Essays, provided for each writing chapter (Chapters 9–17), offer step-by-step support throughout the writing process. Each step is accompanied by explanations, examples, critical thinking questions, and opportunities for students to work on their own writing. (See p. 3.)

- Planning Forms for Paragraphs and Essays offer students additional opportunities to visualize and plan their paragraphs and essays. (See p. 163.)

We have provided self-assessment tools and diagnostic tests so that you can help identify where your students are and where they need to go.

- The Writing Questionnaire gives students the opportunity to reflect on their experience as writers. (See p. 1.)

- Diagnostic Tests help you identify students' areas of strength and weakness so that you can focus your instruction. (See p. 193.)

And we have included additional grammar exercises and tests for further or more focused practice and assessment.

- Review Tests for Editing Chapters serve as handy assessment tools, combining all of the strategies covered in each chapter in a single chapter test. (See p. 229.)

- Supplemental Exercises for Editing Chapters give you plenty of exercises to supplement each editing chapter. (See p. 291.)

Immediately useful, ultimately practical, *Additional Resources* will help you follow through on the pedagogy of *Real Writing.*

For additional help, you can visit the companion Web site for *Real Writing,* available at www.bedfordstmartins.com/realwriting. This Web site includes links for both faculty and students. From Resources for Developmental Professionals, you can find information on (and, for most, links to) Web sites, listservs, books, organizations, and publications as well as additional resources that can be downloaded, including forms, outlines, checklists, and much more. Your students will have access to Exercise Central (online grammar exercises) and the English Research Room, a site that provides help with the research process (including electronic research), interactive tutorials (hands-on practice with electronic search techniques), and research links (access to search engines, online writing centers, dictionaries, and subject sources). Exercise Central's multiple exercise sets on every grammar topic, at two levels, ensure that students get as much practice as they need. Customized feedback turns skills practice into a learning experience, and the reporting feature allows you and your students to monitor and assess student progress.

Name _____ Date _____

This questionnaire will help you become more aware of your own experience as a writer. Take some time to fill it out now to determine where you are before you start the course.

1. List everything that you have written in the past three days. Include any kind of writing: reminder notes, homework, shopping lists, emails, forms—anything that caused you to put words on paper or on a computer screen. You may want to compare your list with some of your classmates' lists or talk about your recent writing experiences in a small group before you make your list. The comparison or discussion may remind you of things you've written.

2. Pick any two of the examples of writing from question 1 to focus on and circle them. For each one, do you consider this *real writing?* Why or why not? What, for you, is *real writing?*

3. Why did you write each one? Who eventually read each one?

4. For each one, did you have any problem getting your message across? Could people figure out what you meant? (If you wrote a note to yourself, did it make sense later?)

5. In general, what is hardest about writing? What is easiest?

Guided Practices for Paragraphs or Essays (*Chapters 9–17*)

Guided Practice: How to Write Illustration

Step 1. Narrow and Explore Your Topic

After you have selected a general topic to explain, narrow it to a topic that you are interested in, know about, or have experienced. Write down a few possible ideas for topics, and then select the one you want to write about. Remember to select a topic for which you can find several examples to illustrate your point.

GENERAL TOPIC	*Theft*
POSSIBLE TOPICS	*from stores, at work, from homes*
NARROWED TOPIC	*Theft at work*
IDEAS	*widespread, conscious and unconscious taking, attitude that it's okay, costly problem*

Thinking Critically to Narrow and Explore an Illustration

FOCUS   Think about your general topic and what you know about it.

ASK
- What observations or experiences have I had with this topic?
- Which of these are interesting to me?
- Which would seem important to my reader?
- What do I want my reader to know about this topic?

WRITE   Write down your narrowed topic and ideas that you have.

PRACTICE 1

Narrowing and Exploring Your Topic

Use the Thinking Critically guide on this page to find two different narrowed topics you might want to write about. Then circle the topic you will use and jot down some of the things that come to your mind as you think about that topic.

GENERAL TOPIC: _____

NARROWED TOPICS *(circle the one you will use):*

1. _____

2. _____

IDEAS ABOUT THE NARROWED TOPIC (*jot down at least five*):

_____

_____

_____

_____

_____

_____

_____

_____

Step 2. Make Your Point in a Topic Sentence or Thesis Statement

Determine What Is Most Interesting or Important about Your Topic.

Reread the ideas that you wrote in Practice 1. Do you see a major focus in your thoughts? If not, write a few more ideas. Your main focus should be one that you can easily support with clear, specific examples.

NARROWED TOPIC	*Theft at work*
WHAT'S IMPORTANT ABOUT THE TOPIC	*A lot of people steal from their employers. Many don't realize that their actions are considered stealing.*
	Many people think it's okay.

Write a Topic Sentence or Thesis Statement.

Your topic sentence or thesis statement should provide your readers with the intent of your paragraph or essay. Write a topic sentence or thesis statement that lets your reader know what to expect in your illustration. Try following this basic formula:

narrowed topic   +   main focus   =   topic sentence or thesis statement

TOPIC SENTENCE	*Many people steal from companies although they don't think it's wrong.*

If your first attempt does not seem interesting enough, try revising so your focus is clearer and stronger.

| REVISED TOPIC SENTENCE | *Although they don't consider it stealing, many people regularly take things from their companies.* |

Thinking Critically to Make Your Point

FOCUS   Reread your narrowed topic and think about why this topic would be important to your reader.

ASK   • Why is this topic important? Why is it interesting?
• What main point do I want readers to understand?
• Can I make the subject interesting to the reader by supplying clear, specific details?

WRITE   Write a topic sentence or thesis statement that includes your narrowed topic and your primary focus.

PRACTICE 2

Making Your Point in a Topic Sentence or Thesis Statement

Using the Thinking Critically guide on this page, complete the sentence about why your subject is important, then write a topic sentence or thesis statement.

THE MOST IMPORTANT POINT I WANT TO MAKE ABOUT THIS SUBJECT IS _____

_____

TOPIC SENTENCE OR THESIS STATEMENT: _____

_____

Step 3. Support Your Main Point with Examples

Find and Choose Supporting Examples.

You already have a topic sentence or thesis statement. Now use a prewriting technique to come up with examples that will show, explain, or prove your main point. Your examples will help your readers understand your main point.

First, use a prewriting technique to find as many examples as you can. Then go over your prewriting and drop examples that will not help you get your point across to your readers. Choose the best examples; think about combining smaller points.

TOPIC SENTENCE: Although they don't consider it stealing, many people regularly take things from their companies.

PREWRITING LIST

pens and pencils

pads of paper

~~erasers~~

products they make

long-distance calls

personal calls

~~paper clips~~

file folders

Add Supporting Details.

Your illustration will only be as good as the examples you provide, and your examples will only be as good as the details you use. Reread the examples you have chosen and look for additional details or examples you can use to make them stronger.

TOPIC SENTENCE: Although they don't consider it stealing, many people regularly take things from their companies.

EXAMPLES AND DETAILS CHOSEN FOR PARAGRAPH

SUPPORTING EXAMPLE: pens and pencils

Added detail: accumulate in bottom of purse or knapsack

SUPPORTING EXAMPLE: personal long-distance calls

Added detail: to family or friends, short but frequent

SUPPORTING EXAMPLE: products they make

Added detail: think they're entitled to; sometimes even give to friends

SUPPORTING EXAMPLE: paper

Added detail: pads of paper, notepads, file folders

Thinking Critically to Support Your Main Point with Examples

FOCUS   Reread your topic sentence or thesis statement carefully.

ASK
- What is a good example of what I mean?
- What are some examples I've experienced myself? What have I heard about from friends and relatives?
- What kinds of examples will my readers relate to?
- Which of these examples are directly related to my main point?
- What details will help my readers see what I mean?

WRITE   List the supporting examples and additional details you will use.

PRACTICE 3

Supporting Your Main Point with Examples and Details

Use the Thinking Critically guide above to help you find supporting examples and details for your illustration. Follow these steps:

1. Use a prewriting technique to find possible examples. List them on the lines labeled "Example."

2. Cross out unrelated ideas and anything that won't help you get your point across to your readers.

3. Circle the three or four strongest examples.

4. Try to add one detail to each example you have circled, to make it lively and clear to your readers. Write each detail on the line labeled "Detail" next to its example.

EXAMPLE: _____   **DETAIL:** _____

_____   _____

EXAMPLE: _____   **DETAIL:** _____

_____   _____

EXAMPLE: _____   **DETAIL:** _____

_____   _____

EXAMPLE: _____   **DETAIL:** _____

_____   _____

EXAMPLE: _____   **DETAIL:** _____

_____   _____

EXAMPLE: _____   **DETAIL:** _____

_____   _____

Step 4. Make a Plan

Arrange Your Examples.

Illustrations may use space order, time order, or order of importance. Reread your topic sentence and your supporting examples to decide how to arrange them so that they will have the most impact on your readers.

Once you have decided how to order your ideas, make a plan by putting them into an informal outline.

INFORMAL OUTLINE

TOPIC SENTENCE: Although they don't consider it stealing, many people regularly take things from their companies.

1. *Pens and pencils*

   — accumulate in bottom of purse or knapsack

2. *Paper*

   — pads of paper, notepads, file folders

3. *Personal long-distance calls*

   — to family or friends, short but frequent

4. *Products they make*

   — think they're entitled to; sometimes even give to friends

Thinking Critically While Planning Your Illustration

FOCUS   Reread your topic sentence or thesis statement and the supporting examples and think about the best way to present your ideas.

ASK   • Which of the three orders (space, time, importance) would work best with these examples to make my point to my readers?
   • Now that I have an order, are there any "gaps" that I should fill in with other examples?

WRITE   Write an outline that shows the plan for your illustration paragraph or essay.

PRACTICE 4

Making a Plan

Use the Thinking Critically guide above to make a plan for your illustration in the spaces that follow.

TOPIC SENTENCE OR THESIS STATEMENT: _____

_____

SUPPORTING EXAMPLE **1**: _____

    ADDED DETAIL(S): _____

_____

SUPPORTING EXAMPLE **2**: _____

    ADDED DETAIL(S): _____

_____

SUPPORTING EXAMPLE **3**: _____

    ADDED DETAIL(S): _____

_____

SUPPORTING EXAMPLE **4**: _____

    ADDED DETAIL(S): _____

_____

Step 5. Write a Draft

Using the outline you have prepared as a guide, write a draft of your paragraph or essay.

FOR A PARAGRAPH

Turn your examples and details into complete sentences, and arrange them in paragraph form.

DRAFT PARAGRAPH

Although they don't consider it stealing, many people regularly take things from their companies. The items that most frequently disappear are pens and pencils that employees almost unconsciously stuff into their purses, knapsacks, or briefcases. Over time, employees may accumulate quite a stash of them. Paper is a big item, including pads of lined paper, notepads, and file folders. Few people consider long-distance personal phone calls at work actually stealing, but it is using company time and money to chat, even briefly, with friends and family. One of the more significant ways people "steal" from their companies is by taking home samples of the products the company makes: food, clothing, supplies, and so on. Employees seem to think they are entitled to these products and even give them to friends. In this way, they hurt the company by robbing it of a product it depends on for revenue.

FOR AN ESSAY

Write a draft essay that includes your thesis statement in the first paragraph. Each of your supporting examples should become the topic sentence for a paragraph. Each body paragraph should include examples and details that support the topic sentence.

Write a Conclusion.

A concluding sentence or paragraph ties your examples back to your main point. It makes a further observation about what the topic sentence or thesis statement and the supporting examples add up to.

CONCLUDING SENTENCE FOR ILLUSTRATION PARAGRAPH: Taking things from work may not seem like stealing, but the results are the same: extra costs to the company, which may result in smaller pay raises.

Thinking Critically to Write a Conclusion

FOCUS As you reread your draft, think about what observation you can make based on the examples you have given.

ASK
- What observation do these examples add up to?
- How can I tie the observation back to my topic sentence or thesis statement?
- What can I say that will end my paragraph or essay on a strong note?

WRITE Write your conclusion.

PRACTICE 5

Writing Your Concluding Sentence

Read your draft paragraph and write two possible concluding sentences here. Then circle the best one and add it to your draft paragraph.

CONCLUDING SENTENCE 1: ______________________________

____

CONCLUDING SENTENCE 2: ______________________________

____

PRACTICE 6

Writing Your Concluding Paragraph

Write two possible concluding paragraphs for your draft essay. Then choose the best one and add it to your draft essay.

Step 6. Revise Your Draft

After completing your draft, take a break. Then reread it, searching for examples that don't fit, additional details to make your examples more lively and specific, and ways to connect the examples so that they flow smoothly. This is your chance to improve your illustration before getting a grade. Do not just copy over your draft; make changes that will improve the paragraph.

Teamwork: Get Feedback

When you have completed your draft, you may want to show it to someone else or to read it aloud in a small group, asking for feedback and suggestions that will help you revise.

GUIDELINES FOR GIVING FEEDBACK

- Start with a positive comment.
- Throughout, offer comments and observations rather than "You should's."
- Start with the draft as a whole and move to smaller points.

  —Tell the writer what you think the main point is.

  —Ask questions about the examples and the writer's meaning.

- Tell the writer what works for you and what you think might be better (and how).
- Be as specific as you can. Don't just say, "It's good," or "I liked it." Explain why.
- If you get confused, tell the writer what's confusing.
- Help the writer.

Here is the revised example paragraph, with notes to show what changes the writer made to revise the draft paragraph.

REVISED PARAGRAPH

Although they don't consider it stealing, many people regu-

larly take things from their companies. The most common items to   *— less wordy —*

disappear are pens and pencils that employees almost unconsciously

stuff into their purses, knapsacks, or briefcases. Over time, they may   *word changed* accumulate quite a stash of them. Another [transition added] big item is all kinds of paper: pads of lined paper, [added detail] handy little notepads that can be used for shopping lists and phone messages, and file folders to organize home records. [added detail] Yet another "innocent theft" [transition] is the long-distance personal phone call. Those calls cost the company in two ways: they use company time for personal business, and the company has to pay for the calls. Even though companies may have special discounted telephone rates, no call is free. [transition added] Finally, one of the more [added more concrete detail] significant ways people steal is by taking home samples of the products the company makes: food, clothing, supplies, and so on. Employees seem to think they are entitled to these products and even give them to friends. By doing so, they hurt the company by robbing it of a product it depends on for revenue. These examples may not seem like stealing, but the results are the same: [added concluding sentence] extra costs to the company, [observation] which may result in smaller pay raises.

Thinking Critically to Revise an Illustration Draft

FOCUS After a break, reread your draft with a fresh perspective. Think about what you want your readers to learn from the paragraph or essay.

ASK
- What do I want to say? Have I said it?
- Are there any examples or details that don't fit?
- Are there enough detailed examples to show my readers what I mean?
- Do the pieces fit together into a whole piece of writing that flows smoothly? Do I need to add transitions or repeat key words?
- Will my readers get my point? Will they find my illustration interesting?

WRITE Revise by making improvements to your draft.

PRACTICE 7

Revising Your Draft

Reread your draft and ask yourself the questions in the Thinking Critically guide above. Revise your draft by making at least three to five changes. Be prepared to explain how those changes improve the draft.

Guided Practice: How to Write Narration

Step 1. Narrow and Explore Your General Topic

After you have chosen a general topic to write about, find your own story within that general topic. Write down one or two ideas for possible stories and ask yourself if there *is* a story to tell, if you are interested in the story, and if you can tell it in a paragraph or essay.

Sometimes people choose experiences that are too big to tell in a paragraph or even in an essay. For instance, one student first chose as his story "life as a Buddhist." There may be a fascinating story there, but it's too big to tell thoroughly in one short writing. The student had to narrow the general topic to something more focused: "an important Buddhist ceremony." You need to be able to communicate the important events in your story in only one to a few paragraphs.

GENERAL TOPIC	*A situation I learned from*
POSSIBLE STORIES	*When I fell before my wedding, when I hurt Naomi's feelings, when my grandfather died*
NARROWED TOPIC / STORY	*When I fell before my wedding*
IDEAS	*A horrible experience, one I learned from, behavior the day before, the fall, how it changed things*

Thinking Critically to Narrow and Explore a Narration Topic

FOCUS   Think about the general topic and your experiences with it.

ASK
- What experiences in my life are connected to this topic?
- Which would make a good story?
- Which seem interesting to me?
- Which one should I focus on?
- When I think of this experience, what are the first things that come to my mind?
- What do I want my readers to get from the story?

WRITE   Write down your narrowed topic and ideas that you have.

PRACTICE 1

Narrowing and Exploring Your General Topic

Use the Thinking Critically guide above to find two different narrowed topics you might write about. Then circle the topic you will use and jot down some of the things that come to your mind as you think about it.

GENERAL TOPIC: _____

NARROWED TOPICS (*circle the one you will use*):

1. _____

2. _____

IDEAS ABOUT THE NARROWED TOPIC (*jot down at least five*):

_____

_____

_____

_____

_____

Step 2. Make Your Point in a Topic Sentence or Thesis Statement

Decide What Is Important about the Story.

The point of the story is simply what makes the story important to you and to your readers.

If you need to discover what about the story is important to you, reread the list you made in Practice 1. Is the point of the story there? Ask yourself what you would want a good friend to get out of this story. (Or what you would answer if your friend asked, "So what?") Consider why the story was interesting to you in the first place. Then write a statement of why you think the story is important.

NARROWED TOPIC/STORY	*When I fell before my wedding*
WHAT'S IMPORTANT ABOUT THE EXPERIENCE	*I learned that getting married was more than the wedding. I focused on what was really happening. I was happy about the important things and forgot about the small things like flowers, weather, how I looked.*

Write a Topic Sentence or Thesis Statement.

In the topic sentence or thesis statement, you introduce the topic and give the reader a preview of what will happen. Your topic sentence or thesis statement should give readers some idea of why the story is important. Try starting with this basic formula:

topic   +   preview   =   **topic sentence or thesis statement**

TOPIC SENTENCE   *An accident the night before my wedding reminded me of what was important.*

Thinking Critically to Make Your Point

FOCUS   Reread your narrowed topic and think about why you chose this experience to write about.

ASK
- How did this experience affect me? Why is it important to me? Why is it interesting?
- What do I want to reveal by telling this story? What do I want readers to learn from it?
- How can I get readers interested in the story without giving it away?

WRITE   Write a topic sentence or thesis statement that identifies your topic and gives a preview.

PRACTICE 2

Making Your Point in a Topic Sentence or Thesis Statement

Using the Thinking Critically guide above, complete the sentence about what's important and then write a topic sentence or thesis statement.

WHAT'S IMPORTANT TO ME ABOUT THE EXPERIENCE IS _____

_____

_____

TOPIC SENTENCE OR THESIS STATEMENT: _____

_____

Step 3. Support Your Main Point with Events That Tell the Story

In a narration, the events you include and the way you describe them create a story with a certain point of view. For example, two people who witness the same event may give very different accounts of it because they focused on different events or perceived those events differently. The stories the two people tell reflect different points of view. Read these two accounts of the same experience.

CHARLENE'S STORY

This morning I could have killed my husband. While I was running around yelling at the kids, trying to get them fed and off to school, he sat there reading the newspaper. When I finally sat down, he just kept on reading that newspaper, even though I needed to talk with him. After several attempts to get through to him, I finally barked out, "Daryl! I have a few things I need to say!" He looked up, smiled, got another cup of coffee, and said, "What?" But as I began talking, he resumed reading the paper. Does he live in another world?

DARYL'S STORY

This morning my family enjoyed some "quality time" together. The children were all in the kitchen eating and talking with each other. After they left for school, my wife and I were able to sit and share some quiet time at the table. We chatted about various things while drinking coffee and looking at the newspaper. It really started the day out right.

As you can see, the events are the same, but the stories aren't; they repeat two different points of view. Be careful to use events that will tell the story you want to tell.

Find and Choose Events.

Once you know the story you want to tell and the message you want to get across, you need to find and choose the events you will use to tell that story to your readers.

Use a prewriting technique to come up with a list of the events in your story. Start by writing down every event that you can think of. Then go back over your prewriting and cross out anything that isn't central to the story you want to tell. Think about what you want your readers to know. Look for minor events that can be combined into larger ones. You should end up with about three to six events that will be useful in telling your story.

TOPIC SENTENCE: An accident the night before my wedding reminded me of what was really important.

PREWRITING LIST OF EVENTS

finding fault with everyone, really nervous

~~stubbed my toe~~

arguments with my mother and Jim

~~couldn't get in touch with maid of honor~~

~~phone kept ringing~~

~~ate too much leftover Halloween candy~~

~~left my raincoat in my apartment~~

~~umbrella broke~~

fell

couldn't sleep

got up

splashed water on my face

went to hospital—35 stitches

talked with Jim, felt better

Add Details.

Look for examples and details that will make each event lively and specific. Remember that you want your readers to share your point of view and see the same message in the story that you do.

TOPIC SENTENCE: An accident the night before my wedding reminded me of what was really important.

EVENTS AND DETAILS CHOSEN FOR THE PARAGRAPH

EVENT: *finding fault with everyone and everything*

Details: *hemline on wedding dress looked crooked, rain predicted, fights with my mother and fiancé*

EVENT: *fell*

Details: *tripped over suitcase and hit corner of night table*

EVENT: *couldn't sleep*

Details: *got up to splash warm water on my face*

EVENT: *went to hospital*

Details: *35 stitches, doctor's reaction, thinking how terrible I'd look*

EVENT: *talked with Jim and felt better*

Details: *he was there when I woke up, said I looked beautiful, remembered what's important*

Use Conversation.

As you remember the experience, you may recall something that someone said or a brief conversation that took place. If what was said was important to the story, put it in your narration. If you are reporting exactly what the speaker said, use quotation marks.

I said, "I'm going to be one ugly bride."

He said, "That would be impossible."

Thinking Critically to Support Your Main Point

FOCUS Reread your topic sentence or thesis statement and think about what happened.

ASK
- What happened first? What next?
- Which events do I need to tell the story? Which get my message across? Which will my readers relate to?
- Should any minor events be combined?
- What details make these events come alive?
- Do I want to report anything that was said?

WRITE List the events and additional details you will use.

PRACTICE 3

Supporting Your Main Point with Events and Details

Use the Thinking Critically guide above to help you find supporting details for your narration. Follow these steps:

1. Use a prewriting technique to find possible events. List them on the lines labeled "Event."

2. Cross out events that are not essential and combine smaller events.

3. Circle the three or four strongest events to use in your writing.

4. Add at least one detail or example to make the events you have chosen lively and specific. Write the details on the lines labeled "Details" next to each event.

5. Write down any pieces of conversation you might use.

EVENT: _____ **DETAILS:** _____

_____ _____

EVENT: _____ **DETAILS:** _____

_____ _____

EVENT: _____ **DETAILS:** _____

_____ _____

EVENT: _____ **DETAILS:** _____

_____ _____

EVENT: _____   DETAILS: _____

_____   _____

CONVERSATION: _____

_____

Step 4. Make a Plan

Arrange Your Events.

When you tell a story, most often you arrange the events according to when they happened: in time order. Before you write a draft of your narration, arrange the events in a logical time sequence, usually working from what happened first to what happened last. Make a plan (usually an outline) for your paragraph.

INFORMAL OUTLINE

TOPIC SENTENCE: An accident the night before my wedding reminded me of what was really important.

1. *Finding fault, nervous and cranky*

   —hemline on wedding dress looked crooked, rain predicted, fights with my mother and fiancé

2. *Couldn't sleep*

   —got up to splash warm water on my face

3. *Fell*

   —tripped over suitcase and hit corner of night table

4. *Went to hospital*

   —35 stitches, doctor's reaction, thinking how terrible I'd look

5. *Talked with Jim*

   —he was there when I woke up, said I looked beautiful, remembered what was really important

Thinking Critically While Planning Your Narration

FOCUS   Reread your topic sentence or thesis statement and details of events and think about how to tell your story.

ASK
- Does time order work best?
- Should I go from what happened first and work up to what happened last?
- Have I left out any important incidents?

WRITE Write an outline that shows the plan for your narration paragraph or essay.

PRACTICE 4

Making a Plan

Use the Thinking Critically guide above to make a plan for your narration in the following spaces.

TOPIC SENTENCE OR THESIS STATEMENT: _____

EVENT 1: _____

    DETAILS: _____

EVENT 2: _____

    DETAILS: _____

EVENT 3: _____

    DETAILS: _____

EVENT 4: _____

    DETAILS: _____

Step 5. Write a Draft

Using the outline you have prepared as a guide, write a draft of your paragraph or essay.

FOR A PARAGRAPH

Turn your event details into complete sentences, and arrange them in paragraph form, using your topic sentence as your first sentence.

DRAFT PARAGRAPH

An accident the night before my wedding reminded me of what was really important. All day I had been nervous and ready to find fault. Nothing was right: The hem on my wedding dress looked crooked, the weather report predicted rain, and one of the bouquets was the wrong color. I argued nonstop with my mother and my fiancé. That night I couldn't sleep, so I got up to splash some warm water on my face. I tripped and crashed headfirst into the corner of the night table. I felt blood, and I screamed for help. At the hospital, the doctor sewed my lip and cheek together with thirty-five stitches. I asked him how I would look for the wedding, and he shrugged his shoulders. When I awoke on my wedding day, my fiancé was sitting in a chair beside the bed holding my hand. I said, "I'm going to be one ugly bride." He placed his hand on the side of my face and said, "That would be impossible."

FOR AN ESSAY

Write a draft essay that includes your thesis statement in the first paragraph. Each of your supporting events should become the topic sentence for a paragraph. Each body paragraph should include specific details and perhaps dialogue that supports the topic sentence.

Write a Conclusion.

A concluding sentence or paragraph relates back to your main point and sums up what is important about the story.

CONCLUDING SENTENCE: At that moment I remembered what was important: not a dress, the weather, or how I looked, but the beauty of our relationship.

Thinking Critically to Write a Conclusion

FOCUS   As you reread your paragraph or essay, think about what is important about the experience.

ASK   • What is the point of my story?
            • What message do I want to leave my readers with?

WRITE   Write your conclusion.

PRACTICE 5

Writing Your Concluding Sentence

Use the Thinking Critically guide on this page to write two possible concluding sentences for your narration paragraph. Then circle the best one and add it to your draft paragraph.

CONCLUDING SENTENCE 1: _____

_____

CONCLUDING SENTENCE 2: _____

_____

PRACTICE 6

Writing Your Concluding Paragraph

Using the Thinking Critically guide on this page, write two possible concluding paragraphs for your draft essay. Then choose the best one and add it to your draft essay.

Step 6. Revise Your Draft

You have your story on paper. Now reread it, looking for ways to improve it: making the point clearer; getting rid of events that don't fit; adding other, more important events; adding detail; connecting the events with transitions. Do not just copy over your draft; make changes that will improve the story.

Add Transitions.

Transitions connect your ideas so that they flow smoothly from one to the next. Because narration usually uses time order to arrange ideas, **time transitions** are the best connectors, indicating when one event occurred in relation to another.

COMMON TIME TRANSITIONS

after	eventually	meanwhile	soon
as	finally	next	then
at last	first	now	when
before	last	second	while
during	later	since	

The revised example paragraph has comments that show where the writer made changes to her draft, including adding transitions.

REVISED PARAGRAPH

An accident the night before my wedding reminded me of what was really important. All day I had been nervous and ready to find fault. Nothing was right: The hem on my wedding dress looked crooked, the weather report predicted rain, and one of the bouquets was the wrong color. I argued nonstop with my mother and my fiancé. That night I couldn't sleep, so I got up to splash some warm

——————— added detail ———————

water on my face. Returning to the bedroom in the dark, I tripped

┌ added detail ┐

and crashed headfirst into the corner of the night table. Blood gushed

———————   ⟋transition

from my face, and I screamed for help. Later at the hospital, the doctor sewed my lip and cheek together with thirty-five stitches,

——————— added detail ———————   ╱transition

a visible seam in the middle of my face. When I asked him how I

——————— added detail ———————

would look for the wedding, he tilted his head, grimaced, and

shrugged his shoulders. When I awoke on my wedding day, my fiancé

was sitting in a chair beside the bed holding my hand. I said, "I'm

⌐detail⌐

going to be one ugly bride." He placed his hand so gently on the side

⌐—detail—⌐   ⌐—detail—⌐

of my face, kissed me, and whispered, "That would be impossible."

At that moment I remembered what was important: not a dress, the

added concluding sentence

weather, or how I looked, but the beauty of our relationship.

Teamwork: Get Feedback

When you have completed your draft, you may want to show it to someone else or read it aloud in a small group, asking for feedback and suggestions that will help you revise.

GUIDELINES FOR GIVING FEEDBACK

- Start with a positive comment.

- Throughout, offer comments and observations rather than "You should's."

- Start with the draft as a whole and move to smaller points.

  —Tell the writer what you think the main idea is.

  —Review the events that make up the story.

  —Ask questions about the events that might help the writer give more detail.

- Tell the writer what works for you and what you think might be done better (and how).

- Be as specific as you can. Don't just say, "It's good," or "I liked it." Explain why.

- If you get confused or lost somewhere in the draft, tell the writer where.

- Help the writer.

Thinking Critically to Revise a Narration

FOCUS   After a break, reread your draft narration with a fresh perspective. Think about what you want your readers to take away from the story.

ASK
- What is the point of my story? Why is it important to me? What do I want my readers to learn or understand?
- Are there any incidents or details I should cut because they are unimportant to the story?
- Have I included all the important incidents? Will my readers be able to follow the sequence of events?
- Have I included enough concrete, specific details?
- Do the pieces fit together and flow smoothly? Do I need to add transitions to show how one event leads to another?
- Is it a good story?

WRITE   Revise by making improvements to your draft.

PRACTICE 7

Revising Your Draft

Use the Thinking Critically guide on this page to revise your draft. Make at least three changes and be prepared to explain how they improve the draft.

Guided Practice: How to Write Description

Step 1. Narrow and Explore Your Topic

When you have selected a general topic to describe, narrow it into a topic you are interested in, have observed directly, and can describe in a paragraph or essay. To narrow the general topic, write down a few possibilities of things you could describe vividly, and choose the one you want to write about. Keep in mind that good description creates a single main impression—or overall feeling, effect, image—about the topic. Jot down some ideas you have about the narrowed topic.

GENERAL TOPIC	*An office*
POSSIBLE TOPICS	~~*doctor's office,*~~ *English professor's office,* ~~*boss's office*~~
NARROWED TOPIC	*English professor's office*
IDEAS	*in Carleton Hall*
	messy
	comfortable
	dusty
	books and papers everywhere
	stuff on the floor

Thinking Critically to Narrow and Explore a Description Topic

FOCUS	Think about the general topic and some things you have observed that you could describe.
ASK	• What narrower topic do I have concrete, specific ideas about?
	• What am I interested in describing?
	• What topic could I actually observe (or observe again) before writing the description so that I remember the details?
	• What are my first thoughts about the possible topic? Do I already know what main impression I have about the topic?
WRITE	Write down your narrowed topic and some ideas you have about it.

PRACTICE 1

Narrowing and Exploring Your Topic

Use the Thinking Critically guide on this page to find two different narrowed topics you might write about. As you narrow, remember that your description should include sensory details, so think about a topic you can describe using your senses (hearing, sight, smell, taste, touch). Circle the topic you will describe and write down some ideas about it.

GENERAL TOPIC: _____

NARROWED TOPICS (*circle the one you will use*):

1. _____

2. _____

IDEAS ABOUT THE NARROWED TOPIC (*jot down at least five*):

_____

_____

_____

_____

_____

_____

Step 2. Make Your Point in a Topic Sentence or Thesis Statement

Decide What Main Impression You Want to Create about Your Topic.

Review the ideas you wrote down. Do they add up to a general impression you could write about? If not, jot down a few more ideas about what main impression *you* have of the topic. Another strategy is to say the topic to yourself and write down the first impression that comes to mind: It may be the main impression you have.

Remember, the main impression should be one that you are interested in describing and can describe with sensory details.

MAIN IMPRESSION *messy*

Write a Topic Sentence or Thesis Statement.

Write a topic sentence or thesis statement that includes your narrowed topic and your main impression. Try starting with the basic formula:

narrowed topic + main impression = topic sentence or thesis statement

TOPIC SENTENCE   *My English professor's office is a mess.*

When you have the basic sentence, revise it to make it sharper and more specific.

REVISED TOPIC SENTENCE   *My English professor's office is a study in clutter.*

Thinking Critically to Make Your Point

FOCUS   Reread your narrowed topic and the ideas you wrote about it.

ASK
- What is the main impression I have of this topic?
- Can I describe the main impression to my readers? (Is my impression of the topic vivid?)
- Can I describe it with concrete, sensory details?

WRITE   Write a topic sentence or thesis statement that includes your topic and main impression.

PRACTICE 2

Making Your Point in a Topic Sentence or Thesis Statement

Using the Thinking Critically guide on this page, complete the sentence about your main impression, and then write a topic sentence or thesis statement. When you have a basic topic sentence, try revising it to make it sound stronger, clearer, or more interesting.

THE MAIN IMPRESSION I WANT TO CREATE ABOUT MY TOPIC IS _____

_____

TOPIC SENTENCE: _____

_____

REVISED TOPIC SENTENCE: _____

_____

Step 3. Support Your Main Point with Details

Use Sensory Details.

As you develop your description, probe your senses for the various sensory details you might use to support your main impression. Keep in mind that your description should *show* your readers what you mean, not just *tell* them. Here are some things to consider.

Sight

Colors?

Shapes?

Sizes?

Textures?

Light/dark/contrast?

Shiny/dull?

Does it look like anything else?

Smell

Sweet? Sour?

Sharp? Mild?

Good? (Like what? How good?)

Bad? (Rotten? Like what?)

New? (New what? Leather? Plastic? How new?)

Old? (What does "old" smell like?)

Does it smell like anything else?

Touch

Hard/soft?

Liquid/solid?

Rough/smooth?

Hot/cold?

Dry/oily?

Does it feel like anything else?

Taste

Good? (What does "good" taste like?)

Bad? (What does "bad" taste like?)

Bitter? Sugary? Metallic?

Burning, spicy?

State (How?)

Does it taste like anything else?

Sound

Loud/soft? (Piercing, soothing?)

Continuous/off-and-on?

Close/far away?

Pleasant/unpleasant (How?)

Does it sound like anything else?

To find details, first reread notes you have made about your topic and main impression to see if they contain details you could use. Then use a prewriting technique to generate as many concrete, sensory details that support the main impression as you can. Think of how the topic looks, smells, sounds, feels, or tastes. Many people find clustering or listing to be good techniques for generating details. The example uses listing.

When you have finished your prewriting, reread what you have written. Cross out details that don't support the main impression.

TOPIC SENTENCE: My English professor's office is a study in clutter.

EARLIER IDEAS

~~in Carleton Hall~~

(messy)

~~comfortable~~

~~dusty~~

(books and papers everywhere)

(stuff on the floor)

NEW IDEAS: PREWRITING LIST

(stuff on the wall)

(piles of paper)

(stacks of books)

~~three coffee mugs~~

~~old tests and papers~~

~~music playing, but can't see radio~~

~~coffee pot~~

~~smells like burnt coffee~~

(bulletin board — covered with stuff)

(pictures of people)

~~bowl of candy~~

(cartoons taped to wall)

~~two dead plants~~

~~dark, overhead light turned off~~

~~old jacket hung on back of door~~

(chairs filled with stuff)

~~picture of some writer on the wall~~

~~tan walls~~

Thinking Critically to Support Your Main Impression

FOCUS Think about your topic and main impression. Try to think about the last time you observed your topic.

ASK
- What does my topic look like? sound like? smell like? feel like? taste like?
- Which details are needed to get my main impression across to my readers?
- What other concrete details can I recall?
- Should any minor details be combined?
- What can I do to "supercharge" these details? How can I make them stronger and more convincing?
- Will the details I've generated give my reader the full experience?

WRITE   Write a list of the concrete, specific details you will use.

PRACTICE 3

Finding Supporting Details for Your Main Impression

MAIN IMPRESSION: _____

TOPIC SENTENCE OR THESIS STATEMENT: _____

SUPPORTING DETAILS: _____

_____

_____

_____

_____

_____

_____

Supercharge the Details.

Because details are key to good description, once you have your basic supporting details, supercharge them by making them more vivid, more specific, more concrete and sensory.

TOPIC SENTENCE: My English professor's office is a study in clutter.

SUPPORTING DETAILS CHOSEN

1. *piles of paper on every surface*

    details added: *four towering piles of paper on the desk, one on chair, two-foot mountain of old, yellowing paper with the edges curled up on the file cabinet*

2. *stacks of books everywhere*

    details added: *books on board on top of radiator (leaning to the left), books jammed into floor-to-ceiling bookcase, books on floor*

3. *stuff on wall (crooked pictures, cartoons)*

   details added: *two pictures of famous authors, both crooked, pictures of former students and friends. Cartoons taped to the wall, many overlapping and rolled up*

4. *two visitor chairs, both filled with stuff*

   details added: *visitor chair, green molded plastic. Piled high with papers, a battered briefcase, a newspaper, and a jacket*

Thinking Critically to Supercharge Your Details

FOCUS   Review the details you have selected.

ASK   • How can I make each of them more vivid and specific?
    • What additional details can I add?

WRITE   Write additional details that make the description more vivid.

PRACTICE 4

Supercharge Your Details

Using the Thinking Critically guide on this page, add at least two details to make your supporting details more specific and vivid. Use concrete, specific words that appeal to sight, sound, smell, taste, or touch.

TOPIC SENTENCE OR THESIS STATEMENT: _____

SUPPORTING DETAIL: _____

    DETAIL ADDED: _____

SUPPORTING DETAIL: _____

    DETAIL ADDED: _____

SUPPORTING DETAIL: _____

    DETAIL ADDED: _____

SUPPORTING DETAIL: _____

    DETAIL ADDED: _____

Step 4. Make a Plan

Arrange Your Details.

In description, details often are presented according to spatial arrangement: what you see first, next, after that, and so on. You want your reader to see and experience what you are describing as *you* see and experience it, so follow your eyes around the topic. As you arrange your details, try using space order.

SPACE ORDER

- top to bottom/bottom to top
- near to far/far to near
- side to side/left to right/right to left
- back to front/front to back

Make a plan (usually an outline) for your paragraph or essay.

INFORMAL OUTLINE

TOPIC SENTENCE: My English professor's office is a study in clutter.

SUPPORTING DETAIL 1. *piles of paper*

—*two-foot mountain of old, yellowing paper with tattered edges on file cabinet*

—*four towering piles of paper on the desk*

SUPPORTING DETAIL 2. *huge bulletin board*

—*covered with pictures (famous authors, students, friends)*

—*cartoons*

—*favorite quotes*

SUPPORTING DETAIL 3. *stacks of books everywhere*

—*on board on top of radiator (leaning to the left)*

—*jammed into floor-to-ceiling metal bookcase*

—*on floor*

SUPPORTING DETAIL 4. *visitor chair, green molded plastic*

—*piled high with papers, a battered briefcase, a newspaper, a jacket, a gym bag*

Thinking Critically While Planning Your Description Paragraph or Essay

FOCUS   Reread your topic sentence or thesis statement and supporting details.

ASK
- How should my details be organized? Should I use space order to help my readers "see" my topic as I do? Would another organization work better?
- Are there other details I can add to make the description more vivid?
- Are there details that seem unrelated to my main impression?

WRITE   Write an outline that shows the plan for your description paragraph or essay.

PRACTICE 5

Making a Plan

Use the Thinking Critically guide above to make a plan for your description paragraph in the following spaces.

TOPIC SENTENCE OR THESIS STATEMENT: _____

SUPPORTING DETAIL 1: _____

_____

_____

SUPPORTING DETAIL 2: _____

_____

_____

_____

SUPPORTING DETAIL 3: _____

_____

_____

_____

_____

Step 5. Write a Draft

Using the plan (outline) you have prepared as a guide, write a draft of your description paragraph or essay.

FOR A PARAGRAPH

Using complete sentences, write a draft paragraph, using your topic sentence as your opening sentence.

DRAFT PARAGRAPH

My English professor's office is a study in clutter. The first thing you notice as you walk in are the many piles of paper around the room. A two-foot mountain of yellowing paper with tattered edges balances on the file cabinet. My professor's desk is walled in by the four towering masses of paper on each corner of his desk. A huge bulletin board is covered with all kinds of paper. There are pictures of famous authors, pictures of students, pictures of friends. Cartoons are tacked on going every which way, and favorite quotes stick out from the corkboard and the wooden frame. Books of all sizes sit on a warped pine board stuck on top of a radiator. The floor-to-ceiling metal bookcase is crammed with books. The overflow is dumped on the floor. No one can sit in the green molded-plastic visitor's chair. It is piled high with papers, a battered briefcase, a newspaper, a jacket, and a gym bag.

FOR AN ESSAY

Write a draft essay that includes your thesis statement in the first paragraph. Each of your supporting details should become the topic sentence for a paragraph. Each body paragraph should include specific, sensory details that support the topic sentence.

Write a Conclusion.

A concluding sentence or paragraph for a description relates back to the main impression, emphasizing it one last time for your readers.

CONCLUDING SENTENCE *My professor doesn't seem to mind the clutter, saying, "Oh, have a seat, if you can find one."*

Thinking Critically to Write a Conclusion

FOCUS As you reread your paragraph or essay, think about what final impression you want to leave your reader with.

ASK • What is my main impression?
 • What observation can I make that will remind my reader of my main impression?

WRITE Write your conclusion.

PRACTICE 6

Writing Your Concluding Sentence

Use the Thinking Critically guide above to write two possible concluding sentences for your description paragraph. Then circle the best one and add it to your draft paragraph.

1. _____

_____

_____

_____

2. _____

_____

_____

_____

PRACTICE 7

Writing Your Concluding Paragraph

Using the Thinking Critically guide on page 38, write two possible concluding paragraphs for your draft essay. Then choose the best one and add it to your draft essay.

Step 6. Revise Your Draft

You have your description on paper. Now reread your draft, looking for ways to improve it. Make sure all of the details are concrete, specific, and relate to the main impression. Add any other good details that occur to you.

Teamwork: Get Feedback

When you have completed your draft, you may want to show it to someone else or read it aloud in a small group, asking for feedback and suggestions that will help you revise.

GUIDELINES FOR GIVING FEEDBACK
- Start with a positive comment.
- Throughout, offer comments and observations rather than "You should's."
- Start with the draft as a whole and move to smaller points.
  —Tell the writer what you think the main idea is.
  —Review the events that make up the story.
  —Ask questions about the events that might help the writer give more detail.
- Tell the writer what works for you and what you think might be done better (and how).
- Be as specific as you can. Don't just say, "It's good," or "I liked it." Explain why.
- If you get confused or lost somewhere in the draft, tell the writer where.
- Help the writer.

Add Transitions.

Transitions connect your ideas so that they flow smoothly. In description, space transitions help your readers to see what is where: The space transitions tell readers how to move their eyes.

COMMON SPACE TRANSITIONS

above	beside	near	to the right
across	beyond	next to	to the side
behind	farther/further	over	under
below	in front of	opposite	where
	inside	to the left	

The revised example paragraph contains the writer's notes to show where he made changes, including adding space transitions.

REVISED PARAGRAPH

added adjective
My English professor's ⌐tiny⌐ office is a study in clutter. The first

thing I notice on walking in is the many piles of paper around the

⌐—— added space transition ——⌐
room. At the rear of the office, a two-foot mountain of yellowing

⌐added detail⌐
paper with tattered edges balances precariously on the file cabinet.

⌐—— added space transition ——⌐
In front of the file cabinet is my professor's desk, where the profes-   } reworked sentence

sor himself is walled in by the four towers of paper, one on each

added space transition
corner. ⌐Beside the desk⌐ a huge bulletin board is covered with all

kinds of paper—pictures of famous authors, pictures of students,

pictures of friends. Cartoons are tacked on going every which way,

and favorite quotes stick out from the corkboard and the wooden

⌐—— added space transition ——⌐
frame. Under the bulletin board, books of all sizes sit on a warped

pine board on top of the radiator. The floor-to-ceiling metal book-

case is crammed with all kinds of books, and the overflow is dumped on the floor. No one can sit in the green molded-plastic visitor's

———— added detail ————

chair wedged between piles of books in front of the desk. It is piled

high with papers, a battered briefcase, a newspaper, a jacket, and a

gym bag. My professor doesn't seem to mind the clutter, saying,   concluding sentence

"Oh, have a seat, if you can find one."

Thinking Critically to Revise a Description

FOCUS   After a break, reread your draft description with a fresh perspective. Imagine that you are not familiar with your topic.

ASK
- Is the main impression stated clearly?
- Have I provided enough detail, particularly concrete, sensory detail?
- Are all of the details related to the main impression?
- Are they arranged in a logical order (probably space)?
- Have I included space transitions to help my reader see what I'm describing?
- How can I make the description better?

WRITE   Revise by making improvements to your draft.

PRACTICE 8

Revising Your Draft

Use the Thinking Critically guide above to revise your draft. Make at least three changes and be prepared to explain how they improve the draft.

Guided Practice: How to Write Process Analysis

Step 1. Narrow and Explore Your Topic

After you have chosen a general topic to write about, decide whether you will explain how to do something or explain how something works. Write down one or two possible processes, and ask yourself if you are interested in the process and can analyze it step-by-step in a paragraph or essay. Avoid processes that are too involved to describe in a short assignment: "learning mathematics" or "learning to drive a car," for example. To narrow the general process, write down a few more focused, less complicated processes, such as "performing simple functions using a calculator" or "parallel parking," if you are writing a single paragraph. Choose a process you want to write about and jot down some of its steps.

GENERAL TOPIC/PROCESS	*How to study*
POSSIBLE PROCESSES	*studying for a test, reading to remember, settling down to do homework*
NARROWED TOPIC/PROCESS	*reading to remember*
IDEAS	*choose a good spot, don't get distracted, concentrate*

Thinking Critically to Narrow and Explore a Process Analysis Topic

FOCUS Think about the general topic and what you know about it.

ASK
- What are some processes that I have actually done or know about (and that I'm interested in)?
- Which of them do I think is worth writing about?
- When I think of this process, what are the first steps that come to my mind?
- Could I describe all the steps in a paragraph or short essay?
- What do I want my reader to learn?

WRITE Write down your narrowed process and some of its steps.

PRACTICE 1

Narrowing and Exploring Your Topic

Use the Thinking Critically guide above to find two different narrowed topics you might write about. Then circle the process you will use and jot down some of its steps as you think about it.

GENERAL TOPIC: _____

NARROWED TOPICS (*circle the one you will use*):

1. _____

2. _____

STEPS IN THE NARROWED PROCESS (*jot down at least five*):

_____

_____

_____

_____

_____

_____

Step 2. Make Your Point in a Topic Sentence or Thesis Statement

When you select a process to write about, you should also decide on the point you want to make about that process. In a process analysis, you explain to your readers either how to do something or how something works by presenting the steps in the process. Most readers will want to know *why* they need to understand the process you are writing about. Your main point should tell them what about the process you want them to know. Your topic sentence (paragraph) or thesis statement (essay) does not simply state the process: It makes a point about it.

To find your point, reread the steps you jotted down in Practice 1 and consider what general point you want to make to your reader about the process.

> **NARROWED TOPIC/PROCESS** *reading to remember*
>
> **POINT I WANT TO MAKE** *requires concentration and thought*

Write a Topic Sentence or Thesis Statement.

In the topic sentence or thesis statement, you should tell the reader what process you are analyzing and include any point you want to make about that process. Try starting with the basic formula:

narrowed process + point about process = topic sentence or thesis statement

> **TOPIC SENTENCE** *Remembering what you read requires concentration.*

Usually you need to rearrange your topic sentence so that it sounds better or makes your point more forcefully. Always try to make your topic sentence or thesis statement stronger after you've written it the first time.

REVISED TOPIC SENTENCE   *To remember what you read, pay attention to what you are doing and why.*

Thinking Critically to Make Your Point

FOCUS   Reread your narrowed topic and think about what point you want to make about this process.

ASK
- What do I want to communicate to my reader about this process?
- As I think about the process, what general observation do I want to make about it?

WRITE   Write a topic sentence that identifies the process and the point you will make about it.

PRACTICE 2

Making Your Point in a Topic Sentence or Thesis Statement

Using the Thinking Critically guide above, complete the sentence about your main point and then write a topic sentence or thesis statement. When you have a basic topic sentence, try revising it to make it stronger, clearer, or more interesting.

THE POINT I WANT TO MAKE ABOUT THE PROCESS IS _____

_____

TOPIC SENTENCE: _____

_____

REVISED TOPIC SENTENCE: _____

_____

Step 3. Support Your Main Point With Essential Steps in the Process (Key Step)

Find and Choose Steps.

To perform or understand the process, your reader must have all the essential steps. Because you are describing a process that you are familiar with, you may not think about the individual steps. For example, as you tie your shoelaces, you probably don't think about the many different steps involved; you just do them. As you prepare to describe a process, you need to think carefully about what the steps are so that you do not leave any essential ones out.

Use a prewriting technique to come up with a list of essential steps. Start by writing down every step you can think of. Then go back over your prewriting and cross out nonessential steps. Look for minor steps that can be combined into larger ones.

TOPIC SENTENCE: To remember what you read, pay attention to what you are doing and why.

PREWRITING LIST OF STEPS

~~find a good place~~

~~think about what you need~~

gather together anything you need

sit up

remind yourself of why you're reading

highlight

make notes

look over what you will read

ask yourself questions

answer questions in book

~~what do you want to remember?~~

~~talk about with others?~~

note anything you don't understand

Add Supporting Details.

The steps in the process will be easier for your reader to understand if you give details about them. In a process analysis, the supporting details often are specific examples of what is involved in the step.

One way to make a step in the process clearer to the reader is to link it to something else that you know the reader is familiar with. Read this excerpt from the example paragraphs in the text about how email travels to its destination.

During times of real congestion, each packet can take a different route to the same place: It's as if every page in a letter were delivered by a separate letter carrier.

The writer linked the way an email travels to the way regular mail might be delivered if it worked the same way. This link makes the step clearer to readers because it is like something in their own experience.

TOPIC SENTENCE: To remember what you read, pay attention to what you are doing and why.

STEP 1: *Think about what you need and gather it together*

    Details: book(s), pen, paper, highlighter, drink, something to eat, glasses

STEP 2: *Remind yourself of why you're reading*

    Details: for a class discussion? a test? to give a report? to summarize for someone else? to learn something specific?

STEP 3: *Read actively*

    Details: highlight important points, make notes, ask yourself questions, mark things you don't understand

STEP 4: *Look over what you will read (preview it)*

    Details: look at major headings, see how long it is, look at material in boxes, pictures

STEP 5: *Review*

    Details: answer questions in book, read summaries, review points you've highlighted, make additional notes

STEP 6: *Remind yourself of your purpose for reading*

    Details: what do you want to remember and how can you best do that? Have you got what you need from the reading?

Thinking Critically to Support Your Main Point

FOCUS Reread your topic sentence or thesis statement and any prewriting you've done. Think about your readers and what you need to explain so they can either perform or understand the process.

ASK
- Exactly how is this process performed? What are the essential steps?
- What steps do my readers need to know to perform or understand the process?
- How much detail do I need to give about each step? What are good examples of the steps?
- Have I left any essential steps out?

> • Will my readers understand the process based on the steps I've chosen?

WRITE   List the steps and the supporting details you'll use.

PRACTICE 3

Choosing the Essential Steps in the Process and Adding Details

Reread your prewriting list, and write down the steps you will use to describe the process below. Then, using the Thinking Critically guide above, add details to make the process more specific for your reader.

STEPS SELECTED AND DETAILS ADDED

TOPIC SENTENCE: _____

STEP: _____

    DETAILS: _____

STEP: _____

    DETAILS: _____

STEP: _____

    DETAILS: _____

STEP: _____

    DETAILS: _____

STEP: _____

    DETAILS: _____

Step 4. Make a Plan (Key Step)

When you are describing a process, most often you will arrange the steps according to time: what should be done first, second, next, and so on. You may find that as you listed the steps, you naturally arranged them in chronological order because you were working through the process in your mind. Be sure steps are in proper order. Then make a plan (usually an outline).

INFORMAL OUTLINE

TOPIC SENTENCE: To remember what you read, pay attention to what you are doing, and why.

1. *Think about what you need; gather it together*

    —book(s), pen, paper, highlighter, drink, something to eat, glasses

2. *Remind yourself why you're reading*

    —for a class discussion? a test? to give a report? to summarize for someone else? to learn something specific?

3. *Look over what you will read*

    —look at major headings, see how long it is, look at material in boxes, pictures

4. *Read actively*

    —highlight important points, make notes, ask yourself questions, mark things you don't understand

5. *Review*

    —answer questions in a book, read summaries, review points you've highlighted, make additional notes

6. *Remind yourself of your purpose for reading*

    —what do you want to remember and how can you best do this? Have you got what you need from the reading?

Thinking Critically While Planning Your Process Analysis

FOCUS   Reread your topic sentence or thesis statement and steps. Think about the best order for presenting the steps.

ASK   • What happens first? What next? What comes after that?
 • What time transitions can I use to emphasize when each step happens?
 • Now that I have an order, are there any gaps that need to be filled?

WRITE   Write an outline that shows the plan for your process analysis. Then write a draft.

PRACTICE 4

Making a Plan

Use the Thinking Critically guide above to make a plan for your process analysis in the following spaces.

TOPIC SENTENCE OR THESIS STATEMENT: _____

STEP **1:** _____

    DETAILS: _____

STEP **2:** _____

    DETAILS: _____

STEP **3:** _____

    DETAILS: _____

STEP **4:** _____

    DETAILS: _____

Step 5. Write a Draft

Using the outline you have prepared as a guide, write a draft of your paragraph or essay. Before you write your draft, review the steps you have chosen to make sure they are arranged in a logical time sequence. If any of them are out of sequence, rearrange the steps.

FOR A PARAGRAPH

Turn your steps and details into complete sentences, and arrange them in paragraph form, using your topic sentence as your first sentence.

DRAFT PARAGRAPH

To remember what you read, pay attention to what you are doing, and why. Think about what you need and gather it together. Get what you will read, along with a pen, some paper, a highlighter, glasses if you wear them, and whatever you might want to drink or eat. Once you have everything together, remind yourself of why you're reading so you think about what to pay attention to. Are you reading for a class discussion? For a test? To give a report? To summarize for someone else? What, specifically, do you need to do with what you are reading? Preview the material, looking at major headings, material in boxes, and pictures. Read—actively. Don't just sit there: Pay attention! Highlight important points, make notes, ask yourself questions. Go back and review what you have read, looking at important points and making additional notes to yourself. If there is a summary in the book, see if it matches what you got from what you read.

FOR AN ESSAY

Write a draft essay that includes your thesis statement in the first paragraph. Each of your steps (or major steps) should become the topic sentence for a paragraph. Each body paragraph should include specific details and perhaps examples that support the topic sentence.

Write a Conclusion.

A concluding sentence or paragraph reminds your reader of the process and your point about it.

CONCLUDING SENTENCE *If you don't pay attention to what you read and how you read it, you may find that when you turn that last page, you don't remember a single thing.*

Thinking Critically to Write a Conclusion

FOCUS   As you reread your draft, think about what you want your reader to understand about the process.

ASK   • What is the point of my process analysis?
     • What thought about the process do I want to leave my reader with?

WRITE   Write your conclusion.

PRACTICE 5

Writing Your Concluding Sentence

Use the Thinking Critically guide above to write two possible concluding sentences for your process analysis paragraph. Then circle the best one and add it to your draft paragraph.

1. _____

_____

2. _____

_____

PRACTICE 6

Writing Your Concluding Paragraph

Using the Thinking Critically guide on this page, write two possible concluding paragraphs for your draft essay. Then choose the best one and add it to your draft essay.

Step 6. Revise Your Draft

You have your process on paper. Now reread your draft looking for ways to improve it: Get rid of steps that don't fit; add other essential steps; add supporting details; connect the steps with transitions. Do not just copy over your draft; make changes that will enable the reader to perform the process.

Teamwork: Get Feedback

When you have completed the draft of your process analysis, you may want to show it to someone else or read it aloud in a small group, asking for feedback and suggestions that will help you revise.

GUIDELINES FOR GIVING FEEDBACK

- Start with a positive comment.
- Throughout, offer comments and observations rather than "You should's."
- Start with the draft as a whole and move to smaller points.
  —Tell the writer what you think the process is and what point the writer is making about it.
  —Review the steps that make up the process.
  —Ask questions about the steps that might help the writer give more detail.
- Tell the writer what works for you and what you think might be done better (and how).
- Be as specific as you can. Don't just say, "It's good," or "I liked it." Explain why.
- If you get confused or lost somewhere in the draft, tell the writer where.
- Help the writer.

Add Transitions.

Transitions connect your ideas so that they flow smoothly. Because process analysis usually uses time order, time transitions are the best connectors, indicating when each step takes place.

COMMON TIME TRANSITIONS

after	during	later	since
as	eventually	meanwhile	soon
at last	finally	next	then
before	first	now	when
	last	second	while

The revised example paragraph contains the writer's notes to show where she made changes to her draft, including adding time transitions.

REVISED PARAGRAPH

To remember what you read, pay attention to what you are

doing, and why. ⌐added time transition⌐ Before beginning, think about what you need and

gather it together. Get your ⌐——reasoning——⌐ reading material, along with a pen, some

paper, a highlighter, glasses if you wear them, and whatever you

might want to drink or eat. ⌐—— added detail ——⌐ Otherwise, you will keep finding ex-

cuses to stop reading and go get something you need. Once you

have everything together, remind yourself of why you are reading

so that you ⌐—— better wording ——⌐ will focus on what is important. Are you reading for a

class discussion? for a test? to give a report? to summarize for some-

one else? What, specifically, do you need to do with what you are

reading? ⟋ time transition Next preview the material quickly, looking at major head-

ings, material in boxes, and pictures. ⟋ time transition Now you are ready to read—

actively. Don't just sit there: Pay attention; do something. High-

light important points, make notes, ask yourself questions. When

you have finished, go back and review what you have read, looking

at important points and making additional notes to yourself. If there

is a summary in the book, see if it matches what you got from what

you read. Finally, ⟋ time transition test yourself: ⌐—added detail—⌐ Do you remember? If you don't pay

attention to what you read and how you read it, you may find that concluding sentence

when you turn that last page, you don't remember anything.

Thinking Critically to Revise a Process Analysis

FOCUS After a break, reread your draft process analysis with a fresh perspective. Think about what you want your readers to learn about the process.

ASK
- What point am I making about this process? Why is it important to me?
- Have I described all of the essential steps? In the right order?
- Should I replace some of the essential steps?
- Have I included the steps in enough specific detail?
- Are the steps connected so that they flow smoothly from one to the next?
- Does my reader have all the information needed to perform the process?
- How can I make the process easier to understand?

WRITE Revise by making improvements to your draft.

PRACTICE 7

Revising Your Draft

Use the Thinking Critically guide above to revise your draft. Make at least three changes and be prepared to explain how they improve the draft.

Guided Practice: How to Write Classification

Step 1. Narrow and Explore Your Topic

After you have selected a general topic to describe, narrow it to one you are interested in, can break into groups, and can handle in a paragraph or short essay. To narrow the general topic, write down a few possibilities for things you could classify by breaking them into categories, and choose the one you want to write about. Consider your purpose for classifying the topic: What do you want to show your readers? Then jot down a few ideas about the topic and possible categories.

GENERAL TOPIC	*How you organize a task*
PURPOSE	*To sort/organize things in order to make the task easier or more efficient*
POSSIBLE TOPICS	*hiring people at work, interviewing people, kinds of applicants/résumés*
PURPOSE	*To decide which candidates are suitable for the job and which aren't*
NARROWED TOPIC	*kinds of applicants/résumés*
HOW CLASSIFIED	*by suitability for the job*
POSSIBLE CATEGORIES	*good candidates, not suitable, maybe good*

In order to use her time more efficiently, the writer decides to classify (sort) the narrowed topic (kinds of applicants/résumés) by suitability for the job. When she has sorted the applicants and their résumés, she has narrowed the number of people she will consider and interview.

Thinking Critically to Narrow and Explore a Classification Topic

FOCUS Think about the general topic and its parts.

ASK
- What narrower topics do I know something about?
- Which of them am I interested in?
- What are several possible ways to sort (classify) this topic?

WRITE Write down your narrowed topic and some ideas you have about it.

PRACTICE 1

Narrowing and Exploring Your Topic

Use the Thinking Critically guide above to find two different narrowed topics you might write about. Then circle the topic you will use and jot down some ideas about how you might sort it.

GENERAL TOPIC: _____

NARROWED TOPICS (*circle the one you will use*):

1. _____

2. _____

WHAT IS MY PURPOSE IN CLASSIFYING THE TOPIC?_____

POSSIBLE WAYS TO CLASSIFY/SORT TOPIC (*circle the one you will use*):

1. _____

2. _____

3. _____

Step 2. Make Your Point in a Topic Sentence or Thesis Statement

Decide How You Want to Classify Your Topic.

There are a couple of ways to write a topic sentence or a thesis statement for classification. One is to tell readers what your topic is and how you are classifying it.

topic + how classified = topic sentence or thesis statement

TOPIC	*applicants/résumés*
HOW CLASSIFIED	*suitability for the job*
TOPIC SENTENCE	*Applicants' résumés show their suitability for the position.*

The writer knows at this point that her writing will classify the applicants into types according to their suitability for the job. But she looks at her sentence and decides that it sounds too wordy and complicated.

Sometimes a topic sentence or thesis statement for a classification will not actually state the classification. Instead, the topic sentence or thesis statement tells the reader the topic and announces that the writer is breaking the topic into types or categories.

topic + announcement of classification = topic sentence or thesis statement

REVISED TOPIC SENTENCE	*There are usually several types of candidates for any job.*

Both types of topic sentences or thesis statements may also include the categories you are using to classify (sort) your topic.

TOPIC SENTENCE
WITH CATEGORIES
There are usually several types of candidates for any job: suitables, unsuitables, and maybes.

If you want to use a topic sentence or thesis statement that states the categories, you can write one now, but be prepared to go back and make changes in the categories after you have completed the next step in the process where you choose useful categories.

Thinking Critically to Make Your Point

FOCUS Review your purpose, your topic, and how you are classifying it.

ASK
- How is the topic classified (by _____)?
- Other than the topic and how it is being classified, is there anything else I want my reader to focus on while reading the paragraph?
- How can I combine the topic and how it is being classified into a sentence that is clear and simple but lets the reader know what to expect?
- Am I certain enough about the categories my topic will be sorted into that I can name them in the topic sentence or thesis statement?

WRITE Write a topic sentence or thesis statement that includes the topic being classified and how it is being classified.

PRACTICE 2

Making Your Point

Using the Thinking Critically guide above, complete the sentence about your topic and how it is being classified. Then write a topic sentence or thesis statement. When you have a basic topic sentence or thesis statement, try revising it to make it sound stronger, clearer, or more interesting.

I WILL CLASSIFY MY TOPIC BY _____

_____

TOPIC SENTENCE OR THESIS STATEMENT: _____

_____

REVISED TOPIC SENTENCE OR THESIS STATEMENT: _____

_____

Step 3. Support Your Main Point with Useful Categories and Examples

Choose Useful Categories.

The categories you choose for your classification will tell your readers how you are organizing your topic. First, you need to find useful categories. Second, you need to make sure all the categories follow a single organizing principle. Third, you need to supply examples for each category.

Begin by listing all of the possible categories that you might use.

TOPIC	*applicants for jobs*
POSSIBLE CATEGORIES	*strong candidates, no-way candidates, maybes*

Use a Single Organizing Principle.

The categories you use to classify the topic must follow the same organizing principle. Review your possible categories to make sure that this is the case. What is the relationship among all of the categories? What do they all have in common? The answer to those questions should give you the organizing principle.

TOPIC	*applicants/résumés*
CATEGORIES	*strong candidates, no-ways, maybes*
ORGANIZING PRINCIPLE	*suitability for the job*

When choosing the categories, make sure that you understand what organizing principle you are using and that all the categories follow it. Otherwise, the classification may not be useful.

Thinking Critically to Support Your Main Point

FOCUS Think about your topic and how you might sort it.

ASK
- What is my purpose in sorting (classifying) the topic? What do I want to show my readers?
- What categories would help me achieve that purpose?
- What organizing principle do these categories follow?
- What examples can I give of things that fit into the categories so that my readers will understand them? Will one example be enough, or do I need several to make the categories clear?
- Have I overlooked any categories?

WRITE Write a list of your categories with examples.

PRACTICE 3

Exploring Your Topic for Categories

Use the Thinking Critically guide on page 58 to explore your topic for the categories you could use to organize it. List your possible categories here.

NARROWED TOPIC: _____

POSSIBLE CATEGORIES: _____

_____

_____

_____

_____

_____

PRACTICE 4

Checking the Categories for an Organizing Principle

Reread the categories you listed. First group the ones that you think follow the same organizing principle. Then write that organizing principle in the space provided. Review the categories again, and drop any that do not follow the same organizing principle.

ORGANIZING PRINCIPLE: _____

CATEGORIES THAT FOLLOW IT: _____

_____

_____

_____

Choose Categories That Are Distinct from Each Other.

One of the problems that can occur when you classify something is that the categories overlap and prevent you from sorting things usefully. For example, if you are packing to move and want to come up with some system for what things go in what boxes, you don't want categories that overlap, such as "kitchen things" and "breakable things." Too many things could go in either box (coffee mugs, glasses, plates, etc.). The purpose of classifying is to make sorting easy, and overlapping categories confuse things.

If your categories all follow the same organizing principle, they are not as likely to overlap, but before selecting the categories, do a test run of sorting things to make sure the categories are distinct and help the organizing process.

Find Examples of Things That Fit into Each Category.

Your readers need specific examples of things that fit into each category, so after you present a category, give an example. You need enough examples to make sure that your readers will understand what kinds of things fit into the category.

TOPIC	*applicants/résumés*
ORGANIZING PRINCIPLE	*suitability for job*
TOPIC SENTENCE	*Applicants for a job usually fall into one of three types: strong candidates, no-ways, and maybes.*
CATEGORY	*strong candidates* ***examples:** related experience, good résumé*
CATEGORY	*no-way candidates* ***examples:** no experience, no qualifications*
CATEGORY	*maybes* ***examples:** not ideal, but okay*

PRACTICE 5

Giving Examples of Things That Fit into Each Category

In the spaces provided, give one or more examples of things that fit into the categories you are using to classify (sort and organize) your topic.

TOPIC SENTENCE OR THESIS STATEMENT: _____

CATEGORY: _____

    EXAMPLES: _____

_____

CATEGORY: _____

    EXAMPLES: _____

_____

CATEGORY: _____

    EXAMPLES: _____

_____

CATEGORY: _____

    EXAMPLES: _____

_____

Step 4. Make a Plan

Decide on an Order of Presentation.

Classification can use any order of organization; your purpose is to sort into categories and give examples of what goes into each category, so you won't necessarily need to use a strict time, space, or importance arrangement. Arrange your categories and their examples in an order that makes the most sense. Think again about your purpose and what order of sorting would help you achieve that purpose.

Make a plan (usually an outline) for your paragraph or essay.

INFORMAL OUTLINE

TOPIC SENTENCE: Applicants for a job usually fall into one of these types: no-ways, definites, and maybes.

1. *No-ways*

    —no experience, no qualifications

2. *Definites*

    —good résumé, related work experience

3. *Maybes*

    —not ideal, but a possibility

Thinking Critically While Planning Your Classification

FOCUS   Reread your topic sentence or thesis statement, categories, and examples, and think about how you want to arrange them.

ASK   • Should the categories be arranged in any of the standard orders (time, space, importance)?
   • What order of presentation will show how I would actually sort them if I were physically dividing the items into piles?
   • How does my sorting of the items relate to my purpose for classifying them?

WRITE   Write an outline that shows the plan for your classification.

PRACTICE 6

Making a Plan

Use the Thinking Critically guide above to make a plan for your classification in the following spaces.

TOPIC SENTENCE OR THESIS STATEMENT: _____

CATEGORY 1: _____

    EXAMPLES: _____

_____

CATEGORY 2: _____

    EXAMPLES: _____

_____

CATEGORY 3: _____

    EXAMPLES: _____

Step 5. Write a Draft

Using the outline you have prepared as a guide, write a draft of your paragraph or essay. As you write, make sure that your order makes sense. If it doesn't, rearrange your categories.

FOR A PARAGRAPH

Turn your categories and details into complete sentences, and arrange them in paragraph form, using your topic sentence as your first sentence.

DRAFT PARAGRAPH

Applicants for a job usually fall into one of three types: no-ways, definites, and maybes. The no-ways are people who have no experience for the job. The definites look good on paper with good experience. The maybes aren't ideal for the job, but they might be worth seeing if none of the definites work out.

FOR AN ESSAY

Write a draft essay that includes your thesis statement in the first paragraph. Each of your categories should become the topic sentence for a paragraph. Each body paragraph should include clear, specific details and examples that support the topic sentence.

Write a Conclusion.

Now that you have presented all of the categories and given examples of each, tie them together with a concluding sentence or paragraph. Your conclusion should remind your reader of the topic that you are classifying and make an observation.

Do not just end limply with something like: "These are the types of applicants." Make an observation that connects the categories and examples to the topic sentence or thesis statement. Your observation might use the organizing principle.

CONCLUDING SENTENCE *Sorting applicants first according to their suitability for the job helps the person doing the hiring to efficiently eliminate unsuitable applicants and pursue qualified candidates.*

Thinking Critically to Write a Conclusion

FOCUS As you rewrite your draft, think about what you want your reader to understand about your topic and the categories.

ASK
- What is the point of my classification?
- What observation can I make that ties the categories back to the topic?
- How can I include the organizing principle as part of my observation?

WRITE Write your conclusion.

PRACTICE 7

Writing Your Concluding Sentence

Use the Thinking Critically guide above to write two possible concluding sentences for your classification paragraph. Then circle the best one and add it to your draft.

1. _____

_____

2. _____

_____

PRACTICE 8

Writing Your Concluding Paragraph

Using the Thinking Critically guide above, write two possible concluding paragraphs for your classification essay. Then choose the best one and add it to your draft essay.

Step 6. Revise Your Draft

You have your classification on paper. Now, reread your paragraph, looking for ways to improve it: Get rid of categories that don't fit or that overlap; add supporting examples; connect the categories with transitions. Do not just copy over your draft; make changes that will enable the reader to see the purpose of your classification.

Teamwork: Get Feedback

When you have completed your draft, you may want to show it to someone else or read it aloud in a small group, asking for feedback and suggestions that will help you revise.

GUIDELINES FOR GIVING FEEDBACK

- Start with a positive comment.

- Throughout, offer comments and observations rather than "You should's."

- Start with the draft as a whole and move to smaller points.

  —Tell the writer what you think the organizing principle is.

  —Tell the writer what you think the purpose of the classification is.

  —Tell the writer what you think the categories and examples are.

  —Ask questions about the categories that might help the writer give more detail.

- Tell the writer what works for you and what you think might be done better (and how).

- Be as specific as you can. Don't just say, "It's good," or "I liked it." Explain why.

- If you get confused or lost somewhere in the draft, tell the writer where.

- Help the writer.

Add Transitions.

Transitions connect ideas so that they flow smoothly from one to the next. In classification, use transitions that let your reader know when you are moving from one category to the next.

COMMON CLASSIFICATION TRANSITIONS

the first category	another type	a third type
the next category	the second kind	the last type
		the final group

The revised example paragraph has comments that show where the writer made changes to her draft, including adding transitions.

REVISED PARAGRAPH

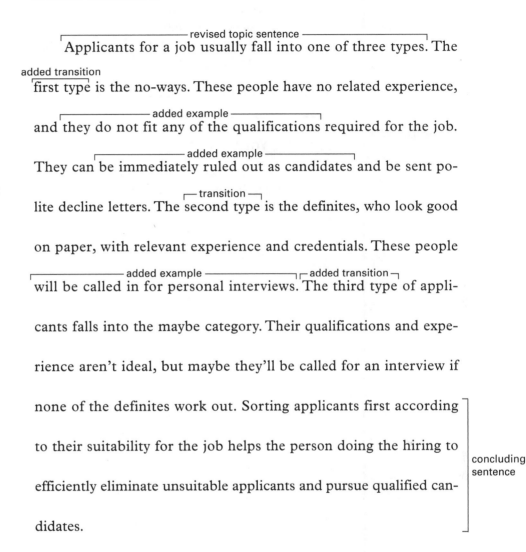

——————————— revised topic sentence ———————————
Applicants for a job usually fall into one of three types. The

added transition
first type is the no-ways. These people have no related experience,

——————— added example ———————
and they do not fit any of the qualifications required for the job.

——————— added example ———————
They can be immediately ruled out as candidates and be sent po-

—— transition ——
lite decline letters. The second type is the definites, who look good

on paper, with relevant experience and credentials. These people

——————— added example ———————— —— added transition ——
will be called in for personal interviews. The third type of appli-

cants falls into the maybe category. Their qualifications and expe-

rience aren't ideal, but maybe they'll be called for an interview if

none of the definites work out. Sorting applicants first according

to their suitability for the job helps the person doing the hiring to

efficiently eliminate unsuitable applicants and pursue qualified can-

didates.

concluding sentence

Thinking Critically to Revise a Classification

FOCUS   After a break, reread your draft from the perspective of your reader, and with your purpose in mind. Think about whether your classification helps organize and explain your topic.

ASK
- What observation am I making about this topic?
- Do the categories all follow the same organizing principle?
- Are they distinct enough so that the same things don't fit into more than one category in a way that makes sorting difficult?
- Have I missed any necessary categories?
- Do I give enough examples so that my readers will understand what kinds of things go into each category?

- Are the categories connected so that they flow smoothly from one to the next?
- Based on what I've written, can I make the topic sentence or thesis statement or the concluding sentence or concluding paragraph stronger?

WRITE   Revise by making improvements to your draft.

PRACTICE 9

Revising Your Draft

Use the Thinking Critically guide on page 65 to revise your draft. Make at least three changes, and be prepared to explain how they improved the draft.

Guided Practice: How to Write Definition

Step 1. Narrow and Explore Your Topic

After you have chosen a general topic to write about, narrow it to a single term that you will define. Think about the term you plan to define and what you would need to tell your reader about it. Can you define it in a paragraph or a short essay? If the term is too broad, list a few related but more specific terms. Choose the term you will define, and jot down a few ideas about it. Keep in mind that you need to understand the term before you can define it for others. You might start by looking up a term's meaning in a dictionary.

GENERAL TOPIC	*A personality trait*
POSSIBLE NARROWED TOPICS/TERMS	*sense of humor, moodiness, assertiveness, optimism*
NARROWED TOPIC/TERM	*assertiveness*
DICTIONARY DEFINITION	*defending or maintaining one's rights*
OTHER IDEAS ABOUT TERM'S MEANING	*standing up for your rights, firm but polite, not angry or aggressive, determined*

Thinking Critically to Narrow and Explore a Definition Topic

FOCUS   As you consider the general term, think about what you know about it.

ASK
- What are some more specific terms related to the general one and that I'm interested in?
- Which of these am I most interested in?
- Can it be defined in a paragraph or essay?
- What's the dictionary definition?
- What do I know about the term that will help my reader understand its meaning?
- What does my reader need to know?

WRITE   Write down your narrowed term and some ideas about what it means.

PRACTICE 1

Narrowing and Exploring the Term You Will Define

Use the Thinking Critically guide above to narrow the general term and write down a few more specific terms. Then circle the term you will define, and jot down some ideas about the term's meaning, including the dictionary definition.

GENERAL TERM: _____

MORE SPECIFIC, RELATED TERMS:

1. _____

2. _____

3. _____

IDEAS ABOUT THE TERM'S MEANING. INCLUDE DICTIONARY DEFINITION AND AT LEAST TWO OTHERS.

DICTIONARY DEFINITION: _____

_____

1. _____

2. _____

Step 2. Make Your Point in a Topic Sentence or Thesis Statement

Decide What Basic Definition You Will Present.

The topic sentence in a definition paragraph or the thesis statement in an essay should tell readers what term is being defined and present a clear, basic definition. When you are developing a definition, first develop that basic definition and then find a good way to present it to your readers. Do *not* just copy the definition from the dictionary.

TERM	*Assertiveness*
BASIC DEFINITION	*Standing up for your rights. Calmly defending your rights without getting angry.*
TOPIC SENTENCE	*Assertiveness means standing up for your rights—politely but firmly.*

Write a Topic Sentence or Thesis Statement.

There are several patterns for a good topic sentence or thesis statement for definition.

term + means/is + basic definition = topic sentence or thesis statement

TOPIC SENTENCE	*Assertiveness means standing up for your rights.*

This pattern is the simplest, presenting the term, the word *means* or *is*, and the basic definition.

term + class + detail = topic sentence or thesis statement

TOPIC SENTENCE   *Assertiveness is a personality trait that requires a firm opinion and a level head.*

The "class" is a larger group that the term belongs to; the "detail" is a unique characteristic that sets it apart from other things in the class. This pattern gives readers a precise, basic definition of the term, as long as you are clear what the class is and can give a brief but revealing detail.

term + *is not* + expected definition = topic sentence or thesis statement

TOPIC SENTENCE   *Assertiveness is not always believing your way is the right way.*

This pattern can be effective when you are defining a word differently than your readers may expect. Because the topic sentence or thesis statement in this example does not give the definition of the term, however, make sure you do provide a basic definition somewhere else in the paragraph or essay.

Thinking Critically to Make Your Point

FOCUS   Read the dictionary definition and any ideas you have written about the term.

ASK
- What do I mean by this term? What do I want to tell my readers about it?
- What basic definition should I use in my topic sentence or thesis statement?
- How can I present my definition in a topic sentence or thesis statement so my readers will know what I mean?

WRITE   Write a topic sentence or thesis statement that includes both the term and the basic definition, using one of the common patterns.

PRACTICE 2

Making Your Point in a Topic Sentence or Thesis Statement

Use the Thinking Critically guide above to complete the sentence about your term and your basic definition. Then write a topic sentence or thesis statement. When you have a basic topic sentence or thesis statement, try revising it to make it sound stronger, clearer, or more interesting.

THE BASIC DEFINITION I WANT TO PRESENT FOR THIS TERM IS _____

_____

TOPIC SENTENCE OR THESIS STATEMENT: _____

_____

REVISED TOPIC SENTENCE OR THESIS STATEMENT: _____

_____

Step 3. Support Your Main Point with Examples That Explain the Definition (Key Step)

Find Details and Examples That Explain the Term.

When you have presented a basic definition in your topic sentence or thesis statement, you then need to provide information to explain your definition. The information can be facts, or examples, or stories—whatever will be most likely to explain the term to your reader.

Use a prewriting technique to find details and examples that explain the term.

EXPLANATIONS OF DEFINITION:

When my friend Teresa sent back food in the restaurant

The time when someone tried to cut in front of her in line

Confident, calm, polite, firm/doesn't get mad or defensive or upset/stays cool

Won't be brushed off, doesn't give up

To select the examples you will use, reread your topic sentence or thesis statement and make a list of the examples you think best demonstrate the meaning of the term you're defining.

TOPIC SENTENCE	*Assertiveness means standing up for your rights—politely but firmly.*
EXAMPLES	**stories:** *Teresa and the person who tried to cut in line; Teresa and the overcooked hamburger*
	other characteristics of assertiveness: *not being brushed off when you need an answer or some action*

Thinking Critically to Support Your Main Point

FOCUS   Read your topic sentence or thesis statement, focusing on the basic definition.

ASK   • What do I know that can explain the term?

- What examples would most appeal to my readers?
- Will a brief story reveal the term's meaning in real life?
- Are there facts or additional information that will fill in the basic definition?
- Which ideas will best help readers understand the term?

WRITE   Write a list of your examples.

PRACTICE 3

Selecting Examples That Explain the Definition

Use the Thinking Critically guide above to select examples that will help explain your definition. Fill in the blanks that follow.

TOPIC SENTENCE OR THESIS STATEMENT

EXAMPLE 1: _____

    CHARACTERISTICS _____

    STORIES _____

EXAMPLE 2: _____

    CHARACTERISTICS _____

    STORIES _____

EXAMPLE 3: _____

    CHARACTERISTICS _____

    STORIES _____

Step 4. Make a Plan

Arrange the Examples into a Plan.

Reread your examples to decide how you should arrange them. First think about the three common orders: space, time, and importance. Should you use one of those orders? And if so, how should the examples be arranged to follow that order? If you aren't going to arrange your examples according to one of those orders, how *do* you want to arrange them? Make a plan (usually an outline) for your paragraph or essay.

In the example, the writer decides not to use any of the three common orders exactly. Instead, when she rereads her topic sentence and examples, she decides she wants to follow the topic sentence with a statement about the characteristics of assertiveness, followed by examples that seem to the writer to be increasingly assertive.

INFORMAL OUTLINE

TOPIC SENTENCE: Assertiveness means standing up for your rights—politely but firmly.

1. **CHARACTERISTICS:** *confidence, calm, cool/not anger or defensiveness*

2. **STORIES**

   A. *Teresa and the hamburger*

   B. *Teresa and the person who tried to cut in line*

3. **ANOTHER CHARACTERISTIC:** *refusing to be brushed off when you need an answer or some action*

Thinking Critically While Planning Your Definition

FOCUS   Reread your topic sentence or thesis statement and examples and think about how they can be arranged to have the most impact. Keep the term and the brief definition in mind.

ASK   • Can I use any of the common orders (space, time, importance)?
   • How *do* I want to arrange the examples, and why?
   • Are there other examples that would explain the term more clearly?

WRITE   Write an outline that shows the plan for your definition.

PRACTICE 4

Making a Plan

Use the Thinking Critically guide above to make a plan for your draft that indicates what examples you will use and the order in which you will present them. Use at least three examples.

TOPIC SENTENCE OR THESIS STATEMENT: _____

EXAMPLE 1: _____

_____

EXAMPLE 2: _____

_____

EXAMPLE 3: _____

_____

EXAMPLE 4: _____

_____

Step 5. Write a Draft

Using the outline you have prepared as a guide, write a draft of your definition paragraph or essay.

FOR A PARAGRAPH

Turn your details from Practice 3 into complete sentences, and arrange them in paragraph form, using your topic sentence as your first sentence.

DRAFT PARAGRAPH

Assertiveness means standing up for your rights—politely but firmly. Assertiveness is characterized by an attitude of confidence and self-assurance. An assertive person is cool and calm as opposed to angry and defensive. My friend Teresa is a good example of assertiveness. When Teresa and I were in a restaurant and her hamburger was well-done instead of rare, she signaled the waiter and asked if she could return the excellent but well-done burger for one that was a bit rarer. I braced myself for an argument, but the waiter just replaced the burger. Another time as we stood in line for tickets to a movie, a guy cut in front of Teresa. She tapped him on the shoulder, smiled, and said, "I see there was a gap that looked as if this were the end of the line, but it's really back there." The guy stared at her and said, "I'll just stay here. You don't mind, right?" She quietly replied, "Well, yes, I do mind." She made sure the people in back of us were listening when she said, "And I'm afraid you're not being fair to all these other people, either." The guy left. An assertive person calmly but persistently refuses to be brushed off.

FOR AN ESSAY

Write a draft essay that includes your thesis statement in the first paragraph. Each of your supporting details should become the topic sentence for a paragraph. Each body paragraph should include specific explanations and examples that support the topic sentence.

Write a Conclusion.

Your concluding sentence or concluding paragraph should remind your reader of the term and its definition by making an observation based on the examples you have given. To do this, reread your draft, then focus on the topic sentence or thesis statement, and write a conclusion.

CONCLUDING SENTENCE   _Assertiveness is invaluable because it helps you get what you want and deserve without creating a scene._

Thinking Critically to Write a Conclusion

FOCUS As you reread your draft, think about what you want your reader to understand about your term and its meaning.

ASK
- What is the point of my definition?
- What observation about my term do I want to leave my reader with?

WRITE Write your conclusion.

PRACTICE 5

Writing Your Concluding Sentence

Use the Thinking Critically guide above to write two possible concluding sentences for your definition paragraph. Then circle the best one and add it to your draft paragraph.

1. _____

_____

_____

2. _____

_____

_____

PRACTICE 6

Writing Your Concluding Paragraph

Using the Thinking Critically guide on this page, write two possible concluding paragraphs for your definition essay. Then choose the best one and add it to your draft essay.

Step 6. Revise Your Draft

You have your definition on paper. Now reread your draft, looking for ways to improve it: Make sure that the characteristics and examples you present actually explain or demonstrate the term's meaning. Add other examples that would help the reader understand the term, and connect them with transitions. Do not just copy over your draft; make changes that will enable the reader to understand the term.

Teamwork: Get Feedback

When you have completed your draft, you may want to show it to someone else or read it aloud in a small group, asking for feedback and suggestions that will help you revise.

GUIDELINES FOR GIVING FEEDBACK

- Start with a positive comment.
- Throughout, offer comments and observations rather than "You should's."
- Start with the draft as a whole and move to smaller points.

    —Tell the writer what you think the term means as the writer defines it.

    —Review the brief definition in the topic sentence or thesis statement to see if it gives you a basic idea of what the term means.

    —Check to see if the examples actually demonstrate or explain the meaning of the term.

- Tell the writer what works for you and what you think might be done better (and how).
- Be as specific as you can. Don't just say, "It's good," or "I liked it." Explain why.
- If you get confused or lost somewhere in the draft, tell the writer where.
- Help the writer.

Add Transitions.

Transitions connect your ideas so that they flow smoothly. In definition, you may use very simple transitions such as *for example*, *another example*, and *also*. Or you may signal a move from one example to the next by repeating a key word, usually the term being defined.

The revised example paragraph contains the writer's notes to show where she made changes to her draft, including adding time transitions.

REVISED PARAGRAPH

Assertiveness means standing up for your rights—politely but ⌉ cut
some
⌐———— example ————⌐ ⟋ transition unneeded
firmly. My friend Teresa is assertive. Once when we were in a restau- ⌋ stuff

rant and her hamburger was well-done instead of rare, she signaled the waiter and nicely asked if she could return the excellent but well-done burger for one that was a bit rarer. I braced myself for an argument, but the waiter just replaced the burger. ⌐time transition¬ Another time as we stood in line for tickets to a movie, a guy cut in front of Teresa. She tapped him on the shoulder, smiled, and said, "I see there was a gap that looked as if it were the end of the line, but it's ⟋ time transition really back there." When the guy stared at her and said, "I'll just stay here. You don't mind, right?" she answered, "Well, yes, I do ⟋ time transition mind." She then made sure the people in back of us were listening and said, "And you're not being fair to all these other people, either." The guy left. An assertive person calmly but persistently refuses to be brushed off. Assertiveness helps you get what you want and deserve without creating a scene.

concluding sentence

Thinking Critically to Revise a Definition Draft

FOCUS   After a break, reread your draft from the perspective of your reader, or someone who is not familiar with the term you are defining.

ASK   • Is the basic definition in the topic sentence or thesis statement clear and understandable?
    • Do the examples I give actually help explain the term?
    • Do I need more examples? How can I make the ones I have more revealing of the term's meaning?
    • Are the examples connected so that they flow smoothly from one to the next?

WRITE   Revise by making improvements to your draft.

PRACTICE 7

Revising Your Draft

Use the Thinking Critically guide above to revise your draft. Make at least three changes and be prepared to explain how they improve the draft.

Guided Practice: How to Write Comparison and Contrast

Step 1. Narrow and Explore Your Topic

Sometimes you are given specific subjects to compare or contrast. Other times, however, particularly in college courses, you may need to narrow the general topic into two specific subjects that you could meaningfully compare or contrast in a paragraph or an essay, or you may need to find a more specific way to compare or contrast your subjects. For example, if the assignment is "Compare two credit cards (Big Card and Mega Card)," you already have your two subjects, but you would need to narrow the general topic of credit cards further before you could say anything meaningful about them. Otherwise, your writing would have no focus and would wander from logos and pictures, to the banks, the terms, the limits, and so on. To narrow the general topic, first list some more specific topics. Then choose one and jot down some ideas about how the two subjects are similar or different.

GENERAL TOPIC	*Two credit cards (Big Card and Mega Card)*
MORE SPECIFIC POSSIBILITIES	*financial terms*
	insurance offered (life, disability, etc.)
	discounts (hotels, car rentals, etc.)
NARROWED TOPIC	*Financial terms of two credit cards*

Thinking Critically to Narrow and Explore a Comparison/Contrast Topic

FOCUS Think about the general topic, what you know about it, and how you could make it more specific.

ASK
- Given the general topic, what two subjects can I compare or contrast? In what specific ways can I think about them?
- Could I find something to say about these two subjects?
- Could I make a fairly complete comparison or contrast in a paragraph or essay?
- What are some points that I might make about the two subjects I am comparing?
- What is the point of my comparison or contrast? Is it to help readers choose between the two subjects? Or is it to give readers a better understanding of their relationship?

WRITE Write down your narrowed subjects and some ideas about their similarities or differences.

<table>
<tr><td>PRACTICE 1</td></tr>
</table>

Narrowing and Exploring Your Topic

Using the Thinking Critically guide on page 77, narrow the general topic by writing three more specific, narrower ones. Then circle the one you will use, and jot down some of the similarities and differences you might consider.

GENERAL TOPIC: _____

NARROWED TOPICS (*circle the one you will use*):

1. _____

2. _____

3. _____

SOME SIMILARITIES OR DIFFERENCES (*jot down at least three*):

_____

_____

_____

Step 2. Make Your Point

Decide What Point You Want to Make about the Subjects You Are Comparing and Contrasting.

In a comparison/contrast, your topic sentence or thesis statement should tell the readers what the subjects are and whether you are comparing or contrasting them. To figure out what your point is, think about what you want the comparison/contrast to accomplish. Do you want to help your readers make a decision, or do you want them simply to have an understanding of the topics?

Try using the basic formula to write a topic sentence or thesis statement, and then revise the sentence to make it stronger.

NARROWED TOPIC   *the financial terms of two credit cards (Big Card and Mega Card)*

subjects + main point = topic sentence or thesis statement

TOPIC SENTENCE   *The financial terms of Big Card and Mega Card are very different.*

To make your topic sentence or thesis statement stronger, you can revise it to include your purpose for the comparison/contrast.

PURPOSE	*to choose between them*

subjects + main point + purpose = topic sentence or thesis statement

REVISED TOPIC SENTENCE	*The different financial terms of Big Card and Mega Card should make the choice between them simple.*

Thinking Critically to Make Your Point

FOCUS Reread the similarities and differences you jotted down and think about your purpose in comparing the two subjects.

ASK
- What do I want to show by comparing/contrasting the two subjects? What point do I want to make?
- What do I want my readers to understand? Do I want to help make a choice, a decision, or what?

WRITE Write a topic sentence or thesis statement that includes the subjects, your main point, and whether you are comparing or contrasting them. You may also want to include your purpose in comparing or contrasting them.

PRACTICE 2

Making Your Point in a Topic Sentence or Thesis Statement

Using the Thinking Critically guide above, complete the sentence about your main point and then write a topic sentence or thesis statement. When you have a basic topic sentence or thesis statement, try revising it to make it sound stronger, clearer, or more interesting.

MY PURPOSE IN COMPARING OR CONTRASTING THESE TOPICS IS: _____

_____

_____

_____

TOPIC SENTENCE OR THESIS STATEMENT: _____

_____

_____

REVISED TOPIC SENTENCE OR THESIS STATEMENT: _____

_____

_____

Step 3. Support Your Main Point with Points of Comparison/Contrast (Key Step)

Find Points of Comparison/Contrast.

The similarities (or differences) you present should be significant ones that help your reader to understand the subjects, to choose between them, and/or to make some decision. It is important that you give parallel similarities/differences for both subjects. Choose points that are important to understanding the subjects.

To find the points of comparison/contrast, use a prewriting technique to come up with as many similarities or differences as you can. Then sort through the possibilities, choosing those that will best show how the subjects are similar or different. Choose points that are of similar importance and weight (don't have one point that is trivial, like the color of the credit cards, and another that is much more important, such as the interest rates on loans). Keep the points balanced.

Many people find that making a two-column list (one for each subject) is a good way to come up with parallel similarities or differences. After you have written your lists, reread them, circling points that are the most important to how the subjects are similar or different.

TOPIC SENTENCE: The different financial terms of Big Card and Mega Card should make the choice between them simple.

Big Card's financial terms	Mega Card's financial terms
no annual fee	$35 annual fee
~~$50 theft liability~~	~~$250 theft liability~~
finance charge: 15.5%	finance charge: 17.9%
$1 per cash advance	$1.50 per cash advance
~~$500 credit limit~~	~~$1,000 credit limit~~
grace period: 30 days	grace period: 25 days
~~card insurance: $10/year~~	~~card insurance: $6/year~~

Thinking Critically to Support Your Main Point

FOCUS As you look for points of comparison or contrast, think about your purpose.

ASK
- Do I want to explain two subjects or help readers to make a choice between two subjects?
- Do I want to show the similarities, the differences, or both?
- What are some parallel points of the two subjects?

- Do these points reveal important characteristics of the two subjects?
- What else would help show how the subjects are alike or different?

WRITE   Write a list of points of comparison or contrast.

PRACTICE 3

Finding Points of Comparison or Contrast

Use the Thinking Critically guide on page 80 to find points of comparison or contrast. Using a column for each subject, make a list of at least five similarities or differences you might use. Then circle three that you will develop in your paragraph or essay.

TOPICS: _____

TOPIC SENTENCE OR THESIS STATEMENT: _____

POSSIBLE POINTS OF EITHER COMPARISON OR CONTRAST (5):

_____   _____

_____   _____

_____   _____

_____   _____

_____   _____

Step 4. Make a Plan

Decide on an Organization. (Key Step)

There are two ways to organize a comparison/contrast: point-by-point or whole-to-whole. A point-by-point organization presents one point about the two subjects with examples of each and then moves to the next point with examples, and so on. A whole-to-whole organization presents all the points about the first subject and then all the points about the second subject. Either organization will work, but before choosing one or the other, think about which one better serves your purpose.

When you have decided which of the two organizations to use, you also need to decide on how you will order the points. Because comparison/contrast is often used to make a choice or a decision, the points are often arranged according to importance (least to most important or most to least important). Make a plan (usually an outline).

In the example, the writer uses point-to-point organization and arranges her points according to how important they are to her and the way she uses credit cards. Another writer might have chosen a different arrangement of points or even a different organization, whole-to-whole.

INFORMAL OUTLINE

TOPIC SENTENCE: The different financial terms of Big Card and Mega Card should make the choice between them simple.

POINT 1: *Annual membership fee*

— *Big Card:* *no fee*

— *Mega Card:* *$35*

POINT 2: *Cash advance fees*

— *Big Card:* *$1.00 per withdrawal*

— *Mega Card:* *$1.50 per withdrawal*

POINT 3: *Grace periods*

— *Big Card:* *30 days*

— *Mega Card:* *25 days*

POINT 4: *Finance charges*

— *Big Card:* *15.5%*

— *Mega Card:* *17.9%*

Thinking Critically While Planning Your Comparison/Contrast

FOCUS   Review your topic sentence or thesis statement and points of comparison or contrast, and think about how to arrange your ideas.

ASK
- Should I use a whole-to-whole or point-by-point organization?
- Which organization would make the comparison or contrast easier for my readers to understand? Which seems more natural?
- Within that organization, how should I arrange my points? by importance? by time? by space?

WRITE   Write an outline that shows the plan for your comparison/contrast.

PRACTICE 4

Making a Plan

Use the Thinking Critically guide above to make a plan for your comparison/contrast draft in the following spaces.

POINT-TO-POINT ORGANIZATION

TOPIC SENTENCE OR THESIS STATEMENT: _____

_____

POINT 1: _____

    SUBJECT 1: _____

    SUBJECT 2: _____

POINT 2: _____

    SUBJECT 1: _____

    SUBJECT 2: _____

POINT 3: _____

    SUBJECT 1: _____

    SUBJECT 2: _____

WHOLE-TO-WHOLE ORGANIZATION

TOPIC SENTENCE OR THESIS STATEMENT: _____

_____

SUBJECT 1: _____

    POINT 1: _____

    POINT 2: _____

    POINT 3: _____

SUBJECT 2: _____

    POINT 1: _____

    POINT 2: _____

    POINT 3: _____

Step 5. Write a Draft

Using the outline you have prepared as a guide, write a draft of your paragraph or essay. If the order doesn't seem logical as you are writing, re-arrange your points.

FOR A PARAGRAPH

Turn your points of comparison or contrast into complete sentences, and arrange them in paragraph form, using your topic sentence as your first sentence.

DRAFT PARAGRAPH

The different financial terms of Big Card and Mega Card should make the choice between them simple. They have different annual membership fees. Big Card has no fee at all; Mega Card charges $35 each year for the privilege of membership. They also have different charges for cash advances. Getting an advance using Big Card costs $1.00 per withdrawal, while the same activity using Mega Card will cost $1.50. Another difference between the two cards is the grace periods each "offers" before imposing finance charges on unpaid balances. Big Card offers a grace period of thirty days; Mega Card starts charging after twenty-five. Big Card's finance charge is 15.5%; Mega Card's is a whopping 17.9%. That difference is even bigger when you recall that Mega has a shorter grace period, so the finance charges start adding up earlier.

FOR AN ESSAY

Write a draft essay that includes your thesis statement in the first paragraph. Each of your supporting points should become the topic sentence for a paragraph. Each body paragraph should include specific details and examples that support the topic sentence.

Write a Conclusion.

A concluding sentence or concluding paragraph for comparison/contrast should pull the similarities or differences together to make an observation about the subjects.

CONCLUDING SENTENCE *The differences in these financial terms point clearly to Big Card as the better choice.*

Thinking Critically to Write a Conclusion

FOCUS As you reread your draft, think about what you want your reader to understand about the subjects you are comparing or contrasting.

ASK
- What is the point of my comparison/contrast?
- What have I learned by comparing or contrasting these two subjects?
- What conclusion do I want to pass along to my reader?

WRITE Write your conclusion.

PRACTICE 5

Writing Your Concluding Sentence

Use the Thinking Critically guide on page 84 to write two possible concluding sentences for your comparison/contrast paragraph. Then circle the best one and add it to your draft paragraph.

1. _____

   _____

2. _____

   _____

PRACTICE 6

Writing Your Concluding Paragraph

Using the Thinking Critically guide on page 84, write two possible concluding paragraphs for your comparison-contrast essay. Then choose the best one and add it to your draft essay.

Step 6. Revise Your Draft

Reread your paragraph or essay, looking for ways to improve it: Make sure that the points of comparison/contrast between the two subjects are parallel and relevant to your purpose; add other points of comparison/contrast if needed, or additional examples; connect the points with transitions. Do not just copy over your draft; make changes that will enable the reader to understand how the subjects are alike or different.

Teamwork: Get Feedback

When you have completed your comparison/contrast draft, you may want to show it to someone else or to read it aloud in a small group, asking for feedback and suggestions that will help you revise. Before asking for comments, explain what your purpose is.

GUIDELINES FOR GIVING FEEDBACK

- Start with a positive comment.
- Throughout, offer comments and observations rather than "You should's."
- Start with the draft as a whole and move to smaller points.

  —Tell the writer what you think is being compared or contrasted.
  —Tell the writer what you think the points of comparison or contrast are.

—Do those points of comparison/contrast seem of similar importance and weight so that they are balanced?

• Tell the writer what works for you and what you think might be better (and how).

• Be as specific as you can. Don't just say, "It's good," or "I liked it." Explain why.

• If you get confused or lost somewhere in the draft, tell the writer where.

• Help the writer.

Add Transitions.

Transitions connect ideas so that they flow smoothly from one to the next. In comparison/contrast, use transitions that let your reader know when you are moving from one point of comparison/contrast to the next.

COMMON COMPARISON TRANSITIONS	COMMON CONTRAST TRANSITIONS
one similarity	one difference
another similarity	another difference
similarly	in contrast
like	unlike
both	while

The revised example paragraph has comments that show where the writer made changes to her draft, including adding transitions.

REVISED PARAGRAPH

As revealed in the fine print, the financial terms offered by Big Card and Mega Card are very different. One difference ⌐transition⌐ is the annual membership fees. Big Card has no fee at all; Mega Card charges $35 each year for the privilege of membership. Another difference ⌐transition⌐ is what they charge for cash advances. Getting an advance using Big Card costs $1.00 per withdrawal, while the same activity using Mega Card will cost $1.50. Also, ⌐transition⌐ Big Card is more gracious than ⌐reworded⌐

Mega Card, offering a "grace" period of thirty days before impos-

ing finance charges on unpaid balances. Mega's charge starts after

twenty-five days. The biggest difference between the two cards is

the finance charge rates. Big Card's finance charge is 15.5%; Mega

Card's is a whopping 17.9%. That ┌─────── added detail ───────┐ difference in percentage rates is

even bigger when you recall that Mega has a shorter grace period,

so the finance charges start adding up earlier. Over the course of a

────────────────── added detail sentence ──────────────────
year, unpaid balances will cost a lot more on the Mega Card than

they would on Big Card. The several differences in the financial ⎤
                                                                 ⎥ concluding
                                                                 ⎥ sentence
terms point to Big Card as the better choice.   ⎦

Thinking Critically to Revise a Comparison/Contrast

FOCUS   After a break, reread your draft from the perspective of your
reader, and with your purpose in mind.

ASK   • Are the points of comparison/contrast related to the purpose
for writing?
• Have I missed any strong similarities or differences?
• Do I have enough points of comparison/contrast to help my
reader understand the subjects and/or make a choice between
them?
• Have I presented the points in enough detail?
• Are the points connected with transitions so that they flow
smoothly from one to the next?
• Does the concluding sentence or paragraph make an observation or choice based on the comparison/contrast?

WRITE   Revise by making improvements to your draft.

PRACTICE 7   ## Revising Your Draft

Using the Thinking Critically guide above, revise your draft. Make at
least three changes and be prepared to explain how they improve the draft.

Guided Practice: How to Write Cause and Effect

Step 1. Narrow and Explore Your Topic

Find an Appropriate Topic.

Cause/effect is frequently used to organize writing whether for a business proposal or for an essay exam in history. In those instances, you know your subject, and you probably are told whether you will need to give causes, effects, or both. However, if you need to choose your own subject, select one that you are familiar with and that you could find logical causes and effects for. After you have selected a general topic to explain, narrow it to a topic that you are interested in and can write about in either a paragraph or an essay. Write down a few possible ideas for topics, and then select the one you want to write about. Remember to select a topic for which you can find several causes and effects to prove your point.

GENERAL TOPIC	*anger*
POSSIBLE TOPICS	*fighting, bad driving, verbal abuse*
NARROWED TOPIC	*road rage*
IDEAS	*growing frequency, accidents, stress*

Thinking Critically to Narrow and Explore Cause/Effect

FOCUS   Think about your general topic and what you know about it.

ASK   • What do I already know about this topic?
   • Which of these ideas are interesting to me?
   • Which would seem important to my reader?
   • What do I want my reader to know about this topic?

WRITE   Write down your narrowed topic and ideas that you have.

PRACTICE 1

Narrowing and Exploring Your General Topic

Use the Thinking Critically guide on this page to find two different narrowed topics you might write about. Then circle the topic you will use and jot down some of the things that come to your mind as you think about it.

GENERAL TOPIC: _____

NARROWED TOPICS *(circle the one you will use):*

1. _____

2. _____

IDEAS ABOUT THE NARROWED TOPIC (*jot down at least five*):

_____

_____

_____

_____

_____

Explore Causes and Effects.

Once you have decided on a narrow topic, you need to further explore the specific causes and effects of the event or situation. Whether you decide later to write about causes or effects or both, you first need to understand the complete topic. Using a ring diagram, you can brainstorm by listing possible causes and possible effects for your narrowed topic. At this stage, you don't need to make any decisions about significance, relationships, or order.

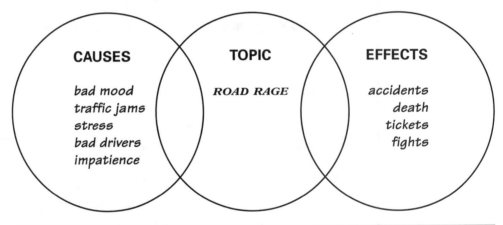

CAUSES

bad mood
traffic jams
stress
bad drivers
impatience

TOPIC

ROAD RAGE

EFFECTS

accidents
death
tickets
fights

PRACTICE 2

Determining True Causes and Effects

Using the ring diagram, write four to five possible causes in the left ring and four to five possible effects in the right one for your narrowed topic. Then circle three or four that you will develop in your paragraph or essay.

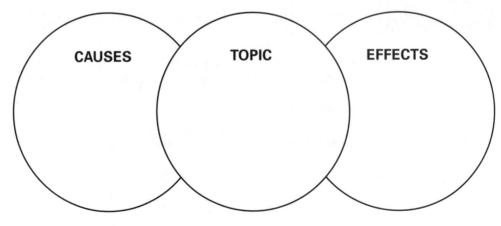

CAUSES

TOPIC

EFFECTS

Step 2. Make Your Point in a Topic Sentence or Thesis Statement

Determine What Is Most Interesting or Important about Your Topic.

Reread the ideas that you wrote in Practices 1 and 2. Do you see a primary focus? Do you see an emphasis on cause or on effect? If not, write a few more ideas. Your main focus should be one that you can easily support with clear, specific examples. Remember that you can usually write about causes, effects, or both unless you are given a topic that dictates which you do.

NARROWED TOPIC	*Road rage*
WHAT'S IMPORTANT ABOUT THE TOPIC	*becoming more frequent; people need to realize the dangers and, perhaps, what causes it*

Write a Topic Sentence or Thesis Statement.

Your topic sentence or thesis statement should provide your readers with the main point of your paragraph or essay. Write a topic sentence or thesis statement that tells your reader what to expect. Using words such as *cause, because, reason, result,* or *effect* will let the reader know if you will concentrate on cause, effect, or both. Try following this basic formula:

narrowed topic + main point + indicator word
= topic sentence or thesis statement

TOPIC SENTENCE OR THESIS STATEMENT

Road rage can result in a wide range of problems. (effects)

OR

Although many people think road rage is merely a result of anger, it actually can be caused by many factors. (causes)

OR

Caused by a variety of factors, road rage can result in a multitude of problems. (both)

If your first attempt does not seem interesting enough, try revising so your focus is clearer and stronger.

REVISED TOPIC SENTENCE OR THESIS STATEMENT	*Road rage can have various results ranging from tickets to death.*

Thinking Critically to Make Your Point

FOCUS   Reread your narrowed topic and think about your purpose for writing.

ASK
- Why is this topic important? Why is it interesting?
- What main point do I want readers to understand?
- Can I make the subject interesting to the reader by supplying clear, specific details?

WRITE   Write a topic sentence or thesis statement that includes your narrowed topic and your main point and indicates whether you are showing causes or effects or both.

PRACTICE 3

Making Your Point in a Topic Sentence or Thesis Statement

Using the Thinking Critically guide on this page, complete the sentence about why your subject is important, then write a topic sentence or thesis statement.

THE MOST IMPORTANT POINT I WANT TO MAKE ABOUT THIS SUBJECT IS _____

_____

TOPIC SENTENCE OR THESIS STATEMENT: _____

Step 3. Support Your Main Point with Clear Examples and Facts

Choose Appropriate and Logical Supporting Details.

Remember that just because one event precedes another doesn't necessarily mean that the first event caused the second. Similarly, when one event follows another, it may not be the result of the first. Therefore, you must select supporting points that have direct cause and effect relationships and that are important. Any event can have a multitude of causes and effects, but not all will be important. For instance, the rising cost of gasoline could increase the prices of airline tickets or bus tickets, affecting many people all over the country, but the fact that you won't be able to drive to the mall as frequently would not seem significant to your reader.

Equally important is the explanation for those causes and effects. The reader cannot read your mind, so you need to give specific examples and details that show how one event or situation caused another or how one event or situation resulted in other events or situations.

TOPIC	*Road rage*
TOPIC SENTENCE OR THESIS STATEMENT	*Road rage can have various results ranging from tickets to death.*

> **CAUSE/EFFECT 1:**   *tickets*
> *example/detail:*   *A policeman could give a citation for reckless driving.*
>
> **CAUSE/EFFECT 2:**   *death*
> *example/detail:*   *newspaper story about one driver shooting another who cut in front of him in traffic*

Thinking Critically to Support Your Main Point

FOCUS   As you look at your points of cause/effect, think about your purpose.

ASK
- Do I want to show the causes of a particular event?
- Do I want to explain the results of a particular event?
- Are my causes and effects direct causes and direct results or merely unrelated happenings?
- What facts or examples can I use to support my point?
- What are the most significant points I could make about the event?

WRITE   Write a list of causes and effects for your topic and add examples and details for each.

PRACTICE 4

Finding Logical, Specific Support

Using the Thinking Critically guide on this page and your responses in Practice 2, think of logical and clear examples for each of the points of cause or effect that you plan to make.

TOPIC: _____

TOPIC SENTENCE OR THESIS STATEMENT: _____

CAUSE/EFFECT 1: _____

     EXAMPLE/DETAIL: _____

CAUSE/EFFECT 2: _____

     EXAMPLE/DETAIL: _____

CAUSE/EFFECT 3: _____

     EXAMPLE/DETAIL: _____

CAUSE/EFFECT 4: _____

     EXAMPLE/DETAIL: _____

Step 4. Make a Plan

Decide on an Organization.

Whether you are writing about effects, causes, or both, you can organize your writing by space order, time order, or order of importance. Sometimes your specific topic will help you determine how to organize your cause/effect. Other times you will need to study the points that you plan to include in order to determine an appropriate organization.

INFORMAL OUTLINE

TOPIC SENTENCE: Road rage can have various results ranging from tickets to death.

POINT 1: *tickets*

—*speeding*

—*following too close*

—*reckless driving*

POINT 2: *accidents*

—*causing someone else to have a wreck*

—*not paying attention to traffic and having an accident yourself*

POINT 3: *fights*

—*car pulls over*

—*someone follows you to your destination*

POINT 4: *death*

—*shootings*

—*woman who miscarried*

Thinking Critically While Planning Your Cause/Effect

FOCUS Review your topic sentence or thesis statement and supporting details, and think about how to arrange your ideas.

ASK • Should I write only about causes, only about effects, or about both?
  • Should I begin with an overview of the situation and then move into the causes and/or effects?
  • How should I arrange my supporting details? By space order? By time order? By order of importance?

WRITE   Write an outline that shows the plan for your cause/effect paragraph or essay.

Making a Plan

Use the Thinking Critically guide on page 94 to make a plan for your cause/effect draft in the following spaces.

TOPIC SENTENCE OR THESIS STATEMENT: _____

CAUSE/EFFECT 1: _____

    EXAMPLES: _____

CAUSE/EFFECT 2: _____

    EXAMPLES: _____

CAUSE/EFFECT 3: _____

    EXAMPLES: _____

Step 5. Write a Draft

Using the outline you have prepared as a guide, write a draft of your paragraph or essay.

FOR A PARAGRAPH

Turn your supporting details into complete sentences, and arrange them in paragraph form, using your topic sentence as your first sentence.

DRAFT PARAGRAPH

Road rage can have various results ranging from tickets to death. Accidents can result from road rage. An angry person who drives erratically can cause someone else to have a wreck when that driver tries to avoid the erratic driver. An enraged driver may not pay close attention to the traffic. Road rage results in fights. If one driver gets mad at another driver, he or she may force the other driver off the road or follow the other driver to his or her destination and start a fight. Death has even occurred because of road rage. One driver can pull out a gun and shoot the other one, and one time a woman who was pregnant lost her baby.

FOR AN ESSAY

Write a draft essay that includes your thesis statement in the first paragraph. Each cause and/or effect should become the topic sentence for a paragraph. Each body paragraph should include specific details and strong examples that support the topic sentence.

Write a Conclusion.

A concluding sentence or concluding paragraph should refer to the main point of the topic sentence or thesis statement and show the significance of the paper.

CONCLUDING SENTENCE FOR CAUSE/EFFECT PARAGRAPH	*If people do not control their rage while driving, they may face disastrous results.*

Thinking Critically to Write a Conclusion

FOCUS As you reread your draft, think about what you want your reader to understand about the subject you are writing about.

ASK
- What is the point of my cause/effect?
- What have I learned by describing the cause/effect relationship?
- What main point do I want my reader to remember?

WRITE Write your conclusion.

PRACTICE 6

Writing Your Concluding Sentence

Use the Thinking Critically guide on this page to write two possible concluding sentences for your cause/effect paragraph. Then circle the best one and add it to your draft paragraph.

1. _____

   _____

2. _____

   _____

PRACTICE 7

Writing Your Concluding Paragraph

Using the Thinking Critically guide on this page, write two possible concluding paragraphs for your draft essay. Then choose the best one and add it to your draft essay.

Step 6. Revise Your Draft

Reread your paragraph or essay, looking for ways to improve it: Make sure that the causes and/or effects are clear and specific, that they have *real* cause and effect relationships and that one does not just follow the other without any connection. Do not just copy over your draft; make changes that will enable the reader to understand how the topics are alike or different.

Teamwork: Get Feedback

When you hve completed your draft, you may want to show it to someone else or read it aloud in a small group, asking for feedback and suggestions that will help you revise.

GUIDELINES FOR GIVING FEEDBACK

- Start with a positive comment.

- Throughout, offer comments and observations rather than "You should's."

- Start with the draft as a whole and move to smaller points.

  —Tell the writer what you think the main idea is.
  —Review the cause/effect relationships.
  —Ask questions about the events or situations that might help the writer give more detail.

- Tell the writer what works for you and what you think might be done better (and how).

- Be as specific as you can. Don't just say, "It's good," or "I liked it." Explain why.

- If you get confused or lost somewhere in the draft, tell the writer where.

- Help the writer.

Add Transitions.

Transitions connect ideas so that they flow smoothly from one to the next. In cause/effect, use transitions that let your reader know whether you are discussing causes or effects and that clearly introduce the next point.

Many cause/effect papers are written in order of importance; you can choose from these transitions that indicate importance.

IMPORTANCE TRANSITIONS

above all	in fact	worst	best
especially	in particular	most	most important

CAUSE/EFFECT TRANSITIONS

one cause, reason, effect, result	a second, third, etc.	another
also	as a result	because

The revised example paragraph has comments that show where the writer made changes to her draft, including adding transitions.

REVISED PARAGRAPH

Road rage can have various results ranging from tickets to death.

┌─transition─┐   ┌─ added information

For instance, accidents can easily result from road rage. If an angry

                              ┌──── added detail ────┐

person is driving erratically, he or she takes risks and can cause some-

one else to have a wreck when that driver tries to avoid the erratic

                ┌─ transition

driver. Also, when enraged, a driver may not pay close attention to

            ┌──────── added detail ────────┐   ┌─ transition

the traffic and may run into another car or into a ditch. Sometimes

road rage results in fights. If one driver gets mad at another driver,

he or she may force the other driver off the road or follow the other

                                          ┌──── transition ────┐

driver to his or her destination and start a fight. More importantly,

                                    ┌──── added detail ────┐

death has even occurred because of road rage. With guns so preva-

┌────────── added detail ──────────┐

lent in society, one never knows when one driver can pull out a gun

                  ┌──── transition ────┐

and shoot the other one. In one recent incident, a woman who was

                                      ┌──────

angry when another driver cut her off rammed the back of the other

driver's vehicle. That driver was pregnant, and the resulting wreck

──────────────── added details and revisions ────────────────

caused her to have a miscarriage. The woman with road rage was

                                              ┌─transition   ┐

charged with causing the death of a fetus. Thus, if people do not   │ concluding
                                                                       │ sentence

control their rage while driving, they may face disastrous results.   ┘

Thinking Critically to Revise a Cause and Effect Draft

FOCUS   After a break, reread your draft from the perspective of your reader and with your purpose in mind.

ASK
- Are the points of cause/effect related to the purpose for writing?
- Have I missed any obvious causes or effects?
- Do I have enough points to help my reader understand my topic?
- Have I presented my points in enough detail?
- Are the points connected with transitions so that they flow smoothly from one to the next?
- Does the conclusion remind the reader of the causes and effects and their significance?

WRITE   Revise by making improvements to your draft.

PRACTICE 8

Revising Your Draft

Using the Thinking Critically guide on this page, revise your draft. Make at least three changes and be prepared to explain how they improve the draft.

Guided Practice: How to Write Argument

Step 1. Explore the Issue and Take a Position

Put Your Issue into Question Form.

After you have chosen a general topic or issue to explore, put the issue into question form. This helps you understand what the issue is, and it also gives you a way to frame your argument: as an answer to the question. Try starting the question with the word *should*.

GENERAL TOPIC/ISSUE	*Ebonics as a separate language*
QUESTION	*Should Ebonics be recognized as a separate language?*

Thinking Critically to Explore an Issue and Take a Position

FOCUS Think about an issue.

ASK
- How can I put the issue in question form?
- Why is the issue important to me? How does this issue affect me and my family? What do I have at stake?
- How would I answer the question? What is my position?
- Why do some people take a different position?
- Can I defend my position with energy and conviction?
- Can I defend it in a single paragraph or a short essay?
- How should I present my position to my readers?

WRITE Write down your topic and position and some ideas you have about it.

PRACTICE 1

Asking a Question

In the spaces provided, write the issue you have chosen, and ask a question that you will answer.

ISSUE: _____

_____

QUESTION: _____

_____

Find Your Position.

You may already know what your position on the issue is, but if you have not decided yet, use a prewriting technique to examine both sides of the issue. Try listing points under "no" and "yes."

Question: Should Ebonics be recognized as a separate language?

No	Yes
1. It's a type of English, not like a foreign language.	1. It is spoken by a particular group of people.
2. It will not help students; in fact, it might hurt them.	2. It will allow schools to get funds to increase their language programs.
3. It is racist.	3. It respects the history of a race.
4. It will hold people back educationally and professionally.	4. It will allow students to get better language training, and it will train teachers to teach students who speak Ebonics.

If you already know what your position is, use a prewriting technique to explore *why* you take the position.

Question: Should Ebonics be recognized as a separate language?

Position: no

Why do I take that position? Maybe the whole idea of Ebonics was started by someone with good intentions, but if it's recognized as a separate language, many students won't bother to learn "standard" English. Whatever you think about that, it's what people speak in the business world, and if you can't speak it and write it, you're hurting your chances of getting ahead. It's like separating off African American students and saying you are really different and that's okay—stay different. I've read that some prominent African Americans are very opposed to the idea. (I should find out more about what these people said and why they're against it.) I don't know, maybe I don't have all the facts, but it seems like a terrible idea to me.

PRACTICE 2

Finding Your Position

Use a prewriting technique either to decide what position you will take or to explore the position you've already taken.

Build Energy.

A good argument has energy; when you read it, you know that the writer is committed to his or her position. Get yourself energized, or you aren't likely to persuade or convince anyone. You should feel like a lawyer about to go to court and present a case.

When you are free to choose the issue to write about, you will proba-bly choose something you care about personally. But even when you are assigned an issue, you still need to defend it powerfully by finding something in it that you care about.

PRACTICE 3

Building Energy

Take a full minute to either think about your issue, talk about it with a partner, or prewrite your issue to build a good energy level. If you need something to get started, here are some techniques.

- Imagine yourself arguing your position to someone you dislike (who, naturally, holds the opposite position).

- Imagine that your whole grade rests on persuading your teacher of your position (he/she, too, holds the opposite opinion).

- Imagine how this issue could affect *you* personally, or your family.

- Imagine that you are representing a large group of people who *do* very much care about the issue and whose lives will be forever changed by it. It's up to you to win their case.

Step 2. Make Your Point in a Topic Sentence or Thesis Statement

Decide How You Will Answer Your Question.

In argument, you should state your position clearly and strongly in the topic sentence or thesis statement. Once you have a position that you feel strongly about, you are ready to answer the question you posed about the issue. The answer to that question is your topic sentence or thesis statement.

Write a Topic Sentence or Thesis Statement.

Let your reader know the point you are making about the issue and where you stand from the start. Jot down several possible topic sentences or thesis statements using the basic formula, and then circle the one you think is best.

issue + position = topic sentence or thesis statement

QUESTION *Should Ebonics be recognized as a separate language?*

ANSWERS/POSSIBLE TOPIC SENTENCES OR THESIS STATEMENTS:

1. *Ebonics should not be recognized as a separate language.*

2. *Ebonics is not a separate language.*

3. *I do not believe that Ebonics is a separate language.*

Thinking Critically to Make Your Point

FOCUS Reread your question carefully.

ASK
- What are some answers to the question?
- Which of the answers is the most forceful?
- When I say it aloud, does it sound definite and energetic?

WRITE Write a topic sentence or thesis statement that answers your question and strongly states your position.

PRACTICE 4

Making Your Point in a Topic Sentence or Thesis Statement

Use the Thinking Critically guide on this page to answer your question and declare your position, and then write a topic sentence or thesis statement. When you have a basic topic sentence or thesis statement, try revising it to make it sound stronger, clearer, or more interesting.

QUESTION: _____

_____

POSSIBLE ANSWERS (2): _____

_____

_____

TOPIC SENTENCE OR THESIS STATEMENT: _____

_____

REVISED TOPIC SENTENCE OR THESIS STATEMENT: _____

_____

Step 3. Support Your Position with Convincing Reasons and Evidence

Consider What Makes Convincing Reasons and Evidence.

Defending your position with convincing reasons and evidence is the most important part of an effective argument. Reasons are the points that support your position—points that must be backed up by evidence. Evidence is more than just your own beliefs stated with conviction. Good evidence is made up of facts, specific examples, and expert opinions.

Your purpose in argument is to convince people of your position—people who don't yet have an opinion and people who have an opposing position. Your reasons and evidence must be chosen to appeal to these people and must take into account whatever objections they might have to your position. As you develop your reasons and evidence, remember two characteristics of good support in an argument:

1. The evidence is made up of facts, experience, and expert opinion, not just your personal beliefs.

2. Your reasons and evidence take your opposition into account and anticipate their objections.

Find Reasons and Evidence.

First reread any notes you made earlier as you decided on your position. Then use a prewriting technique to come up with as much support as you can think of. Try to think of reasons, facts, examples, and expert opinion that you could use.

TOPIC SENTENCE	*Ebonics should not be recognized as a separate language.*
EARLIER FREEWRITING	*Maybe the whole idea of Ebonics was started by someone with good intentions, but if it's recognized as a separate language, <u>many students won't bother to learn "standard" English.</u> Whatever you think about that, <u>it's what people speak in the business world, and if you can't speak it and write it, you're hurting your chances of getting ahead.</u> <u>It's like separating off African American students and saying you are really different</u> and that's okay—stay different. I've read that some <u>prominent African Americans are very opposed to the idea.</u> (I should find out more about what these people said and why they're against it.) I don't know, maybe I don't have all the facts, but it seems like a terrible idea to me.*

The writer underlines some reasons she might use, and then does some more prewriting—this time in list form. She uses an article she has read that gives the opinions of prominent African Americans as evidence. She also adds other facts and experiences to support her position.

She then crosses out reasons and evidence that she thinks aren't as strong as the rest, so what remains can be turned into good, convincing support.

POSSIBLE REASONS AND EVIDENCE

discourages students from learning "standard" English

segregates African Americans as "foreign"

prominent African Americans against it

Maya Angelou quote

Bill Cosby

Eldridge Cleaver

will hurt African Americans' chances of success

~~*not fair to other English speakers*~~

~~*slang isn't recognized as legitimate*~~

~~*only in California*~~

~~*teacher training will cost taxpayers*~~

Thinking Critically to Support Your Main Point

FOCUS   Think about your position and the readers you must persuade.

ASK
- What are my reasons for taking this position? What is my strongest reason? (Save it for last.)
- What facts, examples, and expert opinions can I use to back up my reasons?
- Is all my evidence strictly related to the issue?
- What objections could my opponents raise to each reason or point of evidence? How would I answer those objections?
- What reasons and evidence will appeal strongly to my readers?
- How can I make a final pitch for my position in the conclusion?
- If I were to argue my case with these reasons and this evidence, would I stand a chance of persuading an opponent?

WRITE   List the reasons and evidence you will use.

PRACTICE 5

Finding Convincing Reasons and Evidence

Reread your notes from Practices 1 and 2 to see what you might use as reasons and evidence. Then use a prewriting technique to come up with more. As you prewrite, try to think of facts, experiences, and expert opinions that could be used as evidence. After you have come up with as much possible support as you can think of, read what you've written and cross out points that don't strictly relate to the issue or points that will not be convincing to your reader.

TOPIC SENTENCE OR THESIS STATEMENT: _____

REASON: _____

EVIDENCE: _____

_____

REASON: _____

EVIDENCE: _____

_____

REASON: _____

EVIDENCE: _____

_____

Consider the Opposing Position.

Your reasons and evidence are convincing to you, but will they persuade your opposition? Think about what someone with an opposing view might say to poke holes in your support. By anticipating the objections, you can overcome them.

To do this, list your reasons and evidence, and next to each point list possible objections. Answer the objection, using facts, examples, and expert opinion.

MY SUPPORT	OBJECTION
1. *discourages students from learning "standard" English*	1. *only used as a starting point for language instruction, not the end goal*
2. *segregates African Americans Maya Angelou quote*	
3. *will hurt African Americans' chances of success Eldridge Cleaver* ~~*not fair to other English speakers*~~ ~~*slang isn't recognized as legitimate*~~ ~~*only in California*~~ ~~*teacher training will cost taxpayers*~~	3. *will improve chances of success with more language training and better self-esteem*

PRACTICE 6

Answering Objections

For each reason you have, imagine what your opponent would say to disagree with you. Jot that down, and try to come up with an answer to the objection. At this point, you should have at least three reasons that you plan to use to defend your position. Then answer the objections.

MY REASON

1. _____

_____

2. _____

_____

3. _____

_____

MY OPPONENT'S OBJECTION

1. _____

_____

MY ANSWER:

_____

_____

2. _____

_____

MY ANSWER:

_____

_____

3. _____

_____

MY ANSWER:

_____

_____

Review Your Reasons and Evidence,
and Consider Your Opposition.

Review the support for your argument by using these five strategies:

1. Reread your reasons and evidence from your opponent's perspective, looking for ways to knock them down. Anticipate your opponent's objections and include evidence to answer them.

2. Ask someone else to "cross-examine" your reasons, looking for weak spots.

3. Stay away from generalities. Statements about what "everyone" else does or what "always" happens are easy to disprove.

4. Make sure that you have said enough. Take the time to present your support in full; your argument depends on the quality of your reasons and evidence.

5. Reread your reasons and evidence to make sure that they support your position. If they are the least bit off track, you leave your opponent room to find a hole in your argument.

Step 4. Make a Plan

Arrange the Evidence in Order of Importance.

You now have reasons and evidence, but you need to present them in the most persuasive way possible. Argument almost always uses order of importance: presenting reasons and evidence according to their power to persuade.

Order of Importance
Least important to most important
Most important to least important

Because you are building a case, you probably will want to save your most persuasive reason for last, building up force until the final brilliant stroke. Leave a strong impression that lingers. Save the best reason for last.

INFORMAL OUTLINE

TOPIC SENTENCE: Ebonics should not be recognized as a language that is taught in schools.

Reason: discourages students from learning "standard" English

    —objection: only used as a starting point for language instruction

    —answer: students learn standard English only in school

Reason: segregates African Americans

    —quote by Maya Angelou

Reason: will hurt African Americans' chances of success

    —objection: will offer more language training and better self-esteem

    —answer: spend time on what's necessary to get ahead: standard English

    —quote by Eldridge Cleaver

Make a plan (usually an outline) for your paragraph.

Thinking Critically While Planning Your Argument

FOCUS   Reread your topic sentence or thesis statement and evidence, and think about what evidence will have the most impact on your reader.

ASK
- Have I arranged my reasons in order of importance?
- What would my opponents say about my reasons and evidence?
- Can I make the reasons and evidence I have more convincing by adding detail?
- Are there any other reasons and evidence that will help me make my case?
- How can I build energy in the paragraph so that it ends making a strong and lasting impression?

WRITE   Write an outline that shows the plan for your argument.

PRACTICE 7

Making a Plan

Use the Thinking Critically guide above to make a plan for your argument in the following spaces.

TOPIC SENTENCE OR THESIS STATEMENT: _____

REASON: _____

EVIDENCE: _____

    OBJECTION: _____

    ANSWER: _____

REASON: _____

EVIDENCE: _____

    OBJECTION: _____

    ANSWER: _____

REASON: _____

EVIDENCE: _____

    OBJECTION: _____

    ANSWER: _____

REASON: _____

EVIDENCE: _____

OBJECTION: _____

ANSWER: _____

Step 5. Write a Draft

Using the outline you have prepared as a guide, write a draft of your paragraph or essay. Arrange your reasons according to order of importance. As you write your draft, add evidence to make each reason more persuasive.

FOR A PARAGRAPH

Turn your supporting reasons and evidence into complete sentences, and arrange them in paragraph form, using your topic sentence as your first sentence.

DRAFT PARAGRAPH

Ebonics should not be a recognized language that is taught in the schools. It will discourage African American students from learning "standard" English. Supporters of Ebonics claim that the study of Ebonics would only be used as a starting point for language instruction, not the end goal. But students learn standard English only in school, and that's what should be taught there. Ebonics will segregate African Americans. Poet Maya Angelou stated at a conference, "The very idea that African American language is a language separate and apart is very threatening because it can encourage young men and women not to learn standard English." Teaching Ebonics is a great step backward. Teaching Ebonics could hurt African Americans' chances of success. Supporters of Ebonics say that studying Ebonics will prepare students to learn standard English while at the same time boost their self-esteem by recognizing the legitimacy of their spoken language. But time spent on Ebonics is time not spent on standard English, and there is little enough time to learn what is necessary to get ahead in this world. As former Black Panther leader Eldridge Cleaver wrote in a recent *Los Angeles Times* article, "The only place for Ebonics is in the streets. We don't need it in the classroom; we need to rescue kids from Ebonics."

FOR AN ESSAY

Write a draft essay that includes your thesis statement in the first paragraph. Each of your reasons should become the topic sentence for a paragraph. Each body paragraph should include specific details, facts, examples, and/or expert opinion that support the topic sentence.

Write a Conclusion.

Your concluding sentence or paragraph is the last opportunity you have to win your case. Make it memorable and dramatic. Remind your reader of the issue and reaffirm your position based on the evidence.

Before writing your conclusion, build up your energy again. Then reread your topic sentence or thesis statement and draft. As soon as you finish reading, write the most forceful ending you can think of. Aim for power; you can tone it down later.

> **CONCLUDING SENTENCE:** Ebonics does not belong in the classroom, where students should learn what they don't know and need to know, not what they already know.

Thinking Critically to Write a Conclusion

FOCUS   As you reread your draft, think about what you want your reader to understand about the issue and your position.

ASK
- What is the point of my argument?
- How can I clearly and convincingly state my point once again for my readers?
- What is my final word on this issue?

WRITE   Write your conclusion.

PRACTICE 8

Writing Your Concluding Sentence

Use the Thinking Critically guide above to write two possible concluding sentences for your argument paragraph. Then circle the best one and add it to your draft.

1. _____

_____

2. _____

_____

PRACTICE 9

Writing Your Concluding Paragraph

Using the Thinking Critically guide above, write two possible concluding paragraphs for your draft essay. Then choose the best one and add it to your draft essay.

Step 6. Revise Your Draft

Teamwork: Get Feedback

When you have completed your draft, you should once again get feedback from people acting as opponents to your argument. You may be too involved to see the holes in your argument, so take advantage of others to help you see them.

When you are giving and getting feedback for your argument, remember to be sensitive to the writer, who may have strong feelings about the issue. Your job as the "cross-examiner" is to find holes, but your job as the provider of feedback is to be constructive: to help—not destroy—the writer.

GUIDELINES FOR GIVING FEEDBACK

- Start with a positive comment.
- Throughout, offer comments and observations rather than "You should's."
- Start with the draft as a whole and move to smaller points.
  - —Tell the writer what you think the question he or she is answering is.
  - —Consider whether the topic sentence or thesis statement answers the question.
  - —Tell the writer what you think the reasons and evidence are.
  - —Ask the writer whether each piece of evidence is a fact, an example, or an expert opinion.
  - —Try to come up with an objection for each reason, and ask the writer to answer your objection.
  - —Suggest other possible reasons and evidence.
- Tell the writer what works for you and what you think might be better (and how).
- Be as specific as you can. Don't just say, "It's good," or "I liked it." Explain why.
- If you get confused or lost somewhere in the draft, tell the writer where.
- Help the writer make the case.

Take a break before you revise; you will need some distance from your argument in order to judge it objectively. As you begin to revise, review your reasons and evidence:

- Reread your draft from the perspective of your opponent, looking for ways to knock down your reasons and evidence.

- Reread each reason you have offered to make sure it defends and supports your position. If it is the least bit off track, you leave your opponent room to find a hole in your argument. And once the opponent finds a small hole, he or she can then make it larger.

- Reread each reason, and the evidence that supports it, to make sure you have said enough. In a paragraph, you will probably need more than one sentence to present each reason. In an essay, you may need more than one paragraph. Take the time to present the reasons and evidence in full; your case depends entirely on your support.

- Try to think of one more piece of evidence to add to your case. It doesn't need to be the most important piece, but try now to give your argument one more support.

Add Transitions.

Your case should be seamless, moving smoothly from one reason to another. The idea is to carry your reader along with you until you have presented the whole case. Smooth transitions cut down on the likelihood of your reader stopping after each point and questioning it.

Because argument usually uses order of importance, you may want to use transitions that indicate importance.

COMMON IMPORTANCE TRANSITIONS

above all	in fact	more importantly	best
especially	in particular	worst	
	most important	most	

Other transitions that are also useful in argument include the following:

To move from one point to another:
another thing
in addition
also
another important fact to consider is

To move to your final point:
most importantly
the last point to consider
before making a final decision, remember
the most important thing

The revised example paragraph has comments that show where the writer made changes to her draft, including adding transitions.

REVISED PARAGRAPH

Ebonics should not be a recognized language that is taught in the schools. It will discourage African American students from learning "standard" English. Supporters of Ebonics claim that the [anticipated objection] study of Ebonics would only be used as a starting point for language instruction, not the end goal. But as actor Bill Cosby argued [added evidence to answer objection] in a recent *Wall Street Journal* piece, "If you don't teach Ebonics, students will find it anyway. But legitimizing the street in the classroom is backwards." Students will learn standard English only in school, and that's what should be taught there. [transition] More importantly, [revised reason] Ebonics will segregate African Americans. Poet Maya Angelou stated at a conference, "The very idea that African American language [added evidence/support] is a language separate and apart is very threatening because it can encourage young men and women not to learn standard English." Teaching Ebonics is a great step backward. [transition] The worst possible outcome of teaching Ebonics is that it could hurt African Americans' chances of success. [added support] The world of business communicates in standard English, and if students can't fluently use that language, they are unlikely to go very far. Supporters of Ebonics say that [anticipated objection] studying Ebonics will prepare students to learn standard English while at the same time boost their self-esteem by recognizing the legitimacy of their spoken language. But time spent on Ebonics is [answer objection] time not spent on standard English, and there is little enough time to learn what is necessary to get ahead in this world. As former

Black Panther leader Eldridge Cleaver wrote in a recent *Los Angeles Times* article, "The only place for Ebonics is in the streets. We don't need it in the classroom; we need to rescue kids from Ebonics." Those people who first proposed Ebonics were well intentioned, but Ebonics will hurt, not help, students. Ebonics does not belong in the classroom, where students should learn what they don't know and need to know, not what they already know.

concluding sentence

Thinking Critically to Revise an Argument

FOCUS After a break, reread your draft from the perspective of your opponent so that you can overcome objections to your argument.

ASK
- Are all the points I make actually reason and evidence that support my position?
- Do any of the reasons or evidence need more detail?
- What would my opponent say about my reasons and evidence?
- What other reasons and evidence can I think of?
- Can I make the topic sentence, thesis statement, or conclusion more forceful?
- Could transitions help the reader understand when I'm making a new point?
- Does the argument have energy and conviction?
- How can I make the argument better?

WRITE Revise by making improvements to your draft.

PRACTICE 10

Revising Your Draft

Using the Thinking Critically guide above, revise your draft. Make at least three changes and be prepared to explain how they improved the draft.

Checklists for Paragraphs and Essays
(*Chapters 9–17, 19, 20*)

Checklist: How to Write an Illustration Paragraph

Check off items as you complete them.

1.   **Narrow and explore your general topic.**

_____ Narrow the general topic to a more specific topic that you are interested in and that you can show, explain, or prove in one paragraph.

_____ Jot down some ideas about the narrowed topic and why it's important.

2.   **KEY STEP**   **Make a main point in a topic sentence.** (See p. 116.)

_____ Decide what is most important about your narrowed topic. What do you want to say to your readers? What point do you want to make?

_____ Write a topic sentence that contains both your narrowed topic and the point you want to make about it.

3.   **KEY STEPS**   **Support your main point with specific examples, and give details that explain the examples.** (See pp. 116 and 118.)

_____ Use a prewriting technique to find supporting examples that will show, explain, or prove your main point.

_____ Drop unrelated ideas. Select the best specific examples to use in your paragraph.

_____ Add supporting details to explain the examples.

4.   **Make a plan.**

_____ Using the topic sentence as the first sentence, make a plan by listing your examples under it, in the order in which you will present them.

5.   **Write a draft.**

_____ Write a draft paragraph using complete sentences in paragraph form.

_____ Write a concluding sentence that relates back to your main point but does not just repeat it.

_____ Title your paragraph, if required.

(continued)

6.   **Revise your draft.**

_____   Get feedback from others. (See Chapter 8, pp. 93–94 for guidelines for giving and getting feedback, including Questions for Reviewers of a Draft.)

_____   Cut any details that do not support your main point.

_____   Make sure that you have enough examples to appeal to your audience and to get your point across.

_____   Make sure your paragraph flows. Add transitions and repeat key words as necessary.

_____   Do not just copy over your draft. Make at least three changes to improve it.

7.   **Edit your revised draft.**

_____   Find and correct any problems with grammar, spelling, word use, or punctuation.

_____   Produce a clean, final copy.

_____   Ask yourself: Is this the best I can do?

Checklist: How to Write an Illustration Essay

Check off items as you complete them.

1.   **Narrow and explore your general topic.**

_____ Narrow the general topic to a more specific topic that you are interested in and that you can show, explain, or prove in an essay that is several paragraphs long.

_____ Jot down some ideas about the narrowed topic and why it's important.

2.   **KEY STEP Make a main point in a thesis statement.** (See p. 116.)

_____ Decide what is most important about your narrowed topic. What do you want to say to your readers? What point do you want to make?

_____ Write a thesis statement that contains both your narrowed topic and the point you want to make about it.

3.   **KEY STEPS Support your main point with specific examples, and give details that explain the examples.** (See pp. 116 and 118.)

_____ Use a prewriting technique to find supporting examples that will show, explain, or prove your main point.

_____ Drop unrelated ideas. Select the best specific examples to use in your essay.

_____ Add supporting details to explain the examples.

4.   **Make a plan.**

_____ Arrange your examples. Write a topic sentence for each example.

_____ Make a plan or outline that arranges the topic sentences in the correct order.

5.   **Write a draft.**

_____ Write a draft essay with an introduction that includes your thesis statement and supporting body paragraphs with examples and details.

_____ Write a concluding paragraph that relates back to your main point but does not simply repeat it.

_____ Title your essay.

(continued)

6.   **Revise your draft.**

_____   Get feedback from others. (See Chapter 8, pp. 93–94, for guidelines for giving and getting feedback, including Questions for Reviewers of a Draft.)

_____   Cut any examples that do not support your main point.

_____   Make sure that you have enough examples to appeal to your audience and to get your point across.

_____   Add details to support examples that seem weak or need explanation.

_____   Make sure your essay flows. Add transitions and repeat key words as necessary. Add transitional sentences between paragraphs as necessary.

_____   Do not just copy over your draft. Make at least five changes to improve it.

7.   **Edit your revised draft.**

_____   Find and correct any problems with grammar, spelling, word use, or punctuation.

_____   Produce a clean, final copy.

_____   Ask yourself: Is this the best I can do?

Checklist: How to Write a Narration Paragraph

Check off items as you complete them.

1.   Narrow and explore your general topic (the story you will tell).

_____   Narrow the general topic to a specific experience that you are interested in—one you can tell about in a paragraph.

_____   Jot down some ideas about the story and why it's important.

2.   KEY STEP   Make a main point in a topic sentence. (See p. 132.)

_____   Decide what is most important about the experience. What do you want your story to reveal? How were you or others affected by what happened?

_____   Write a topic sentence that includes your narrowed topic and your main point.

3.   KEY STEP   Support your main point with the essential events that tell the story, and give details about those events. (See p. 134.)

_____   Use a prewriting technique to find the events that were part of the experience.

_____   Read your prewriting, and choose the events that are most important to the reader's understanding of the story. Drop events that are not essential to the story.

_____   Add details to make the events come to life. Consider adding conversation.

4.   Make a plan.

_____   Arrange the events in time order, and make a plan.

5.   Write a draft.

_____   Write a draft paragraph using complete sentences in paragraph form.

_____   Write a concluding sentence that sums up what is important about the story and relates back to your topic sentence.

_____   Title your paragraph, if required.

(continued)

6.   **Revise your draft.**

_____ Get feedback from others. (See Chapter 8, pp. 93–94, for guidelines for giving and getting feedback, including Questions for Reviewers of a Draft.)

_____ Cut any details that distract readers from the story.

_____ Add any other events that are important to the story.

_____ Make sure the sequence of events is logical.

_____ Add transitions (especially time transitions) to take readers from one event to another.

_____ Do not just copy over your draft. Make at least three changes to improve it.

7.   **Edit your revised draft.**

_____ Find and correct any problems with grammar, spelling, word use, or punctuation.

_____ Produce a clean, final copy.

_____ Ask yourself: Is this the best I can do?

Checklist: How to Write a Narration Essay

Check off items as you complete them.

1. Narrow and explore your general topic (the story or experience you will tell).

_____ Narrow the general topic to a specific experience that you are interested in and can tell about in an essay. Jot down some ideas about the story and why it's important.

2. KEY STEP Make a main point in a thesis statement. (See p. 132.)

_____ Decide what is most important about the experience. What do you want your story to reveal? How were you or others affected by what happened?

_____ Write a thesis statement that includes both your narrowed topic and the point your story will make.

3. KEY STEP Support your main point with the essential events that tell the story, and give details about those events. (See p. 134.)

_____ Use a prewriting technique to find the events that were part of the experience.

_____ Read your prewriting, and choose the events that are most important to the reader's understanding of the story. Drop events that are not essential to the story.

_____ Add details to make the events come to life. Consider adding conversation.

4. Make a plan.

_____ Arrange the events in time order.

_____ Write a topic sentence for each major event.

_____ Make a plan or outline that arranges the topic sentences in the correct order.

5. Write a draft.

_____ Write a draft essay with topic sentences and paragraphs for each major event.

_____ Write a concluding paragraph that reminds your reader of the main point of the story or experience; your conclusion should relate back to your thesis statement but not simply repeat it.

_____ Title the essay.

(continued)

6.   **Revise your draft.**

_____   Get feedback from others. (See Chapter 8, pp. 93–94, for guidelines for giving and getting feedback, including Questions for Reviewers of a Draft.)

_____   Cut any details that distract readers from the story.

_____   Add any other events that are important to the story.

_____   Make sure the sequence is logical.

_____   Add transitions (especially time transitions) to take readers from one event to another. Add transitional sentences between paragraphs as necessary.

_____   Do not just copy over your draft. Make at least five changes to improve it.

7.   **Edit your revised draft.**

_____   Find and correct any problems with grammar, spelling, word use, or punctuation.

_____   Produce a clean, final copy.

_____   Ask yourself: Is this the best I can do?

Checklist: How to Write a Description Paragraph

Check off items as you complete them.

1.   **Narrow and explore your general topic (the person, place, or thing you will describe).**

_____   Narrow the general topic to a specific topic that interests you and that you have observed directly—one you can describe in a paragraph.

_____   Jot down a few ideas you have about the narrowed topic.

_____   Consider your purpose for describing this topic.

2.   **KEY STEP** **Convey your main impression in a topic sentence.** (See p. 154.)

_____   Review your ideas, and decide what main impression you want to create about your topic. What overall effect do you want your description to make on your readers?

_____   Write a topic sentence that includes your narrowed topic and your main impression.

3.   **KEY STEP** **Support your main impression with sensory details.** (See p. 156.)

_____   Use a prewriting technique to discover concrete, sensory details (sight, hearing, smell, taste, and touch) that will support your main impression and make the topic come alive for your readers.

_____   Drop details that don't support the main impression, and select those that do.

_____   Add information to make the details more vivid and concrete.

4.   **Make a plan.**

_____   Arrange the details in a logical order (probably space order), and make a plan.

5.   **Write a draft.**

_____   Write a draft paragraph using complete sentences in paragraph form.

_____   Write a concluding sentence that relates back to the main impression, emphasizing it one last time for your readers.

(continued)

6.   **Revise your draft.**

_____   Get feedback from others. (See Chapter 8, pp. 93–94, for guidelines for giving and getting feedback, including Questions for Reviewers of a Draft.)

_____   Cut any details that do not support your main impression or help show readers what you mean.

_____   Add any sensory details that will make your paragraph stronger.

_____   Make sure the order of details is logical. Add transitions (especially space transitions) to take readers from one detail to another.

_____   Do not just copy over your draft. Make at least three changes to improve it.

7.   **Edit your revised draft.**

_____   Find and correct any problems with grammar, spelling, word use, or punctuation.

_____   Produce a clean, final copy.

_____   Ask yourself: Is this the best I can do?

Checklist: How to Write a Description Essay

Check off items as you complete them.

1.   **Narrow and explore your general topic (the person, place, or thing you will describe).**

_____   Narrow the general topic to a specific topic that interests you and that you have observed directly. Make sure you can write an essay-length description of your narrowed topic.

_____   Jot down a few ideas you have about the narrowed topic.

_____   Consider your purpose for describing this topic. What main quality do you want your readers to learn about the topic?

2.   **KEY STEP** **Convey your main impression in a thesis statement.** (See p. 154.)

_____   Review your ideas, and decide what main impression you want to create about your topic.

_____   Write a thesis statement that includes both your narrowed topic and the main impression you want to convey about it.

3.   **KEY STEP** **Support your main impression with sensory details.** (See p. 156.)

_____   Use a prewriting technique to find concrete, sensory details (sight, hearing, smell, taste, and touch) that will support your main impression and make the topic come alive for your readers.

_____   Drop details that don't support the main impression, and select those that do.

_____   Add information to make the details more vivid and concrete.

4.   **Make a plan.**

_____   Arrange the major details in a logical order. (Descriptions are often organized by spatial order.)

_____   Write a topic sentence for each major detail.

_____   Make a plan or outline that arranges the topic sentences in the correct order.

(continued)

5.   **Write a draft.**

_____   Write a draft essay with topic sentences and paragraphs for each major detail.

_____   Write a concluding paragraph that relates back to the main impression in your thesis statement and makes an observation based on the points you have made.

_____   Title the essay.

6.   **Revise your draft.**

_____   Get feedback from others. (See Chapter 8, pp. 93–94, for guidelines for giving and getting feedback, including Questions for Reviewers of a Draft.)

_____   Cut any details that do not support your main impression or help show readers what you mean.

_____   Add any sensory details that will make your essay stronger.

_____   Make sure the order of details is logical. Add transitions (especially space transitions) to make the details within each paragraph easy to follow, and repeat key words as necessary. Add transitional sentences between paragraphs to help readers follow your ideas.

_____   Do not just copy over your draft. Make at least five changes to improve it.

7.   **Edit your revised draft.**

_____   Find and correct any problems with grammar, spelling, word use, or punctuation.

_____   Produce a clean, final copy.

_____   Ask yourself: Is this the best I can do?

Checklist: How to Write a Process Analysis Paragraph

Check off items as you complete them.

1. **Narrow and explore your topic (the process you will analyze).**

_____ Narrow the general topic to a specific process that you know about, are interested in, and can describe in a paragraph.

_____ Jot down a few ideas about the narrowed topic.

_____ Consider your purpose for describing this process: Do you want to teach your readers how to do it themselves? Do you want to give your readers an idea of how it happens?

2. **KEY STEP** **Make a main point in a topic sentence.** (See p. 172.)

_____ Decide what is most important about the process. What do you want readers to understand about it?

_____ Write a topic sentence that includes both the process you are analyzing and the main point you want to make about it.

3. **KEY STEP** **Choose the essential steps in the process to support your main point.** (See p. 172.)

_____ Use a prewriting technique to find all steps you can think of.

_____ Drop any steps that are not essential to the process.

_____ Choose steps that are necessary for the reader to perform the process or to understand how it works.

_____ Add details to make the steps more concrete, specific, and easy to follow.

4. **KEY STEP** **Make a plan. Arrange the steps in a logical order.** (See p. 175.)

_____ Arrange the steps in time order and make a plan, using the topic sentence as the first sentence.

5. **Write a draft.**

_____ Write a draft paragraph using complete sentences in correct paragraph form.

(continued)

_____ Write a concluding sentence that reminds the reader of your main point about the process.

_____ Title your paragraph, if required.

6. Revise your draft.

_____ Get feedback from others. (See Chapter 8, pp. 93–94, for guidelines for giving and getting feedback, including Questions for Reviewers of a Draft.)

_____ Cut unnecessary steps and detours.

_____ Add any other steps that readers need in order to understand the process, and add details to any steps that aren't clear.

_____ Make sure the sequence of steps is logical; add time transitions where connections are unclear.

_____ Do not just copy over your draft. Make at least three changes to improve it.

7. Edit your revised draft.

_____ Find and correct any problems with grammar, spelling, word use, or punctuation.

_____ Produce a clean, final copy.

_____ Ask yourself: Is this the best I can do?

Checklist: How to Write a Process Analysis Essay

Check off items as you complete them.

1.   **Narrow and explore your general topic (the process you will analyze).**

_____   Narrow the general topic to a specific process that you know about, are interested in, and can describe in an essay.

_____   Jot down a few ideas about the specific process.

_____   Consider your purpose for describing this process: Do you want to teach your readers how to do it themselves? Do you want to give your readers an idea of how it happens?

2.   **KEY STEP**   **Make a main point in a thesis statement.** (See p. 172.)

_____   Decide what is most important about the process. What do you want readers to understand about it?

_____   Write a thesis statement that includes both the process you are analyzing and the main point you want to make about it.

3.   **KEY STEP**   **Choose the essential steps in the process to support your main point.** (See p. 172.)

_____   Use a prewriting technique to find all the steps you can think of.

_____   Drop any steps that are not essential to the process.

_____   Choose steps that are necessary for the reader to perform the process or to understand how it works.

_____   Add details to make the steps more concrete, specific, and easy to follow.

4.   **KEY STEP**   **Make a plan. Arrange the steps in a logical order.** (See p. 175.)

_____   Arrange the major steps in a logical order. (A process analysis is often organized by time order, the order in which the steps occur.)

_____   Write a topic sentence for each major step.

_____   Make a plan or outline that arranges the topic sentences in the correct order.

(continued)

5. **Write a draft.**

_____ Write a draft essay with topic sentences and paragraphs for each of the major steps.

_____ Write a concluding paragraph that relates back to your main point about the process.

_____ Title the essay.

6. **Revise your draft.**

_____ Get feedback from others. (See Chapter 8, pp. 93–94, for guidelines for giving and getting feedback, including Questions for Reviewers of a Draft.)

_____ Cut unnecessary steps or detours.

_____ Add any other steps that readers need in order to understand the process, and add details to any steps that aren't clear.

_____ Make sure the sequence is logical; add time transitions where connections are unclear. Add transitional sentences to help readers move from one paragraph to the next.

_____ Do not just copy over your draft. Make at least five changes to improve it.

7. **Edit your revised draft.**

_____ Find and correct any problems with grammar, spelling, word use, or punctuation.

_____ Produce a clean, final copy.

_____ Ask yourself: Is this the best I can do?

Checklist: How to Write a Classification Paragraph

Check off items as you complete them.

1. **Narrow and explore your general topic (the collection of people or items you will categorize).**

_____ Narrow the general topic to one that you are familiar with, are interested in, and can break into groups.

_____ Jot down a few ideas about the narrowed topic and some possible categories.

_____ Consider your purpose for classifying the topic: What do you want to show your readers?

2. **Make a main point in a topic sentence.**

_____ Review your ideas and decide how you want to sort your topic.

_____ Write a topic sentence that includes both your narrowed topic and your organizing principle—how you are classifying (sorting) your topic. You may also want to mention the categories in the topic sentence.

3. **KEY STEPS Choose useful categories, and make sure that they follow the same organizing principle.** (See pp. 192 and 194.)

_____ Use a prewriting technique to find possible categories into which you could sort your topic.

_____ Drop categories that do not follow the organizing principle. Choose the most useful categories.

4. **KEY STEP Give examples of people or items that fit in the categories, and include facts and details to explain your examples.** (See p. 196.)

_____ Find examples of people or items that fit into each category.

_____ Add facts and details for each example you find.

5. **Make a plan.**

_____ Decide on an order of presentation and make a plan, using the topic sentence as the first sentence.

(continued)

6.   **Write a draft.**

_____   Write a draft paragraph using complete sentences in correct paragraph form.

_____   Write a concluding sentence that reminds readers of your topic and makes an observation about the topic and the categories.

_____   Title your paragraph, if required.

7.   **Revise your draft.**

_____   Get feedback from others. (See Chapter 8, pp. 93–94, for guidelines for giving and getting feedback, including Questions for Reviewers of a Draft.)

_____   Cut any categories that do not follow the one organizing principle you've chosen and any examples that do not fit their categories.

_____   Add transitions to let readers know you are moving from one category to another.

_____   Add any other necessary categories, examples, facts, or details.

_____   Do not just copy over your draft. Make at least three changes to improve it.

8.   **Edit your revised draft.**

_____   Find and correct any problems with grammar, spelling, word use, or punctuation.

_____   Produce a clean, final copy.

_____   Ask yourself: Is this the best I can do?

Checklist: How to Write a Classification Essay

Check off items as you complete them.

1.   **Narrow and explore your general topic** (the collection of people or items you will categorize).

_____   Narrow the general topic to one that you are familiar with, are interested in, and can break into groups. Make sure you can write an essay-length classification of your narrowed topic.

_____   Jot down a few ideas about the narrowed topic and some possible categories.

_____   Consider your purpose for classifying the topic: What do you want to show your readers?

2.   **Make a main point in a thesis statement.**

_____   Review your ideas and decide how you want to sort your topic.

_____   Write a thesis statement that includes both your narrowed topic and your organizing principle—how you are classifying (sorting) your topic. You may also want to mention the categories in the thesis statement.

3.   **KEY STEPS** **Choose useful categories, and make sure that they follow the same organizing principle.** (See pp. 192 and 194.)

_____   Use a prewriting technique to find possible categories into which you could sort your topic.

_____   Drop categories that do not follow the organizing principle. Choose the most useful categories.

4.   **KEY STEP** **Give examples of people or items that fit in the categories, and include facts and details to explain your examples.** (See p. 196.)

_____   Find examples of people or items that fit into each category.

_____   Add facts and details for each example you find.

(continued)

5.   **Make a plan.**

_____   Arrange the categories in a logical order.

_____   Write a topic sentence for each category.

_____   Make a plan or outline that arranges the topic sentences in the correct order.

6.   **Write a draft.**

_____   Write a draft essay with topic sentences and paragraphs for each category.

_____   Write a concluding paragraph that reminds readers of your topic and makes an observation about the topic and the categories.

_____   Title the essay.

7.   **Revise your draft.**

_____   Get feedback from others. (See Chapter 8, pp. 93–94, for guidelines for giving and getting feedback, including Questions for Reviewers of a Draft.)

_____   Cut any categories that do not fit the organizing principle you've chosen and any examples that do not fit their categories.

_____   Add transitions and transitional sentences to let readers know you are moving from one category to another.

_____   Add any other necessary categories, examples, facts, or details.

_____   Do not just copy over your draft. Make at least five changes to improve it.

8.   **Edit your revised draft.**

_____   Find and correct any problems with grammar, spelling, word use, or punctuation.

_____   Produce a clean, final copy.

_____   Ask yourself: Is this the best I can do?

Checklist: How to Write a Definition Paragraph

Check off items as you complete them.

1.   **Narrow and explore your general topic (the term you will define).**

_____ Use a dictionary to find the meaning(s) of the word you plan to define.

_____ Make sure your topic is a term that you can define in a paragraph.

_____ Jot down a few ideas about the term's meaning. Consider both the dictionary meaning(s) and other meanings.

_____ Consider your purpose for defining this term: What do you want your readers to know about it?

2.   **KEY STEP** **Write a topic sentence that presents a clear, basic definition.** (See p. 213.)

_____ Review your ideas, and decide what basic definition you will give in your paragraph.

_____ Write a topic sentence that includes both the term and a basic definition. You may want to use one of these patterns:

      term + *means/is* + basic definition = topic sentence

      term + class + detail = topic sentence

      term + *is not* + expected definition = topic sentence

_____ Do not just copy the dictionary definition. Write the definition in your own words.

3.   **KEY STEP** **Support your definition with examples and details.** (See p. 216.)

_____ Use a prewriting technique to find examples and details that explain the term.

_____ Drop examples that do not support the definition.

_____ Select the best examples to use in your paragraph. Add any details necessary to make your definition clearer.

(continued)

4. **Make a plan.**

——— Arrange the examples and make a plan, using your topic sentence as the first sentence. A definition might use any of the three ways to order ideas: space, time, or importance. Arrange your ideas so that readers will understand them.

5. **Write a draft.**

——— Write a draft paragraph using complete sentences in correct paragraph form.

——— Write a concluding sentence that reminds readers of the term and its meaning and makes an observation about it based on the examples you've given.

——— Title your paragraph, if required.

6. **Revise your draft.**

——— Get feedback from others. (See Chapter 8, pp. 93–94, for guidelines for giving and getting feedback, including Questions for Reviewers of a Draft.)

——— Cut examples or details that don't help to communicate your definition.

——— Add other examples or details that help explain the term.

——— Make sure the sequence is logical; add transitions to take readers smoothly from one example to the next.

——— Do not just copy over your draft. Make at least three changes to improve it.

7. **Edit your revised draft.**

——— Find and correct any problems with grammar, spelling, word use, or punctuation.

——— Produce a clean, final copy.

——— Ask yourself: Is this the best I can do?

Checklist: How to Write a Definition Essay

Check off items as you complete them.

1. **Narrow and explore your general topic (the term you will define).**

   _____ Use a dictionary to find the meaning(s) of the word you plan to define.

   _____ Make sure you can write an essay-length definition of your term.

   _____ Jot down a few ideas about the term's meaning. Consider both the dictionary meaning(s) and other meanings.

   _____ Consider your purpose for defining this term: What do you want your readers to know about it?

2. **KEY STEP** **Write a thesis statement that presents a clear, basic definition.** (See p. 214.)

   _____ Review your ideas, and decide what basic definition you will give or if you want to give several different meanings.

   _____ Write a thesis statement that includes both the term and a basic definition. You may want to use one of these patterns:

   term + *means/is* + basic definition = thesis statement

   term + class + detail = thesis statement

   term + *is not* + expected definition = thesis statement

   _____ Do not just copy the dictionary definition. Write the definition in your own words.

3. **KEY STEP** **Support your definition with examples and details.** (See p. 216.)

   _____ Use a prewriting technique to find examples and details that explain the term.

   _____ Drop examples that do not support the definition.

   _____ Select the best examples to use in your essay. Add any details necessary to make your definition clearer.

4. **Make a plan.**

   _____ Write a topic sentence for each main support point, which will usually be an example.

(continued)

_____ Arrange the examples and make a plan or outline, using the thesis statement as the first sentence and topic sentences for main support points. A definition might use any of the three ways to order ideas: space, time, or importance. Arrange your ideas so that readers will understand them.

5. **Write a draft.**

_____ Write a draft essay with topic sentences and paragraphs for each major example.

_____ Write a conclusion that reminds readers of the term and its meaning and makes an observation about it based on the examples you've given.

_____ Title the essay.

6. **Revise your draft.**

_____ Get feedback from others. (See Chapter 8, pp. 93–94, for guidelines for giving and getting feedback, including Questions for Reviewers of a Draft.)

_____ Cut examples or details that don't help to communicate your definition.

_____ Add other examples or details that help explain the term.

_____ Make sure the sequence is logical; add transitions to take readers smoothly from one example to the next.

_____ Do not just copy over your draft. Make at least five changes to improve it.

7. **Edit your revised draft.**

_____ Find and correct any problems with grammar, spelling, word use, or punctuation.

_____ Produce a clean, final copy.

_____ Ask yourself: Is this the best I can do?

Checklist: How to Write a Comparison/Contrast Paragraph

Check off items as you complete them.

1.   **Narrow and explore your general topic.**

_____   Narrow your general topic to two subjects that you are interested in, that have enough in common to be compared or contrasted, and that can be compared or contrasted in a paragraph.

_____   Jot down some ideas about the two subjects.

_____   Decide why you are comparing or contrasting these two subjects. Is it to help readers choose between them? Or is it to give readers a better understanding of their relationship?

_____   Decide whether you will compare or contrast your subjects.

2.   **KEY STEP** **Find points of comparison or contrast, and write a topic sentence.** (See p. 231.)

_____   Review your ideas about the subjects you want to compare or contrast.

_____   Use a prewriting technique to find similarities or differences. Many people find that making a two-column list (one for each subject) is the easiest way to come up with parallel similarities or differences.

_____   Write a topic sentence that includes your subjects, the main point you want to make about them, and whether you are comparing or contrasting them.

_____   Select the points of comparison or contrast you will use, choosing points that your readers will understand.

_____   Add details, facts, or examples of points, if necessary.

3.   **KEY STEP** **Decide on an organization, and arrange the points. Make a plan.** (See p. 234.)

_____   Decide whether to use point-by-point or whole-to-whole organization.

_____   Outline or diagram the paragraph by arranging the points of comparison or contrast in the order you want to present them.

4.   **Write a draft.**

_____   Turn the points of comparison or contrast into complete sentences and put them in paragraph form.

(*continued*)

_____ Write a concluding sentence that reminds readers of what you are comparing or contrasting, and make an observation or decision based on the similarities or differences.

_____ Title your paragraph, if required.

5. Revise your draft.

_____ Get feedback from others. (See Chapter 8, pp. 93–94, for guidelines for giving and getting feedback, including Questions for Reviewers of a Draft.)

_____ Make sure your points of comparison or contrast are parallel and important. Cut anything that does not help make your point.

_____ Add any other information that will help you show important similarities or differences.

_____ Add transitions to move readers smoothly from one part of the comparison or contrast to the next.

_____ Do not just copy over your draft. Make at least three changes to improve it.

6. Edit your revised draft.

_____ Find and correct any problems with grammar, spelling, word use, or punctuation.

_____ Produce a clean, final copy.

_____ Ask yourself: Is this the best I can do?

Checklist: How to Write a Comparison/Contrast Essay

Check off items as you complete them.

1. **Narrow and explore your general topic.**

_____ Narrow your general topic to two subjects that you are interested in, that have enough in common to be compared or contrasted, and that can be compared or contrasted in an essay.

_____ Jot down some ideas about the two subjects.

_____ Decide why you are comparing and/or contrasting these two subjects. Is it to help readers choose between them? Or is it to give readers a better understanding of their relationship?

_____ Decide whether you will use comparison, contrast, or both.

2. **KEY STEP** **Find points of comparison or contrast, and write a thesis statement.** (See p. 231.)

_____ Review your ideas about the subjects you want to compare and/or contrast.

_____ Use a prewriting technique to find similarities and/or differences. Many people find that making a two-column list (one for each subject) is the easiest way to come up with parallel similarities or differences.

_____ Write a thesis statement that includes your subjects, the main point you want to make about them, and whether you are comparing or contrasting them (or both).

_____ Select the points of comparison and/or contrast you will use, choosing points that your readers will understand. You might want to preview your points of comparison or contrast in your thesis statement.

_____ Add details, facts, or examples of points, if necessary.

3. **KEY STEP** **Decide on an organization, and arrange the points. Make a plan.** (See p. 234.)

_____ Decide whether to use point-by-point or whole-to-whole organization.

_____ Write a topic sentence for each point (point-by-point organization) or each subject (whole-to-whole organization).

_____ Make a plan or outline that arranges the topic sentences in the correct order.

(continued)

4.   **Write a draft.**

_____ Write a draft essay with topic sentences and paragraphs for each point or subject. If necessary, add details, facts, and examples for each point.

_____ Write a concluding paragraph that reminds readers of what you are comparing and/or contrasting, and make an observation or decision based on the similarities or differences.

_____ Title the essay.

5.   **Revise your draft.**

_____ Get feedback from others. (See Chapter 8, pp. 93–94, for guidelines for giving and getting feedback, including Questions for Reviewers of a Draft.)

_____ Make sure your points of comparison/contrast are parallel and important. Cut anything that does not help make your point.

_____ Add any other information that will help you show important similarities or differences.

_____ Add transitions and transitional sentences to move readers smoothly from one part of the comparison/contrast to the next.

_____ Do not just copy over your draft. Make at least five changes to improve it.

6.   **Edit your revised draft.**

_____ Find and correct any problems with grammar, spelling, word use, or punctuation.

_____ Produce a clean, final copy.

_____ Ask yourself: Is this the best I can do?

Checklist: How to Write a Cause/Effect Paragraph

Check off items as you complete them.

1. **Narrow and explore your general topic (the situation or event for which you will present causes and/or effects).**

_____ Narrow the general topic to one that you are familiar with, are able to determine logical causes and effects for, and can describe in a paragraph.

_____ Jot down a few ideas about the narrowed topic.

_____ Consider your purpose for writing: Do you want to explain why something happened, do you want to show what happened as a result of it, or both?

2. **KEY STEP** **Choose direct and important causes and/or effects. Write a topic sentence.** (See p. 254.)

_____ Use a prewriting technique to find causes and/or effects.

_____ Review the causes and/or effects to make sure that they were direct causes and/or direct results of the situation or event, not just things that happened before or after.

_____ Decide whether you will discuss causes, effects, or both.

_____ Write a topic sentence that presents the situation or event and tells the reader whether you will present causes, effects, or both.

_____ Do not state: "In this paragraph, I will discuss causes and/or effects." Instead, write a statement that explains what you plan to do, not one that is just an announcement.

_____ Choose the most significant causes and/or effects to use in your paragraph.

3. **KEY STEP** **Give specific examples of and details about the causes and/or effects to support your topic sentence.** (See p. 256.)

_____ For each cause and/or effect, give an example or details that support your topic sentence.

_____ Drop details that do not directly relate to your topic sentence, and add details that will make the point clearer to your readers.

(continued)

4.   **Make a plan.**

_____   Arrange the causes/effects and make a plan, using your topic sentence as the first sentence. A cause/effect paragraph might use any of the three ways of organizing ideas: space, time, or importance. Arrange your ideas so that readers will understand them.

5.   **Write a draft.**

_____   Write a draft paragraph using complete sentences in correct paragraph form.

_____   Write a concluding sentence that reminds readers of the importance of the causes and/or effects you have presented and makes some observation about them.

_____   Title your paragraph, if required.

6.   **Revise your draft.**

_____   Get feedback from others. (See Chapter 8, pp. 93–94, for guidelines for giving and getting feedback, including Questions for Reviewers of a Draft.)

_____   Cut anything that doesn't directly explain what caused or resulted from the situation or event.

_____   Add other examples or details that will explain each cause or effect more clearly.

_____   Make sure the sequence is logical; add transitions to guide readers smoothly from one example to the next.

_____   Do not just copy over your draft. Make at least three changes to improve it.

7.   **Edit your revised draft.**

_____   Find and correct any problems with grammar, spelling, word use, or punctuation.

_____   Produce a clean, final copy.

_____   Ask yourself: Is this the best I can do?

Checklist: How to Write a Cause/Effect Essay

Check off items as you complete them.

1.   **Narrow and explore your general topic (the situation or event for which you will present causes and/or effects).**

_____   Jot down a few ideas about the narrowed topic.

_____   Consider your purpose for writing: Do you want to explain why something happened, do you want to show what happened as a result of it, or both?

2.   **KEY STEP**   **Choose direct and important causes and/or effects. Write a thesis statement.** (See pp. 254 and 255.)

_____   Use a prewriting technique to find causes and/or effects.

_____   Review the causes and/or effects to make sure that they were direct causes and/or direct results of the situation or event, not just things that happened before or after.

_____   Decide whether you will discuss causes, effects, or both.

_____   Write a thesis statement that presents the situation or event and tells the reader whether you will present causes, effects, or both. Consider including a preview of the causes and/or effects you will present.

_____   Do not state: "In this essay, I will discuss causes and/or effects." Instead, write a statement that explains what you plan to do, not one that is just an announcement.

_____   Choose the most significant causes and/or effects to use in your essay.

3.   **KEY STEP**   **Give specific examples of and details about the causes and/or effects.** (See p. 256.)

_____   For each cause and/or effect, give an example and details that support your thesis statement.

_____   Drop examples that do not directly relate to your thesis statement, and add examples and details that make your main point clearer to your readers.

(continued)

4.   Make a plan.

_____   Write a topic sentence for each cause or effect.

_____   Make a plan or outline that arranges the topic sentences in a logical order. A cause/effect essay might use any of the three ways of organizing ideas: space, time, or importance. Arrange your ideas so that readers will understand them.

5.   Write a draft.

_____   Write a draft essay with topic sentences and paragraphs for each cause and/or effect.

_____   Write a concluding paragraph that reminds readers of your topic and makes an observation about the causes and effects.

_____   Title the essay.

6.   Revise your draft.

_____   Get feedback from others. (See Chapter 8, pp. 93–94, for guidelines for giving and getting feedback, including Questions for Reviewers of a Draft.)

_____   Cut anything that doesn't directly explain what caused or resulted from the situation or event.

_____   Add other examples or details that you think will explain each cause or effect more clearly.

_____   Make sure the organization is logical; add transitions and transitional sentences to guide readers smoothly from one cause or effect to the next.

_____   Do not just copy over your draft. Make at least five changes to improve it.

7.   Edit your revised draft.

_____   Find and correct any problems with grammar, spelling, word use, or punctuation.

_____   Produce a clean, final copy.

_____   Ask yourself: Is this the best I can do?

Checklist: How to Write an Argument Paragraph

Check off items as you complete them.

1.   **KEY STEP** **Explore the issue, and take a definite position.** (See p. 273.)

_____   Turn the issue into a question. Jot down some ideas about the issue and what your position is.

_____   Build enthusiasm and energy by taking a few minutes to think about how you are personally affected or involved. Take a position.

_____   Make sure the issue and your position are narrow enough to be covered in a single paragraph.

2.   **Write a topic sentence that states your position.**

_____   Write a topic sentence that answers your question. It should include both the issue and your position on that issue.

3.   **KEY STEP** **Present convincing reasons and evidence to support your position.** (See p. 275.)

_____   Use a prewriting technique to come up with reasons and evidence.

_____   Clearly state your reasons.

_____   Consider what makes strong, persuasive evidence (facts, examples, expert opinions).

_____   Consider whether you will need to consult outside sources at the library or on the Internet. (See Chapter 19.)

_____   Consider what your readers' position on the issue probably is and what types of reasons and evidence will most likely convince them.

_____   Drop reasons and evidence that are unrelated to your position and evidence that will not be convincing to your readers.

_____   Consider opposing views and anticipate objections.

_____   Select the best reasons and evidence to use in your paragraph. Find additional facts, examples, or expert opinions as needed to back up your position.

(continued)

4.   **Make a plan.**

_____ Arrange the reasons in order of importance (probably from least important to most important). Make a plan, using the topic sentence as the first sentence.

5.   **Write a draft.**

_____ Write a draft using complete sentences in correct paragraph form.

_____ Write a concluding sentence that reminds readers of the issue and reaffirms your position based on your reasons and evidence. Make your final pitch—with energy.

_____ Title your paragraph, if required.

6.   **Revise your draft.**

_____ Get feedback from others. (See Chapter 8, pp. 93–94, for guidelines for giving and getting feedback, including Questions for Reviewers of a Draft.)

_____ Read your draft from the perspective of someone who strongly defends the opposite position.

_____ Cut any reasons or evidence that does not support your position.

_____ Add other support that might strengthen your argument.

_____ Make sure the sequence of ideas is logical. Add transitions, especially transitions for emphasis, as needed.

_____ Do not just copy over your draft. Make at least three changes to improve it.

7.   **Edit your revised draft.**

_____ Find and correct any problems with grammar, spelling, word use, or punctuation.

_____ Produce a clean, final copy.

_____ Ask yourself: Is this the best I can do?

Checklist: How to Write an Argument Essay

Check off items as you complete them.

1.   **KEY STEP**   **Explore the issue, and take a definite position.** (See p. 273.)

_____   Turn the issue into a question.

_____   Use a prewriting technique to find and explore your position, your readers' position, and the opposition's position. Make sure you can write an essay-length argument about this issue and your position.

_____   Build energy, get involved with the issue, and take a stand. Take a few minutes to think about how this issue affects you or your family.

2.   **Write a thesis statement.**

_____   Write a thesis statement that answers your question. Make it strong and clear. Consider adding a preview of your reasons.

3.   **KEY STEP**   **Present convincing reasons and evidence to support your position.** (See p. 275.)

_____   Use a prewriting technique to come up with reasons and evidence (facts, examples, expert opinions).

_____   Clearly state each reason.

_____   Consider what makes good persuasive evidence (facts, examples, expert opinions).

_____   Consider whether you will need to use outside sources in the library or on the Internet. (See Chapter 19.)

_____   Consider what your readers' position on the issue probably is and what types of support will most likely convince them.

_____   Consider opposing views and anticipate objections.

_____   Drop reasons or evidence that don't support your thesis well, and select those that do.

_____   Ask someone to listen to and challenge your reasons and evidence. Find new reasons or evidence if necessary.

4.   **Make a plan.**

_____   Write a topic sentence for each reason.

(continued)

_____ Make a plan or outline that arranges the topic sentences and supporting evidence in a logical order (usually from least important to most important). In your outline, give facts, examples, or expert opinions to back up each reason.

5. **Write a draft.**

_____ Write a draft with topic sentences and paragraphs for each reason.

_____ Write an introduction that draws readers in. Write a strong conclusion that makes your final pitch with energy.

_____ Title the essay.

6. **Revise your draft.**

_____ Get feedback from others. (See Chapter 8, pp. 93–94, for guidelines for giving and getting feedback, including Questions for Reviewers of a Draft.)

_____ Cut any reasons or evidence that does not help you persuade readers of your position.

_____ Add other reasons or evidence that might strengthen your argument.

_____ Make sure the order is logical. Add transitions, especially transitions for emphasis, and transitional sentences as needed.

_____ Do not just copy over your draft. Make at least five changes to improve it.

7. **Edit your revised draft.**

_____ Find and correct any problems with grammar, spelling, word use, or punctuation.

_____ Produce a clean, final copy.

_____ Ask yourself: Is this the best I can do?

Checklist: How to Write a Research Essay

Check off items as you complete them.

1.   Get organized. (See p. 311.)

_____   Make a schedule. Set a realistic timetable for researching and writing your research paper. Post it where you can see it, often, and stick to it!

_____   Keep all of your material together in one folder, envelope, or computer disk.

2.   Find and narrow your topic. (See p. 312.)

_____   Narrow the general topic or issue to a more specific one that you are interested in and care about.

_____   Do some pre-research. Use the library and search the Internet to make sure there are enough sources on your topic for you to consult.

_____   Quickly read over a couple of available sources and jot down some ideas.

_____   Reconsider your topic and modify it if necessary.

3.   Write a thesis statement. (See p. 315.)

_____   Turn the topic or issue into a guiding question that you want to answer in your research.

_____   Write a thesis statement that answers your guiding question and puts forth the main point of your essay.

4.   Find sources. (See p. 317.)

_____   Consult the reference librarian.

_____   Use the library's catalog and reference materials.

_____   Use the Internet.

_____   Interview people.

5.   Evaluate your sources. (See p. 321.)

_____   Make sure that the outside sources you plan to use for support are reliable. (Answer the Ten Questions for Evaluating a Source on p. 321.)

6.   Build support and take careful notes. (See p. 322.)

_____   Take lots of notes. Look for facts, evidence, examples, and direct quotations that support your thesis statement.

(continued)

_____ Avoid plagiarism by documenting your sources. (See p. 322.)

_____ Keep a running bibliography in correct documentation format. (See p. 324.)

7. **Organize your notes and plan your draft.** (See p. 324.)

_____ Reread all of your notes.

_____ Evaluate your information, facts, and evidence.

_____ Add your own ideas and observations that support your points.

_____ Make an outline of your thesis statement and major support points, leaving spaces to fill in supporting details and information. (See p. 168 for outline form.)

_____ Use your outline to arrange your index cards. Determine the information that fits best under each support point. (See p. 325.)

_____ Write a topic sentence for each major support point.

_____ Write sentences with details and information that demonstrate, explain, or prove the major support points.

_____ Write an introduction that draws your readers into the topic or issue.

_____ Write a conclusion that reviews your topic or issue and the points you have made, and make a final pitch for your position.

8. **Revise your draft and cite your sources correctly.**

_____ Get feedback from others. (See Chapter 8, pp. 93–94, for guidelines for giving and getting feedback, including Questions for Reviewers of a Draft.)

_____ Cut any information that does not help answer your research question.

_____ Decide if you need more information to answer the question convincingly and with confidence.

_____ Add transitions to move from one point to another.

_____ Check your in-text citations to make sure that you have properly credited someone else's work. Cite your sources using correct in-text citation format for direct quotations, indirect quotations, or summaries. (See pp. 325–327.)

_____ Prepare your final list of works cited, using correct documentation format. (See pp. 327–329.)

(continued)

_____ Research papers always require final touches and some re-working to arrange the information smoothly and logically. Make sure that you make changes; otherwise, you are probably missing something.

9. **Edit your revised draft.**

_____ Find and correct any problems with grammar, spelling, word use, or punctuation.

_____ Alphabetize and proofread your list of works cited, checking each entry carefully for correct format and complete information. (See pp. 327–329.)

_____ Produce a clean, final copy.

_____ Ask yourself: Is this the best I can do?

Checklist: How to Write a Formal Email

Check off items as you complete them.

1.   **Consider your audience and have a clear purpose.**

_____   Think about what your audience already knows.

_____   Jot down ideas about what information you need to provide in order to achieve your purpose.

2.   **State your subject and purpose early.**

_____   In the "SUBJECT" line of the email, type the subject of your message.

_____   State the purpose of the email at its start (e.g., *This will give you an update on the Mannix Project.*).

3.   **Decide what information you need to include.**

_____   Review your ideas to make sure you have included all necessary information. Do not include unrelated information.

4.   **Make a plan.**

_____   Organize your points in a logical order of presentation.

5.   **Write a draft.**

_____   Decide if using a bulleted or numbered list would make the individual points stand out and be easier for the recipient to read.

_____   Write a draft.

6.   **Revise your email.**

_____   Reread your email from your reader's point of view.

_____   Change anything that is not clear.

_____   Add any additional information that you need to include to be accurate and thorough, but not chatty or wordy.

7.   **Edit your email.**

_____   Find and correct problems with grammar, spelling, word use, or punctuation.

_____   Send your message and make a file copy.

Checklist: How to Write a Memo

Check off items as you complete them.

1.   **Consider your audience and have a clear purpose.**

_____ Think about what your audience already knows.

_____ Jot down ideas about what information you need to provide in order to achieve your purpose.

2.   **State your subject and purpose early.**

_____ In the "SUBJECT" line of the standard memo format, state the subject.

_____ State the purpose of the memo at its start (e.g., *Here are the changes in the plans for the conference.*).

3.   **Decide what information you need to include.**

_____ Review your ideas to make sure you have included all necessary information. Do not include unrelated information.

4.   **Make a plan.**

_____ Organize your points in a logical order of presentation.

5.   **Write a draft.**

_____ Decide if using a bulleted or numbered list would make the individual points stand out and be easier for the recipient to read.

_____ Write a draft memo using standard memo format.

6.   **Revise your memo.**

_____ Reread your memo from your reader's point of view.

_____ Change anything that is not clear.

_____ Add any additional information that you need to include to be accurate and thorough, but not chatty or wordy.

7.   **Edit your memo.**

_____ Find and correct problems with grammar, spelling, word use, or punctuation.

_____ Print a clean, final copy.

_____ Make a file copy.

Planning Forms for Paragraphs and Essays
(*Chapters 9–17, 19*)

Prewriting on Your Purpose and Audience

Prewrite to find answers to these questions before you write any paper. Prewrite again later if it seems helpful. Keep your responses in mind as you draft and revise your paper.

PURPOSE

- What is my assignment? What topic will I be writing about?

- What point do I want to make about my topic?

- What do I want my audience to think about my topic?

- What do I need to tell my audience so that they will get my point?

AUDIENCE

- Who is my audience?

- What does my audience already know about my topic?

- What does my audience want or need to know about my topic?

- Does my audience have a particular attitude or opinion about my topic? Do I need to address that specifically?

Clustering Form

Use this form when you are clustering to explore a topic. Write your narrowed topic in the center circle. Then write three ideas or questions about that topic in the three circles that connect to the center circle. Add three more ideas about each of those items in the circles that connect to them, and so on.

You can add more circles and lines as you need them. In the beginning, try to add at least three items at each level. As you progress in your clustering, you may want to focus on a certain part of your cluster.

For more about using clustering to explore ideas, see Chapter 3 in *Real Writing*.

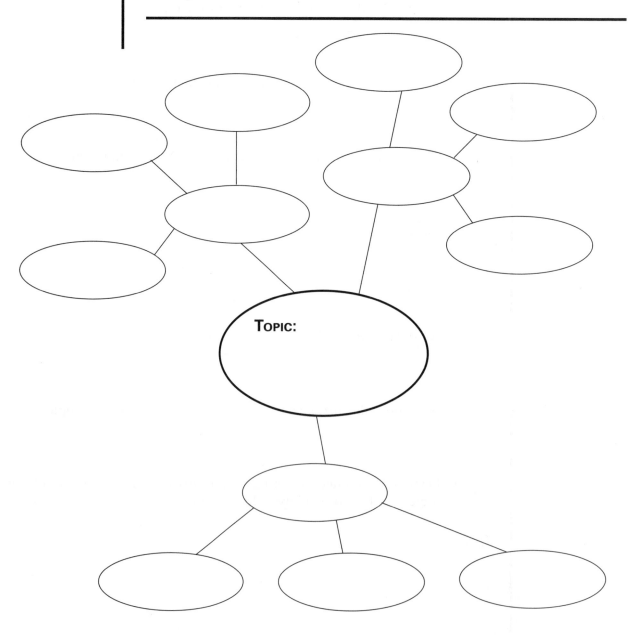

Paragraph Plan

TOPIC SENTENCE

BODY

Supporting point 1:
 	
    Details and examples:
 	
Supporting point 2:
 	
    Details and examples:
 	
Supporting point 3:
 	
    Details and examples:
 	
Supporting point 4:
 	
    Details and examples:

CONCLUDING SENTENCE

Essay Outline

   I. Introduction

     A. Thesis: _____

        _____

     B. Method of getting reader's attention: _____

  II. Topic sentence for first support paragraph: _____

       _____

     A. Supporting idea 1: _____

     B. Supporting idea 2: _____

     C. Supporting idea 3: _____

  III. Topic sentence for second support paragraph: _____

       _____

     A. Supporting idea 1: _____

     B. Supporting idea 2: _____

     C. Supporting idea 3: _____

  IV. Topic sentence for third support paragraph: _____

       _____

     A. Supporting idea 1: _____

     B. Supporting idea 2: _____

     C. Supporting idea 3: _____

  V. Conclusion

     A. Main point: _____

       _____

     B. Method of linking back to introduction: _____

Planning Form for Illustration

Illustration is writing that uses examples to show, explain, or prove a point.

The **topic sentence** or **thesis statement** for illustration usually includes the topic and the point the writer wants to make about it.

The **support** for illustration is a series of examples or a single example explained thoroughly. Use details to bring your examples to life.

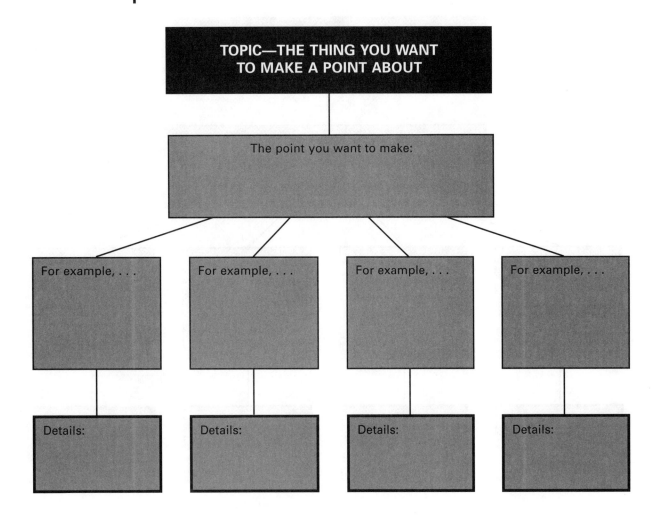

Illustration can use **space, time,** or **importance order.** If the order of the examples in your paper will be different from the order in which you wrote them down here, use the lines under the boxes to write in numbers indicating the order you want to use.

For more help with your illustration paper, see Chapter 9 in *Real Writing.*

Planning Form for Narration

Narration is writing that tells a story of an event or experience that has some importance.

The **topic sentence** or **thesis statement** for narration usually includes the topic and a preview of what is important about it. The **support** for narration is a series of events. Use details to show readers your point of view about why this story is important.

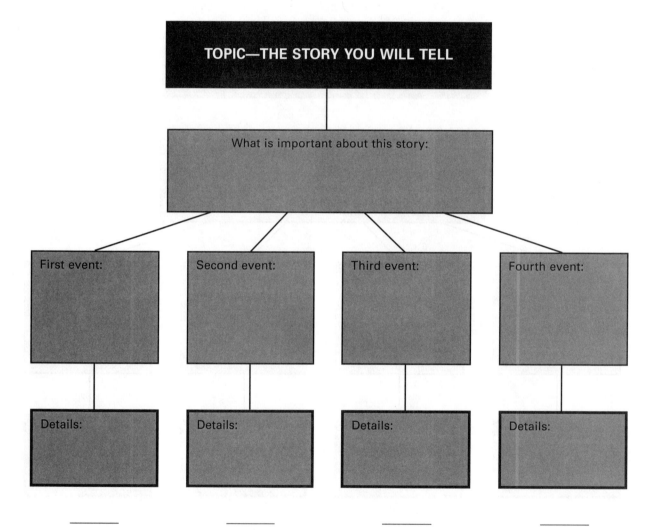

TOPIC—THE STORY YOU WILL TELL

What is important about this story:

First event:

Second event:

Third event:

Fourth event:

Details:

Details:

Details:

Details:

Narration usually uses **time order.** If the order of the events in your paper will be different from the order in which you wrote them down here, use the lines under the boxes to write in numbers indicating the order you want to use.

For more help with your narration paper, see Chapter 10 in *Real Writing.*

Planning Form for Description

Description is writing that creates a clear and vivid impression of the topic.

The **topic sentence** or **thesis statement** for description usually includes the topic and conveys the main impression about it that you want to communicate to your readers. The **support** for description is the sensory details that contribute to the main impression. Use additional information to make the details more concrete and specific.

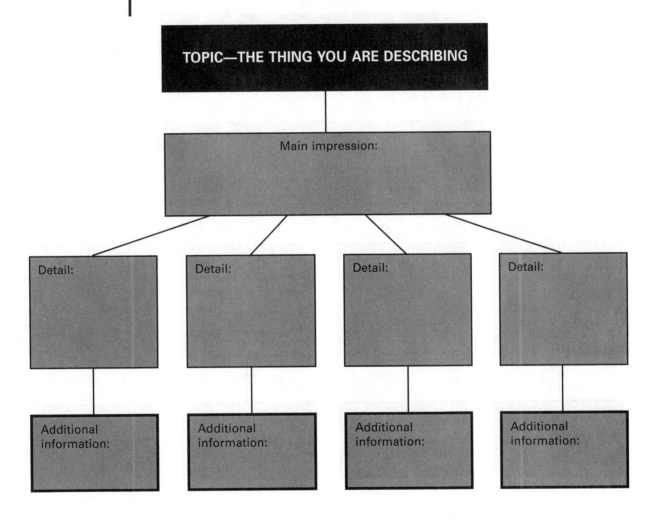

Description usually uses **space order**. If the order of the details in your paper will be different from the order in which you wrote them down here, use the lines under the boxes to write in numbers indicating the order you want to use.

For more help with your description paper, see Chapter 11 in *Real Writing*.

Planning Form for Process Analysis

Process analysis is writing that either explains how to do something or explains how something works.

The **topic sentence** or **thesis statement** for process analysis usually includes the process and the point you want to make about it. The **support** for process analysis is a series of steps. Use details to make the steps easier to imagine and follow.

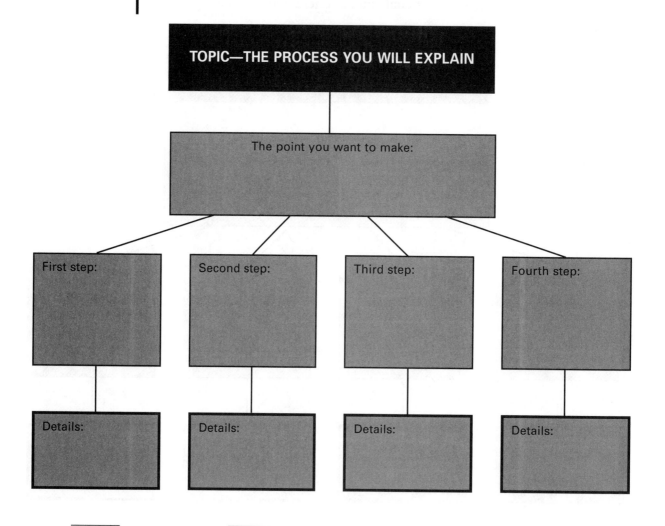

Process analysis usually uses **time order**. If the order of the steps in your paper will be different from the order in which you wrote them down here, use the lines under the boxes to write in numbers indicating the order you want to use.

For more help with your process analysis paper, see Chapter 12 in *Real Writing.*

Planning Form for Classification

Classification is writing that organizes, or sorts, things into categories. The **topic sentence** or **thesis statement** for classification usually includes the topic being classified and the organizing principle used to organize it. Sometimes the categories themselves are named. The **support** for classification is a group of categories that all follow a single organizing principle. Use examples to show what you mean by each category.

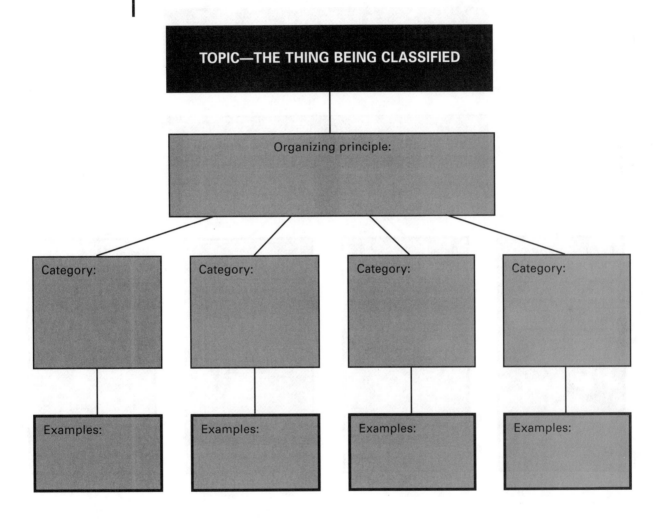

Classification can use **time, space,** or **importance order.** If the order of the categories in your paper will be different from the order in which you wrote them down here, use the lines under the boxes to write in numbers indicating the order you want to use.

For more help with your classification paper, see Chapter 13 in *Real Writing.*

Planning Form for Definition

Definition is writing that explains what a term means.

The **topic sentence** or **thesis statement** for definition usually includes the term and a brief, basic definition. The **support** for definition is details and examples that help readers see what you mean.

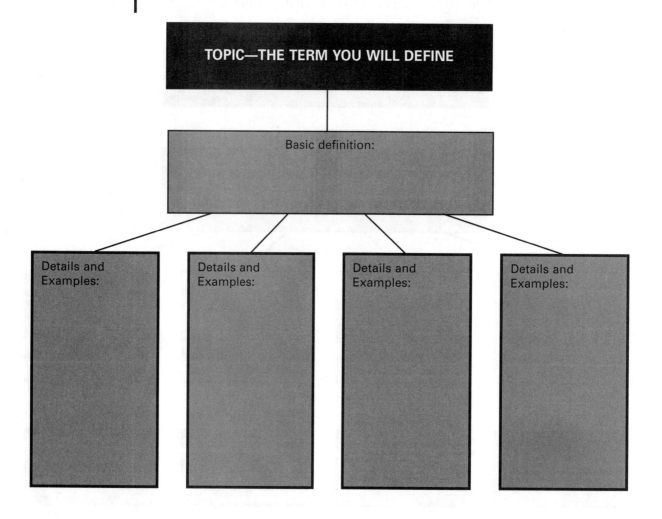

TOPIC—THE TERM YOU WILL DEFINE

Basic definition:

Details and Examples:

Details and Examples:

Details and Examples:

Details and Examples:

Definition can use **space, time,** or **importance order**. If the order of the examples in your paper will be different from the order in which you wrote them down here, use the lines under the boxes to write in numbers indicating the order you want to use.

For more help with your definition paper, see Chapter 14 in *Real Writing*.

Planning Form for Comparison/Contrast

Comparison is writing that shows the similarities among things; **contrast** shows the differences.

The **topic sentence** or **thesis statement** for comparison/contrast usually identifies the subjects and tells the main point you want to make about them.

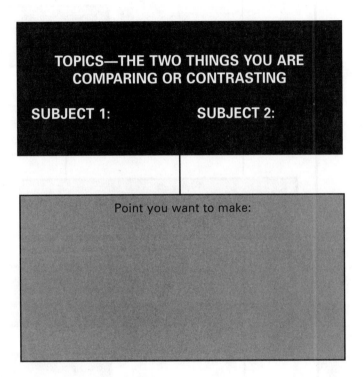

The **support** in a comparison/contrast is a series of important, parallel points of similarity or differences between the two subjects. Comparison/contrast usually uses one of two standard **organizations**: point-by-point or whole-to-whole.

For more help with your comparison/contrast paper, see Chapter 15 in *Real Writing*.

Point-by-Point Organization for Comparison/Contrast

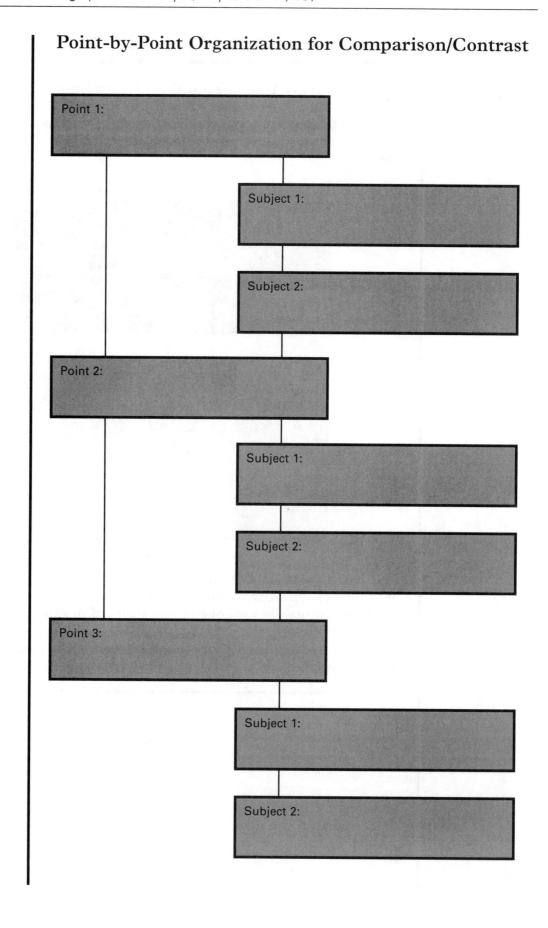

Whole-to-Whole Organization for Comparison/Contrast

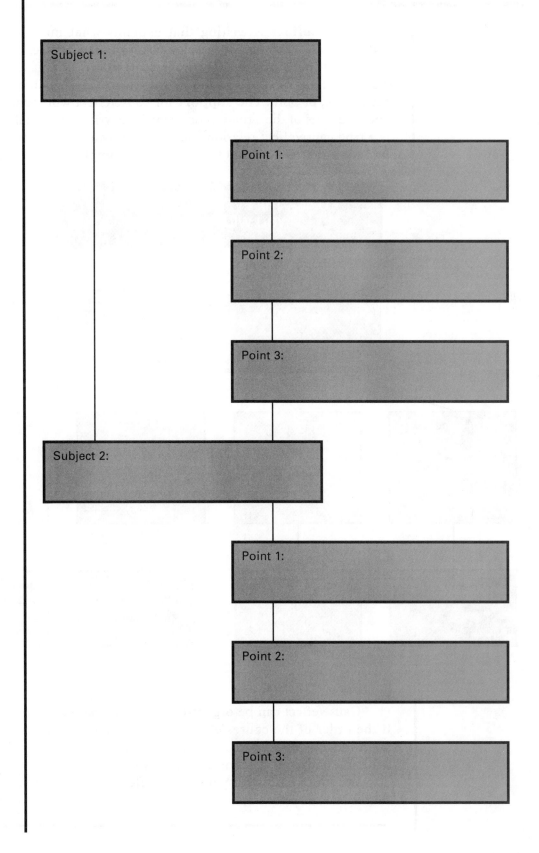

Subject 1:

Point 1:

Point 2:

Point 3:

Subject 2:

Point 1:

Point 2:

Point 3:

Planning Form for Cause/Effect

Cause/effect is writing that explains what made an event happen (cause) and/or what happened as a result of the event (effect).

The **topic sentence** or **thesis statement** for cause/effect should include the event or situation and indicate whether you will discuss the causes, the effects, or both. The **support** for cause/effect will include major causes and/or effects of the situation or event. The writer must make sure that there is a true cause/effect relationship, not merely a time sequence coincidence. For a stronger paper, choose details and examples that are significant.

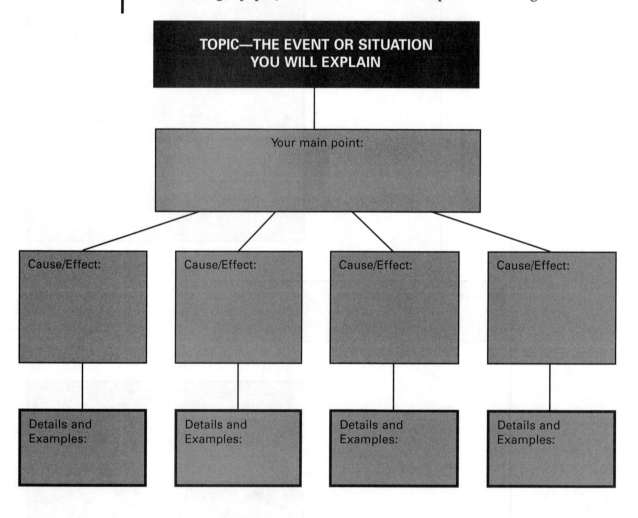

Cause/effect can be organized by **time**, **space**, or **importance order**. If the order of the causes/effects in your paper will be different from the order in which you wrote them down here, use the lines under the boxes to write in numbers indicating the order you want to use.

For more help with your cause/effect paper, see Chapter 16 in *Real Writing*.

Planning Form for Argument

Argument is writing that takes a position on an issue and defends it with evidence to persuade someone else of the position.

The **topic sentence** or **thesis statement** for argument should include the issue and your position on that issue. The **support** for argument is reasons and evidence that persuade readers that your position is a good one. Use details and examples to make your evidence concrete and persuasive.

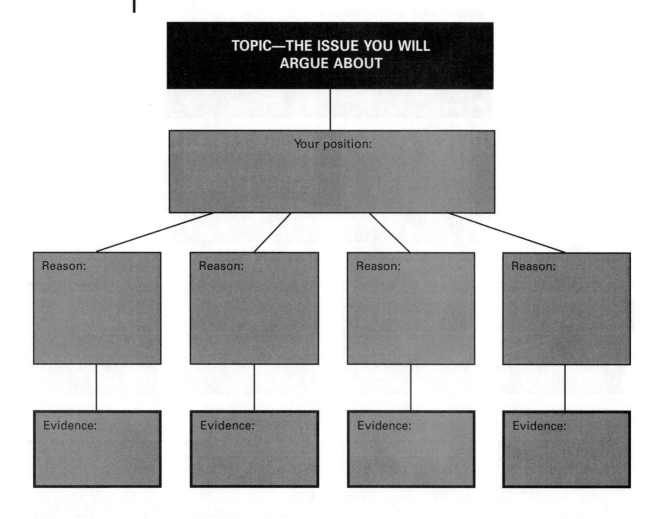

Argument usually uses **importance order**. If the order of the pieces of evidence in your paper will be different from the order in which you wrote them down here, use the lines under the boxes to write in numbers indicating the order you want to use.

For more help with your argument paper, see Chapter 17 in *Real Writing.*

Planning Form for Research Essay

Research is finding information that will help you or others understand a subject.

The **thesis statement** for a research essay should include the narrowed topic and the point you want to make about it. The **support** for a research essay will include evidence you gather through personal research (e.g., interviews, personal knowledge) and secondary research (e.g., materials from the library or the Internet). For a more persuasive paper, choose details and examples that are significant.

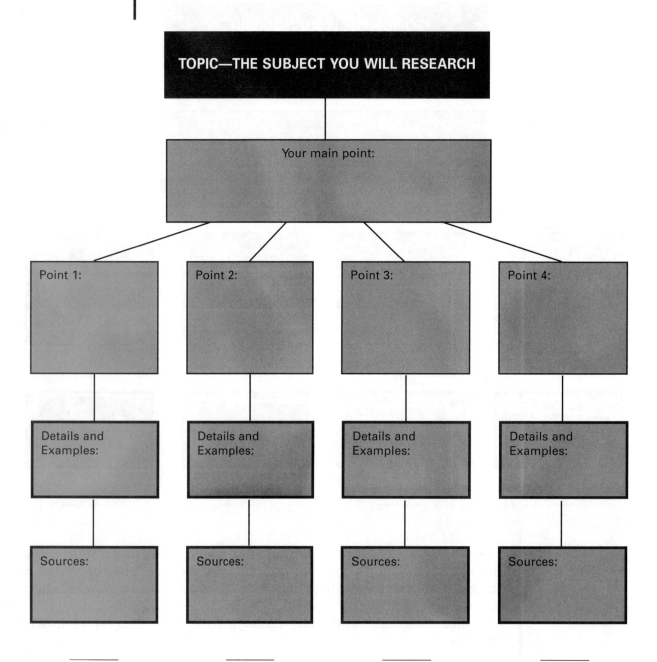

TOPIC—THE SUBJECT YOU WILL RESEARCH

Your main point:

Point 1:	Point 2:	Point 3:	Point 4:
Details and Examples:	Details and Examples:	Details and Examples:	Details and Examples:
Sources:	Sources:	Sources:	Sources:

Because topics and purposes are so varied when conducting research, the resulting essay could follow almost any of the writing strategies (e.g., illustration, comparison/contrast, cause/effect, argument, definition) that you have studied so far. Therefore, a research essay can be organized in a number of ways, depending on the purpose of the research. The most common forms would include **time**, **space**, or **importance order**. If the order of the major points in your paper will be different from the order in which you wrote them down here, use the lines under the boxes to write in numbers indicating the order you want to use.

For more help with your research essay, see Chapter 19 in *Real Writing*.

Peer Review Evaluation Form

TO BE COMPLETED BY STUDENT WRITER:

Your name:

Title of the paper:

One or two focused questions for the reviewer (optional):

TO BE COMPLETED BY THE STUDENT REVIEWER:

Your name:

1. What is the writer's main point?

2. What is the strongest part of the paper? Why is it good?

3. What could be improved? How could it be better?

4. Were any parts confusing?

5. Did you want to learn more about anything?

6. What are your responses to any questions the writer asked you above?

7. Do you have any other comments?

Supplemental Exercises for Chapter 19 ("The Research Essay")

19-1: Integrating and Citing Sources within Your Paper

When using information you have gathered from other sources, you may want to use direct quotes, indirect quotes, summaries, or paraphrases. You also need to make sure that you do not plagiarize (use the author's exact words without using quotation marks and/or referencing the source). Using the following passage, write on separate paper or your computer a one-sentence summary of the entire passage, a paraphrase of the part of the passage that is in bold type, and a direct quote that could be used in a research essay about the effects of music on the brain. (Be sure to introduce the quote with a signal phrase.) At the end of your summary, paraphrase, or quote, include a parenthetical reference to the original source.

ORIGINAL SOURCE

Music has charms to soothe a savage breast, but scientists are finding that it works those charms through the brain. At a recent conference of the New York Academy of Sciences, [Sandra] Trehub and dozens of other scientists interspersed their PET scans and MRIs with snatches of Celine Dion and Stravinsky as they reported on the biological foundations of music. Several lines of evidence suggest that the human brain is wired for music, and that some forms of intelligence are enhanced by music. **Perhaps the most striking hint that the brain holds a special place in its gray matter for music is that people can typically remember scores of tunes, and recognize hundreds more. But we can recall only snatches of a few prose passages ("Four score and seven years ago . . .").** Also, music affects the mind in powerful ways: it not only incites passion, belligerence, serenity or fear, but does so even in people who do not know from experience, for instance, that a particular crescendo means the killer is about to pop out on the movie screen. All in all, says psychologist Isabelle Peretz of the University of Montreal, "the brain seems to be specialized for music."

—Sharon Begley, "Music on the Mind,"
Newsweek, July 24, 2000, p. 51

19-2: Integrating and Citing Sources within Your Paper

When using information you have gathered from other sources, you may want to use direct quotes, indirect quotes, summaries, or paraphrases. You also need to make sure that you do not plagiarize (use the author's exact words without using quotation marks and/or referencing the source). Using the following passage, write on separate paper or your computer a one-sentence summary of the entire passage, a paraphrase of the part of the passage that is in bold type, and a direct quote that could be used in a research essay about feng shui. (Be sure to introduce the quote with a signal phrase.) At the end of your summary, paraphrase, or quote, include a parenthetical reference to the original source.

ORIGINAL SOURCE

Feng shui, for those who have somehow missed its myriad references in pop culture, means wind and water in Chinese. **The 3,500-year-old system, once used only by China's Emperor, is based on the idea that landscapes, buildings and even whole cities have hidden zones of energy *(qi)*, which can be manipulated by the shape, size and color of a structure as well as its entrances. A building that allows *qi* to flow freely is said to have good feng shui, which brings prosperity and success.**
—Ajay Singh, "Luck Be a Stone Lion," *Time*, July 3, 2000, p. 53

19-3: Integrating and Citing Sources within Your Paper

When using information you have gathered from other sources, you may want to use direct quotes, indirect quotes, summaries, or paraphrases. You also need to make sure that you do not plagiarize (use the author's exact words without using quotation marks and/or referencing the source). Using the following passage, write on separate paper or your computer a one-sentence summary of the entire passage, a paraphrase of the part of the passage that is in bold type, and a direct quote that could be used in a research essay on the causes of divorce. (Be sure to introduce the quote with a signal phrase.) At the end of your summary, paraphrase, or quote, include a parenthetical reference to the original source.

ORIGINAL SOURCE

Even though each broken marriage is unique, we can still find the common perils, the common causes for marital despair. Each marriage has crisis points, and each marriage tests endurance, the capacity for both intimacy and change. Outside pressures such as job loss, illness, infertility, trouble with a child, care of aging parents, and all the other plagues of life hit marriage the way hurricanes blast our shores. Some marriages survive these storms, and others don't. Marriages fail, however, not simply because of the outside weather but because the inner climate becomes too hot or too cold, too turbulent or too stupefying.

—Anne Roiphe, "Why Marriages Fail"

The entire essay "Why Marriages Fail" by Anne Roiphe is printed in Chapter 49 of *Real Writing*.

19-4: Integrating and Citing Sources within Your Paper

When using information you have gathered from other sources, you may want to use direct quotes, indirect quotes, summaries, or paraphrases. You also need to make sure that you do not plagiarize (use the author's exact words without using quotation marks and/or referencing the source). Using the following passage, write on separate paper or your computer a one-sentence summary of the entire passage, a paraphrase of the part of the passage that is in bold type, and a direct quote that could be used in a research essay about stereotypes and clichés. (Be sure to introduce the quote with a signal phrase.) At the end of your summary, paraphrase, or quote, include a parenthetical reference to the original source.

ORIGINAL SOURCE

Stereotype and cliché serve a purpose as a form of shorthand. **Our need for vast amounts of information in nanoseconds has made the stereotype vital to modern communications.** Unfortunately, it often shuts down original thinking, giving those hungry for truth a candy bar of misinformation instead of a balanced meal. The stereotype explains a situation with just enough truth to seem unquestionable.

All the *isms*—racism, sexism, ageism, et al.—are founded on and fueled by the stereotype and the cliché, which are lies of exaggeration, omission, and ignorance. They are always dangerous. They take a single tree and make it a landscape. They destroy curiosity. They close minds and separate people. The single mother on welfare is assumed to be cheating. A black male could tell you how much of his identity is obliterated daily by stereotypes. Fat people, ugly people, beautiful people, large-breasted women, short men, the mentally ill, and the homeless all could tell you how much more they are like us than we want to think. I once admitted to a group of people that I had a mouth like a truck driver. Much to my surprise, a man stood up and said, "I'm a truck driver, and I never cuss." Needless to say, I was humbled.

—Stephanie Ericsson, "The Ways We Lie"

The entire essay "The Ways We Lie" by Stephanie Ericsson is printed in Chapter 46 of *Real Writing*.

19-5: **Integrating and Citing Sources within Your Paper**

When using information you have gathered from other sources, you may want to use direct quotes, indirect quotes, summaries, or paraphrases. You also need to make sure that you do not plagiarize (use the author's exact words without using quotation marks and/or referencing the source). Using the following passage, write on separate paper or your computer a one-sentence summary of the entire passage, a paraphrase of the part of the passage that is in bold type, and a direct quote that could be used in a research essay about college students' expectations. (Be sure to introduce the quote with a signal phrase.) At the end of your summary, paraphrase, or quote, include a parenthetical reference to the original source.

ORIGINAL SOURCE

The relationship students want with their college is like the one they already have with their banks, supermarkets, and the other organizations they patronize. They want education to be nearby and to operate during convenient hours. They want easy, accessible parking, short lines, and polite and efficient personnel and services. They also want high-quality products but are eager for low costs. They are very willing to comparison shop—placing a premium on time and money.

What they don't want are the extras colleges traditionally offer. Just as they do not expect their banks to arrange softball games for them or family picnics or religious services or mental health clinics, increasingly they do not expect these things of their colleges. They prefer to tend to their own entertainment, health care, and spiritual needs and do not want to pay a college for these services. **All they want of higher education is simple procedures, good service, quality courses, and low costs—with course quality ranked as the highest priority and price, procedures, and service ranking lower.** Students are bringing to higher education exactly the same consumer expectations they have for every other commercial enterprise with which they deal.

—Arthur Levine, "Student Expectations of College"

The entire essay "Student Expectations of College" by Arthur Levine is printed in Chapter 41 of *Real Writing*.

Answer Key

Answers to Exercises 19–1 through 19–5 will vary depending on what passages the student selects. Possible answers are given below.

Answers to 19–1

Possible answers:

SUMMARY

Recent scientific findings suggest that the human brain is preprogrammed for music (Begley 51).

PARAPHRASE

Humans can store a large number of songs in their memory, compelling evidence that our minds are preprogrammed for music. By contrast, people rarely remember more than a few sentences of written material (Begley 51).

DIRECT QUOTE

As Begley states, "several lines of evidence suggest that the human brain is wired for music" (Begley 51).

Answers to 19–2

Possible answers:

SUMMARY

Feng shui, an ancient Chinese method of designing and organizing spaces to maximize energy and bring wealth, has become a trend in modern interior design (Singh 53).

PARAPHRASE

Feng shui relies on *qi,* energy that can be affected by a space's character— its shape and dimensions. A building with good feng shui, which allows *qi* to move freely throughout a space, rewards its owner with worldly success (Singh 53).

DIRECT QUOTE

As Singh states, "A building that allows *qi* to flow freely is said to have good feng shui" (53).

Answers to 19–3

Possible answers:

SUMMARY

The reasons why marriages end in divorce are unique and include both internal and external stresses (Roiphe 703).

PARAPHRASE

There is a unique set of circumstances behind each marriage that ends in divorce, but there are also predictable flash points (Roiphe 703).

DIRECT QUOTE

According to Roiphe, internal and external stresses "hit marriage the way hurricanes blast our shores" (Roiphe 703).

Answers to 19–4

Possible answers:

SUMMARY

Stereotypes and clichés are substitutes for thinking and getting to know people as individuals rather than as members of a group (Ericsson 683).

PARAPHRASE

In today's world, the need to process a great deal of information quickly leads to the use of stereotypes (Ericsson 683).

DIRECT QUOTE

According to Ericsson, a stereotype "explains a situation with just enough truth to seem unquestionable" (Ericsson 683).

Answers to 19–5

Possible answers:

SUMMARY

Students want colleges that offer good services at low costs, not the traditional "extras" like entertainment, health care, and religion, which they can provide for themselves (Levine 638).

PARAPHRASE

Students are looking for colleges that offer excellent courses and low tuition rates; they are less concerned with other aspects of college life (Levine 638).

DIRECT QUOTE

According to Levine, today's students want higher education that offers "simple procedures, good service, quality courses, and low costs" (Levine 638).

Diagnostic Tests for Editing Skills
(*Chapters 21–40*)

Diagnostic Test–A

Sentence Completeness

In the blank, write **RO** for run-on (two sentences joined incorrectly), **F** for fragment (incomplete sentence), and **S** for complete sentence.

_____ 1. Because the language barrier is the greatest obstacle that I have faced since I have been living in this country.

_____ 2. My employer made me do just about everything at once, such as running the cash register, taking orders, and preparing food.

_____ 3. Always go to dinner after my night class.

_____ 4. College is not just educational, it also makes you feel better about yourself.

_____ 5. That was the first show in which I didn't win an award for sculpture I was still proud of my hard work.

_____ 6. I remember the first day of school; I couldn't speak English very well and had a lot of trouble with my classes.

_____ 7. For example, spending your last few dollars on a lottery ticket.

_____ 8. I also feel more mature by handling responsibilities at home— for example, helping my parents out by paying bills, cleaning house, and taking care of my brother.

_____ 9. Which in turn made me and the customers mad.

_____ 10. Although my landlord lives right above me, is hard to find when I need him.

_____ 11. At UPS, the atmosphere is very different everybody runs around yelling and screaming about one thing or another.

_____ 12. They work outside the house, when they come back home, they still have to take care of the children and be responsible for their comfort, school, and clothes.

Misplaced and Dangling Modifiers

Edit the following sentences to correct errors with dangling or misplaced modifiers.

13. Opening the envelope, a check fell out into her hands.

14. Fran and Albert decided to hang the painting in the den with the African jungle scene.

15. In the middle of the test, Keith discovered that he could only answer ten of the fifty questions.

16. The mothers dressed their babies to protect them from bad weather in snowsuits.

17. After throwing a red towel into the washing machine, Troy's T-shirts turned pink.

Correct Word Choice, Verbs, Modifiers

Circle the correct word or words in parentheses.

18. Today, women (has, have) a lot of opportunities to get better jobs.

19. I hope the man I marry someday treats me as (good, well) as my father treats my mother.

20. I want to take (a, the) computer class that you recommended yesterday.

21. The stationary bicycle and the treadmill are excellent exercise machines to help an older person improve (his, his or her, their) fitness.

22. I had never thought it possible to be in the honor society because of the obstacles that (lay, lied) in my way.

23. Combat troops are tough, heartless, dirty, and (smell, smelly).

24. As the doctor entered the emergency room, the patient (asks, asked) for assistance.

25. My sister had difficulty (scheduling, to schedule) personal appointments during her hectic work week.

26. The (rapid, rapidly) moving car ran the red light and hit the bus.

27. At 68, he has experienced the pain and agony that (comes, come) from having two heart attacks.

28. There should be no limitations placed on people because of (his, his or her, their) gender.

29. When I told her the position was no longer available, she sounded (disappointed, bummed out).

30. (Due to the fact that, Because) she had to stop by the day care center, Amanda missed the first ten minutes of class.

31. I get the majority of my information from newspapers and from (watching television, television).

32. There (is, are) several reasons to finish your homework before class.

33. The child behaved (bad, badly) when his mother told him he couldn't have any ice cream.

34. The government agency announced that (it, they) would refund money to anyone who had the proper documents.

35. The weather this winter seems (cold, colder) than it was last year.

36. Dr. Percy (has spoke, has spoken) at our nursing club's awards banquet for the past three years.

37. Being able to use the computers (has, have) improved my writing skills.

38. After Charlie changed the engine, the Corvette was (faster, fastest, more fast) than the Mustang.

39. The coach named Sebastian and (he, him) to the All-Star team.

40. The Writing Center tutor told us that we are each responsible (about, for) our own disks.

Punctuation and Capitalization

Add the correct punctuation and capitalization in the following sentences.

41. The family will spend christmas in san juan this december.

42. Where are you going? John asked Tran.

43. We will need the following supplies a three-ring notebook, notebook paper, a pen, and a red pencil.

44. If you dont want to go swimming, you wont need to pay a fee because its not required by the state.

45. Luisa who enjoys Tejana music volunteered to find a band for the school dance.

46. We elected Sue, president, Bill, vice-president, Quinn, treasurer, and Sam, secretary.

47. in american literature, professor martinez asked us to read the novel *the old man and the sea.*

48. Although both cars are very fast the Mustang has a v-8, 289 carburetor.

49. With the lottery, people buy tickets by choice therefore, they are not forced to spend money they do not have.

50. Theres no way to determine if theyre receiving assistance on the project.

51. The students who studied made excellent grades on their tests the others were not satisfied with their grades.

52. During the long holiday weekend we are planning to mow the yard clean the house go to the lake and see a movie.

53. Fellow citizens, the president announced, the events of today will be remembered for many years.

54. Although we had a substitute teacher we still had to take a test and we had to write a paragraph before we could leave class.

55. The smith family moved to 925 henderson lane in albany, new york.

Spelling

Correct any spelling errors. Put **C** in the blank if you see no error.

_____ 56. Three hundred dollars is alot of money.

_____ 57. The doctors were egar to help my father.

_____ 58. An on-campus day care offers convience.

_____ 59. Don't embarass me.

_____ 60. We past the same park three times.

_____ 61. Who's car is parked in the driveway?

_____ 62. It was a solemn ocassion.

_____ 63. Did the child brake his arm?

_____ 64. John enjoyed writting.

_____ 65. My opinon is always right.

_____ 66. Amy will pursue a law degree.

_____ 67. I enjoy the peace and quite.

_____ 68. It was a common occurrence.

_____ 69. That cat can preform tricks.

_____ 70. Cars are taxed according to their wieght.

Diagnostic Test–A: Answer Key

Sentence Completeness

1. F. 2. S. 3. F. 4. RO. 5. RO. 6. S. 7. F. 8. S. 9. F. 10. F.
11. RO. 12. RO.

Misplaced and Dangling Modifiers

Possible edits shown.
13. When Alice opened the envelope, a check fell out into her hands.
14. Fran and Albert decided to hang the painting with the African jungle scene in the den.
15. In the middle of the test, Keith discovered that he could answer only ten of the fifty questions.
16. To protect them from bad weather, the mothers dressed their babies in snowsuits.
17. After he threw a red towel into the washing machine, Troy's T-shirts turned pink.

Correct Word Choice, Verbs, Modifiers

18. have. 19. well. 20. the. 21. his or her. 22. lay. 23. smelly.
24. asked. 25. scheduling. 26. rapidly. 27. come. 28. their.
29. disappointed. 30. Because. 31. television. 32. are. 33. badly.
34. it. 35. colder. 36. has spoken. 37. has. 38. faster. 39. him.
40. for.

Punctuation and Capitalization

Edits shown.
41. The family will spend **C**hristmas in **S**an **J**uan this **D**ecember.
42. "Where are you going?" John asked Tran.
43. We will need the following supplies**:** a three-ring notebook**,** notebook paper, a pen, and a red pencil.
44. If you **don't** want to go swimming, you **won't** need to pay a fee because **it's** not required by the state.
45. Luisa**,** who enjoys Tejana music, volunteered to find a band for the school dance.
46. We elected Sue, president**;** Bill, vice-president**;** Quinn, treasurer**;** and Sam, secretary.
47. **I**n **A**merican **L**iterature, **P**rofessor **M**artinez asked us to read the novel *The Old Man and the Sea.*
48. Although both cars are very fast, the Mustang has a v-8, 289 carburetor.
49. With the lottery, people buy tickets by choice**;** therefore**,** they are not forced to spend money they do not have.

50. **There's** no way to determine if **they're** receiving assistance on the project.
51. The students who studied made excellent grades on their tests; the others were not satisfied with their grades.
52. During the long holiday weekend, we are planning to mow the yard, clean the house, go to the lake, and see a movie.
53. "Fellow citizens," the president announced, "the events of today will be remembered for many years."
54. Although we had a substitute teacher, we still had to take a test, and we had to write a paragraph before we could leave class.
55. The **S**mith family moved to 925 **H**enderson **L**ane in **A**lbany, **N**ew **Y**ork.

Spelling

56. a lot.　57. eager.　58. convenience.　59. embarrass.　60. passed.
61. Whose.　62. occasion.　63. break.　64. writing.　65. opinion.
66. C.　67. quiet.　68. C.　69. perform.　70. weight.

Diagnostic Test–A

Identification of Problem Areas

The following table will help you identify your students' strengths and weaknesses in grammar, sentence structure, punctuation, and spelling skills. Use the table to match chapter content in *Real Writing* with individual items from the diagnostic test.

Chapter in **Real Writing**		*Test Items*
22	Fragments	1, 3, 7, 9, 10
23	Run-ons	4, 5, 11, 12
24	Problems with subject-verb agreement	18, 27, 32, 37
25	Verb problems	22, 24, 36
26	Pronouns	21, 28, 34, 39
27	Adjectives and adverbs	19, 26, 33, 35, 38
28	Misplaced and dangling modifiers	13, 14, 15, 16, 17
29	Coordination and subordination	48, 51, 54
30	Parallelism	23, 31
32	ESL	3, 10, 20, 25, 40
33	Word choice	29, 30
34	Commonly confused words	60, 61, 63, 67
35	Spelling	56, 57, 58, 59, 62, 64, 65, 69, 70
36	Commas	45, 52, 54
37	Apostrophes	44, 50
38	Quotation marks	42, 53
39	Other punctuation	43, 46, 49, 51
40	Capitalization	41, 47, 55

Diagnostic Test–B

Part One

Each of the following sentences has three boldfaced sections labeled **A, B,** and **C.** Read each sentence carefully, looking for errors in grammar, punctuation, or spelling. If you find an error in any of the boldfaced sections, write the letter of the problem area in the space provided. If there is no error, write the letter **C** in the space provided.

_____ 1. **By going back to college,** I will have an automatic jump on
other people applying for the **position this** shows an employer
my initiative. **No error.**

_____ 2. **Debates have started** on implementing user fees or
increase the tax base for recreational services. **No error.**

_____ 3. After all the trauma of living with my **mom; living** with my
dad **has changed** my life. **No error.**

_____ 4. Another **responsibility is** paying for my tuition and my
clothes. Which I could not really afford five years ago.
No error.

_____ 5. While listening to the Bob Marley **album, Tyson** started
moving his body to the **rythm** of the music. **No error.**

_____ 6. To save money on car insurance for a **teenager, buy** an older
used car **equipped** with airbags. **No error.**

_____ 7. In the eleventh grade, **I transferred** to West High
School, I was finally mainstream. **No error.**

_____ 8. I enjoy **to cook** for **a big crowd. No error.**

_____ 9. If a family **member disagrees** with a **doctor's choices,** who

          wins? **No error.**

_____ 10. Travel **games, such** as Battleship, **provides** several hours of

          fun for children when you are traveling long distances in your

          car. **No error.**

_____ 11. The United States will be stronger in the **future; if** it helps all

          children **receive** education and medical care. **No error.**

_____ 12. A **family's** insurance policy may not cover medical expenses

          when students are away from their **parents** home area.

          No error.

_____ 13. See if you can buy insurance **direct** from the college, since

          some schools make coverage available for **their** students.

          No error.

_____ 14. **Is difficult** to imagine **myself designing** my own Web page.

          No error.

_____ 15. Stan Weston, creator of G.I. Joe action figures, **advises,**

          "You don't have to be a genius to make a living with your

          imagination". **No error.**

_____ 16. My dad did both jobs when my mom was **working, he** cooked

          for us and took care of **my sisters and me** when we were sick.

          No error.

_____ 17. The best time to water lawns is between 4 A.M. and **8 A.M. but**

          if that's too early for **you, water** between 8 A.M. and noon.

          No error.

_____ 18. We must **decide if** saving a life is more important than saving
the **countries money. No error.**
A · B · C

_____ 19. My **Mother** prefers to drive ten miles out of her **way in order**
to avoid driving on the freeway. **No error.**
A · B · C

_____ 20. A college education **will help me** find a job in the field
that I like. After I earn my degree in accounting. **No error.**
A · B · C

_____ 21. To avoid traffic **tickets, you** need to obey all the **rules: speed**
limits, red lights, and stop signs. **No error.**
A · B · C

_____ 22. When he dropped the letter in the mailbox, Joe **realized** that
he **had wrote** the check for the wrong amount. **No error.**
A · B · C

_____ 23. A federal law **gives** employers the right to monitor all electronic messages stored on **its** system. **No error.**
A · B · C

_____ 24. Many people believe that it will take **goverment** intervention
to stem the rising cost of medical **care, including** doctor visits, prescriptions, and hospital stays. **No error.**
A · B · C

_____ 25. My dad was always there when I needed someone to
talk to. Unlike my mom, who would **act like she didn't have**
time to listen to my problems. **No error.**
A · B · C

_____ 26. For **valentine's day,** I'm planning a **February** cruise to
Jamaica. **No error.**
A · B · C

_____ 27. After the bee **stang** the baby, his arm swelled **tremendously.**
No error.
A · B · C

Part Two

In each of the following sentences, decide which of the words in parentheses is the correct choice for that sentence. Then write the letter indicating the correct word in the space provided.

_____ 28. When he walked on stage, Brock knew that he would
             A   B
             (loose, lose) his confidence.

                                                    A   B
_____ 29. Andrew's purple suit did not produce the (affect, effect)

             that he wanted.

_____ 30. One of the differences between living alone and living with my
             A B
             parents (is, are) the expenses.

                                            A   B
_____ 31. People under stress are often unable to drive (safe, safely).

_____ 32. When the Nguyen family returned home from vacation, they dis-
                                     A   B
             covered that all of Mrs. Nguyen's (jewelry, jewlery) was missing.

                                                  A B
_____ 33. In order to get to the main campus, you need to take (a, the)

             subway east.

                                  A   B
_____ 34. Everything in this country (was, were) new to me; plus, I had

             to learn a different language.

             A   B
_____ 35. (Their, There) are conflicting opinions about women holding

             military commands in combat situations.

                                                  A
_____ 36. My supervisor told me that I need to (get my act together,
                          B
             improve my performance) before my next review.

             A   B
_____ 37. (If, In the event that) your health insurance doesn't cover eye

             exams, you can get discount vouchers from the campus health

             center.

_____ 38. All the money that people spend on the lottery should be
A   **B**
(gave, given) to help poor children who need food and clothes.

A   **B**
_____ 39. She (appears, is appearing) to be very familiar with basic nurs-

ing procedures.

A B
_____ 40. Professor Alberts gave (we, us) students a study guide before

the final exam.

A   B
_____ 41. When you (seperate, separate) the egg yolk from the egg white,

try not to break the yolk.

A   B
_____ 42. We decided that we (are'nt, aren't) going to Italy until next

summer because we spent too much money this year.

A   B
_____ 43. Although Anthony auditioned (good, well), he was disappointed

when he didn't get the part in the school play.

_____ 44. If we don't have taxes, where will we get money to improve our
A B
city and (its, it's) recreational facilities?

A B
_____ 45. When I first started working here, I wasn't aware (about, of)

the dress code.

Part Three

For each number, choose the sentence that is correctly worded and punctuated. Write the letter indicating the correct sentence in the space provided.

_____ 46. **A.** Men and women, who eat high levels of margarine, are at higher risk than those who eat less.

B. Men and women who eat high levels of margarine are at higher risk than those who eat less.

_____ 47. **A.** Women are deciding to be construction workers rather than secretaries.

B. Women are deciding to be construction workers rather than being a secretary.

_____ 48. **A.** Not only do tax-funded recreational facilities help communities as a whole, but it also helps each individual.

B. Not only do tax-funded recreational facilities help communities as a whole, but they also help each individual.

_____ 49. **A.** Five years from now I will get a bachelor's degree; and I will become a teacher.

B. Five years from now I will get a bachelor's degree, and I will become a teacher.

_____ 50. **A.** Therefore, after I go to college, the world is mine.

B. Therefore, after going to college, the world is mine.

_____ 51. **A.** During her first semester in college, Cam took Reading, English, History, and Math.

B. Cam took reading, English, history, and math during her first semester in college.

_____ 52. **A.** I would much rather call than sitting down and writing a letter.

B. I would much rather call than sit down and write a letter.

_____ 53. **A.** My sister always has a plan and sticks to it, while I often do things at the last minute or change my plans.

B. My sister always has a plan and sticks to it, while, I often do things at the last minute or change my plans.

_____ 54. **A.** This job carried a heavy load on me because if I do not put the belt on correctly, I will probably ruin the engine.

B. This job carried a heavy load on me because if I did not put the belt on correctly, I probably would have ruined the engine.

_____ 55. **A.** "Don't belittle your child's fears," says Dr. Leah Klungness, school psychologist, "or he will not discuss them with you."

B. "Don't belittle your child's fears", says Dr. Leah Klungness, school psychologist, "Or he will not discuss them with you".

_____ 56. **A.** Female athletes suffer eight times more knee injuries than male athletes; however, they can avoid injuries if they strengthen their hamstrings by jumping rope for a few minutes three times a week.

B. Female athletes suffer eight times more knee injuries than male athletes, however, they can avoid injuries if they strengthen their hamstrings by jumping rope for a few minutes three times a week.

_____ 57. **A.** You can keep deer and rabbits out of your garden with a homemade repellent: two tablespoons of hot pepper sauce, one gallon of water, and a tablespoon of nondetergent dish soap.

B. You can keep deer and rabbits out of your garden with a homemade repellent, two tablespoons of hot pepper sauce, one gallon of water, and a tablespoon of nondetergent dish soap.

_____ 58. **A.** Working on a computer is no more damaging to the eyes than paperwork or any other close-up labor.

B. Working on a computer is no more damaging to the eyes than doing paperwork or any other close-up labor.

_____ 59. **A.** Doctors, not families, should determine a patient's treatment because the doctors are the ones with the professional degrees and years of experience.

B. Doctors, not families, should determine a patient's treatment; because, the doctors are the ones with the professional degrees and years of experience.

_____ 60. **A.** "Why am I feeling so angry?" Jonathan asked his counselor.

B. "Why am I feeling so angry?", Jonathan asked his counselor.

_____ 61. **A.** All children deserve the best education, and the best medical care they can get.

B. All children deserve the best education and the best medical care they can get.

_____ 62. **A.** Rosemary almost lost $200 on her trip to Atlantic City.

B. Rosemary lost almost $200 on her trip to Atlantic City.

_____ 63. **A.** The professor told Sasha and I that we had the highest grades in the class.

              B. The professor told Sasha and me that we had the highest grades in the class.

_____ 64. **A.** Physical play, drawing, painting, and small tasks help children master their world and can make them less fearful.

              B. Physical play, drawing, painting, and doing small tasks help children master their world and can make them less fearful.

_____ 65. **A.** The television news reported a huge fire near the campus as I was waiting for my ride to school.

              B. Waiting for my ride to school, the television news reported a huge fire near the campus.

Diagnostic Test–B: Answer Key

1. B	18. B	35. B	52. B
2. B	19. A	36. B	53. A
3. A	20. B	37. A	54. B
4. B	21. C	38. B	55. A
5. B	22. B	39. A	56. A
6. C	23. B	40. B	57. A
7. B	24. A	41. B	58. B
8. A	25. A	42. B	59. A
9. C	26. A	43. B	60. A
10. B	27. A	44. A	61. B
11. A	28. B	45. B	62. B
12. B	29. B	46. B	63. B
13. A	30. A	47. A	64. B
14. A	31. B	48. B	65. A
15. B	32. A	49. B	
16. A	33. B	50. A	
17. A	34. A	51. B	

Diagnostic Test–B

Identification of Problem Areas

The following table will help you identify your students' strengths and weaknesses in grammar, sentence structure, punctuation, and spelling skills. Use the table to match chapter content in *Real Writing* with individual items from the diagnostic test.

Chapter in **Real Writing**		*Test Items*
22	Fragments	4, 20, 25
23	Run-ons	1, 7, 16, 56
24	Problems with subject-verb agreement	10, 30, 34
25	Verb problems	22, 27, 38, 54
26	Pronouns	23, 40, 48, 63
27	Adjectives and adverbs	13, 31, 43
28	Misplaced and dangling modifiers	50, 62, 65
29	Coordination and subordination	3, 11, 17, 59
30	Parallelism	2, 47, 52, 58, 64
32	ESL	8, 14, 33, 39, 45
33	Word choice	36, 37
34	Commonly confused words	28, 29, 35, 44
35	Spelling	5, 24, 32, 41
36	Commas	1, 17, 46, 49, 53, 61
37	Apostrophes	9, 12, 18, 42
38	Quotation marks	15, 55, 60
39	Other punctuation	3, 10, 21, 57, 59
40	Capitalization	19, 26, 51

Diagnostic Test–C

Sentence Completeness

In the blank, write **RO** for run-on (two sentences joined incorrectly), **F** for fragment (incomplete sentence), and **S** for complete sentence.

_____ 1. To get through college as quickly as possible.

_____ 2. Although the hours are long and the pay is mediocre.

_____ 3. The Internet has made it easier for students to buy term papers and pass them off as their own work.

_____ 4. Household chores never really end they just go on and on.

_____ 5. Debbie wants to buy a greyhound, however, the landlord does not allow pets.

_____ 6. Since the Beatles, the Rolling Stones, and other British groups "invaded" America in the 1960s.

_____ 7. If you own a home, you can deduct expenses from your tax return, there's no such allowance for those of us who rent.

_____ 8. A computer allows a doctor to monitor the vital signs of a fetus and its mother without being in the same room.

_____ 9. A pencil is more useful than a yellow highlighter, the pencil allows you to jot down comments and questions in the margins of the page.

_____ 10. Some foods believed to reduce the risk of cancer.

_____ 11. The bus offers a quicker, more direct way to reach my apartment, but it does not run as often as the subway train.

_____ 12. In the beginning of the summer, and again at the end of summer.

Misplaced and Dangling Modifiers

Edit the following sentences to correct errors with dangling or misplaced modifiers.

13. Lacking strong math skills, the course was too difficult.

14. The parts of the book are left out of the film that Liza found most interesting to read.

15. Several months behind in their rent payments, the landlord insisted that Jenny and Steve find a new place to live.

16. After sleeping in it, the cat's basket was covered with a thick layer of fur.

17. Martha nearly meets with each of her clients every week.

Correct Word Choice, Verbs, Modifiers

Circle the correct word or words in the parentheses.

18. Prozac is the best known of the newer drugs that (fight, fights) depression with only minor side effects.
19. Students who own computers have an advantage over (his or her, their) classmates.
20. Monica met with colleagues, spoke with her supervisor, and (discussed her concerns, her concerns were discussed) with friends before asking for a transfer.
21. Investing your money in overseas markets (is, are) often riskier than buying stocks in the United States.
22. Tim avoids (to buy, buying) fruits and vegetables that are not organically grown.
23. Trish did (good, well) in her management course, which had only eight students and an energetic professor.
24. (It is the opinion of many Americans, Many Americans believe) that the death penalty gives murderers what they deserve.
25. Although the plot was slow, the film was photographed (beautiful, beautifully).
26. Some people can sleep on an airplane, but I have to be (laying, lying) down.
27. (A, The) classroom that my business class meets in has a noisy heating system.
28. After Pam lifted up a large rock from the tidepool, she (discovers, discovered) an unusual species of hermit crab.
29. In my neighborhood, unemployment is (worse, worst) today than when my parents were young.
30. According to psychologist Joel D. Block, a typical friendship between men (has, have) less emotional depth than a friendship between women.
31. Darlene wants to build her new home near the (green large, large green) hills at the edge of town.
32. I am (psyched, excited) to be offered one of your paid internships.
33. Should the school year for elementary, middle, and high school students last (long, longer) than nine months?
34. The university offers health insurance only to (its, their) full-time employees.
35. One problem with portable phones (occur, occurs) when you can't find the receiver.

36. Li Zhen was proud (for, of) the improvements she made in her spoken and written English.
37. It is important to use up a supply of antibiotics even if the infection appears to have (gone, went) away.
38. Many scientists believe that severe storms are occurring (more frequent, more frequently) because of global warming.
39. We can use our money either to repair the porch or (for buying, to buy) a new dining-room table.
40. A doctor shouldn't claim to always know exactly what is best for (his, his or her, their) patients.

Punctuation and Capitalization

Add the correct punctuation and capitalization to the following sentences.

41. Mount Rainier which is near Seattle has taken the lives of a lot of mountain climbers.
42. My italian grandparents arrived in san pedro, near los angeles, around the time of world war I.
43. Two friends are majoring in economics and international relations and Justin is interested in these subjects himself.
44. When she broke the school record in the quarter-mile, Kate said, This is the most satisfying thing I've ever done!
45. The childrens room at the library is colorfully decorated.
46. Writers revise their drafts by emphasizing key ideas removing unneeded information and paying special attention to clarity.
47. Is it still possible for me to get into this course? Nathan asked, but the professor shook his head.
48. Kevin wouldnt have applied for the job if he didnt think he was qualified.
49. Don't stop now there are only two weeks left in the semester.
50. I must do three things before the end of the month pay the rent have the brakes checked on the Toyota and meet with the career counselor.
51. Centuries ago, latin was the international language of europe, just as english is today.
52. A professor whos sensitive to students feelings will earn the students respect.
53. Theresa was disappointed by her grade on her essay she went to see the professor to ask if she could revise it.
54. Julian a teammate of mine in high school is transferring to this college.
55. As anyone who has met him already knows Jim is an extremely smart guy.

Spelling

Correct any spelling errors. Put **C** in the blank if you see no error.

_____ 56. Rosana has the necesary skills.

_____ 57. This software is a definate improvement.

_____ 58. Their is nothing wrong with my eyesight.

_____ 59. My score was higher then hers.

_____ 60. Kim use to work in an automotive shop.

_____ 61. The fly got traped in the spider's web.

_____ 62. We recieve our grades in the mail.

_____ 63. This arguement could go on forever.

_____ 64. Separate the paper from the glass.

_____ 65. Promise not to deceive me.

_____ 66. She made a valueable contribution.

_____ 67. He should have taken the orignal offer.

_____ 68. I have acheived all of my goals.

_____ 69. The bull got lose from its pen.

_____ 70. It's time to protect the enviroment.

Diagnostic Test–C: Answer Key

Sentence Completeness

1. F. 2. F. 3. S. 4. RO. 5. RO. 6. F. 7. RO. 8. S. 9. RO. 10. F.
11. S. 12. F.

Misplaced and Dangling Modifiers

Possible edits shown.

13. Because he lacked strong math skills, the course was too difficult for him.
14. The parts of the book that Liza found most interesting to read are left out of the film.
15. The landlord insisted that Jenny and Steve, who were several months behind in their rent payments, find a new place to live.
16. After the cat slept in it, the basket was covered with a thick layer of fur.
17. Martha meets with each of her clients nearly every week.

Correct Word Choice, Verbs, Modifiers

18. fight. 19. their. 20. discussed her concerns. 21. is. 22. buying.
23. well. 24. Many Americans believe. 25. beautifully. 26. lying.
27. The. 28. discovered. 29. worse. 30. has. 31. large green.
32. excited. 33. longer. 34. its. 35. occurs. 36. of. 37. gone.
38. more frequently. 39. to buy. 40. his or her.

Punctuation and Capitalization

Edits shown.

41. Mount Rainier**,** which is near Seattle**,** has taken the lives of a lot of mountain climbers.
42. My **I**talian grandparents arrived in **S**an **P**edro, near **L**os **A**ngeles, around the time of **W**orld **W**ar I.
43. Two friends are majoring in economics and international relations**,** and Justin is interested in these subjects himself.
44. When she broke the school record in the quarter-mile, Kate said**,** "This is the most satisfying thing I've ever done!"
45. The children**'**s room at the library is colorfully decorated.
46. Writers revise their drafts by emphasizing key ideas**,** removing unneeded information**,** and paying special attention to clarity.
47. "Is it still possible for me to get into this course?" Nathan asked, but the professor shook his head.
48. Kevin **wouldn't** have applied for the job if he **didn't** think he was qualified.

49. Don't stop now. **T**here are only two weeks left in the semester.
50. I must do three things before the end of the month**:** pay the rent, have the brakes checked on the Toyota**,** and meet with the career counselor.
51. Centuries ago, **L**atin was the international language of **E**urope, just as **E**nglish is today.
52. A professor **who's** sensitive to **students'** feelings will earn the **students'** respect.
53. Theresa was disappointed by her grade on her essay. **S**he went to see the professor to ask if she could revise it.
54. Julian**,** a teammate of mine in high school**,** is transferring to this college.
55. As anyone who has met him already knows**,** Jim is an extremely smart guy.

Spelling

56. necessary.   57. definite.   58. There.   59. than.   60. used.
61. trapped.   62. receive.   63. argument.   64. C.   65. C.
66. valuable.   67. original.   68. achieved.   69. loose.   70. environment.

Diagnostic Test–C

Identification of Problem Areas

The following table will help you to identify your students' strengths and weaknesses in grammar, sentence structure, punctuation, and spelling skills. Use the table to match chapter content in *Real Writing* with individual items from the diagnostic test.

Chapter in **Real Writing**	*Test items*
22 Fragments	1, 2, 6, 10, 12
23 Run-ons	4, 5, 7, 9
24 Problems with subject-verb agreement	18, 21, 30, 35
25 Verb problems	26, 28, 37
26 Pronouns	19, 34, 40
27 Adjectives and adverbs	23, 25, 29, 33, 38
28 Misplaced and dangling modifiers	13, 14, 15, 16, 17
29 Coordination and subordination	41, 43, 53, 55
30 Parallelism	20, 39
32 ESL	22, 27, 31, 36
33 Word choice	24, 32
34 Commonly confused words	58, 59, 60, 69
35 Spelling	56, 57, 61, 62, 63, 64, 65, 66, 67, 68, 70
36 Commas	41, 43, 46, 50, 54, 55
37 Apostrophes	45, 48, 52
38 Quotation marks	44, 47
39 Other punctuation	49, 50, 53
40 Capitalization	42, 51

Diagnostic Test–D

Part One

Each of the following sentences has three boldfaced sections labeled **A, B,** and **C.** Read each sentence carefully, looking for errors in grammar, punctuation, and spelling. If you find an error in any of the boldfaced sections, write the letter of the problem area in the space provided. If there is no error, write the letter **C** in the space provided.

_____ 1. Kel **spend** last summer working as a clerk in a law firm. The
          year before, he **did** volunteer work at a training and employ-
          ment agency. **No error.**

_____ 2. I **decided** to attend college to make something out of my
          life. To end up with a career I can be proud of. **No error.**

_____ 3. Some books **written** about the assassination of John F.
          Kennedy **claims** that Lee Harvey Oswald did not act alone.
          No error.

_____ 4. On **the advice** of a friend, I went back to the registrar's office
          and discovered that **an information** I had received earlier was
          not correct. **No error.**

_____ 5. James spent many long hours in the weight room trying to
          develope the **necessary** strength in his upper body. **No error.**

_____ 6. Although the minivan was **expensive, Mike** and Sheri thought
          it was worth the **money; it** had a better safety record than any
          of the other vans they looked at. **No error.**

_____ 7. **Apple, which** introduced **their** first personal computer back in
          the late 1970s, later fell behind in the highly competitive PC
          market. **No error.**

_____ 8. Even though Marie graduated from high school with a high
grade point average and **winning** several top **awards, she**
<u>A</u>   <u>B</u>
decided to wait a year before attending college. **No error.**
<u>C</u>

_____ 9. That was quite a **surprise** to hear about your **promotion, I**
<u>A</u>   <u>B</u>
thought it would go to someone with more experience.
<u>C</u>
No error.

_____ 10. Sometimes a course **is seeming** hard when you first begin, but
<u>A</u>
then you **realize** that it is not so difficult after all. **No error.**
<u>B</u>   <u>C</u>

_____ 11. **One of the presidents** most important **powers is** the ability
<u>A</u>   <u>B</u>
to veto legislation passed by Congress. **No error.**
<u>C</u>

_____ 12. Our vacation is in **March,** which is too early to enjoy the nice
<u>A</u>
Spring weather. **No error.**
<u>B</u>   <u>C</u>

_____ 13. Everywhere I went in that little **town, distant** relatives of mine
<u>A</u>
offered me food. But I already had **ate** all I could. **No error.**
<u>B</u>   <u>C</u>

_____ 14. Dawn and Glen are from the same city in **Illinois but** they did
<u>A</u>
not know each other until they came to **college; they** attended
<u>B</u>
different high schools. **No error.**
<u>C</u>

_____ 15. If anybody tries to tell you that **it's** easy to work and go to
<u>A</u>
school at the same time, **they** don't know what they're talking
<u>B</u>
about. **No error.**
<u>C</u>

_____ 16. **There** are three good reasons not to own a **car, the** cost of
<u>A</u>   <u>B</u>
the car itself, the cost of insurance, the cost of fuel and repairs.
No error.
<u>C</u>

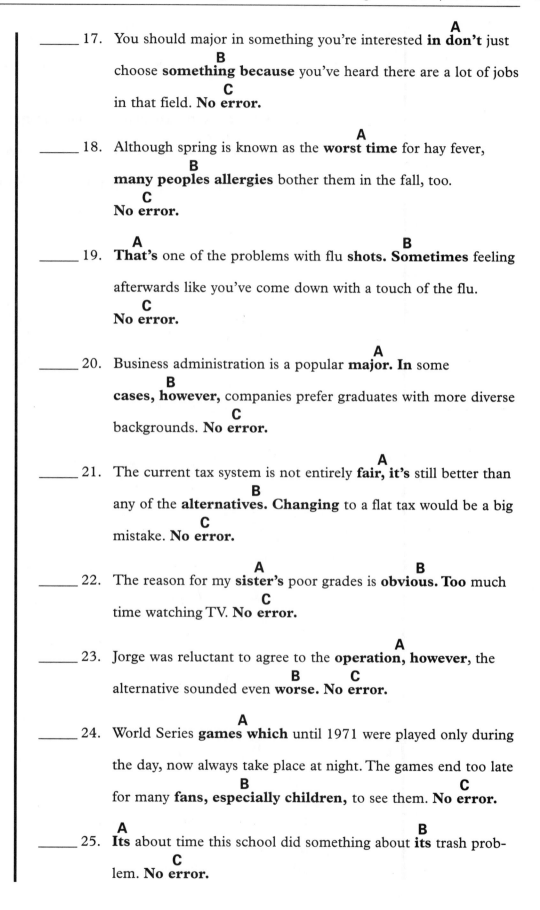

_____ 17. You should major in something you're interested **in don't** just
choose **something because** you've heard there are a lot of jobs
in that field. **No error.**

_____ 18. Although spring is known as the **worst time** for hay fever,
many peoples allergies bother them in the fall, too.
No error.

_____ 19. **That's** one of the problems with flu **shots. Sometimes** feeling
afterwards like you've come down with a touch of the flu.
No error.

_____ 20. Business administration is a popular **major. In** some
cases, however, companies prefer graduates with more diverse
backgrounds. **No error.**

_____ 21. The current tax system is not entirely **fair, it's** still better than
any of the **alternatives. Changing** to a flat tax would be a big
mistake. **No error.**

_____ 22. The reason for my **sister's** poor grades is **obvious. Too** much
time watching TV. **No error.**

_____ 23. Jorge was reluctant to agree to the **operation, however,** the
alternative sounded even **worse. No error.**

_____ 24. World Series **games which** until 1971 were played only during
the day, now always take place at night. The games end too late
for many **fans, especially children,** to see them. **No error.**

_____ 25. **Its** about time this school did something about **its** trash problem. **No error.**

_____ 26. **Hopeing** for a lighter **sentence, the** defendant pleaded guilty
            A   **B**

to a lesser charge. **No error.**
              C

_____ 27. Chandra decided to take another course from the same

writing teacher. Because it allowed her to save money
     A

by not having to buy a different textbook. **No error.**
    B   **C**

Part Two

In each of the following sentences, decide which of the words in parentheses is the correct choice for that sentence. Then write the letter indicating the correct word or words in the space provided.

_____ 28. Familiarity with computer software programs (is, are) required for many different types of jobs today.

_____ 29. I won't be able to sleep (until, untill) I finish writing this paper.

_____ 30. Please (advice, advise) me on what courses I should take.

_____ 31. A (large white, white large) sign marked the entrance to the zoo.

_____ 32. Carrie (wouldnt have, wouldn't have) taken on the second job if she didn't think she could handle it.

_____ 33. Larry and (me, I) have been friends for years.

_____ 34. *Schindler's List* is one of the (most powerful, powerful) films I have ever seen.

_____ 35. Andy's (neice, niece) began kindergarten this fall.

_____ 36. There (are, is) only three days left to drop a course without receiving a "W" mark on your transcripts.

_____ 37. (Although, In spite of the fact that) Gwen had taken a year of chemistry in high school, she decided to take the Introduction to Chemistry course her first semester.

_____ 38. I'm sorry, but I cannot (accept, except) the position you've offered me.

_____ 39. Xiao considered (to transfer, transferring) to another school.

_____ 40. The (dog's, dogs') owners were not paying attention when the two animals began to fight with each other.

_____ 41. Although our overall score was lower, we performed better than (them, they) in several important categories.

_____ 42. Ilse had not (expect, expected) them to ask her what she thought was a fair salary.

_____ 43. Some students are not (aware of, aware about) the services offered by the tutorial center.

_____ 44. Employees were told (not to worry too much, not to get freaked out) about the strange odors circulating through the building.

_____ 45. I had to work (quick, quickly) in order to leave the office in time to make it to the party.

Part Three

For each number, choose the sentence that is correctly worded and punctuated. Write the letter indicating the correct sentence in the space provided.

_____ 46. **A.** Waiting in a long line outside the adviser's office, the adviser told the students he was about to break for lunch.

B. Waiting in a long line outside the adviser's office, the students learned that the adviser was about to break for lunch.

_____ 47. **A.** After class Jill spoke with the professor, and she complimented her on her good ideas.

B. After class Jill spoke with the professor, who complimented Jill on her good ideas.

_____ 48. **A.** Swimming, canoeing, and sailing are among the many popular activities at the lake.

B. Swimming, canoeing, and sailboats are among the many popular activities at the lake.

_____ 49. **A.** The union president said that "he now felt that a strike was unavoidable."

B. The union president said that he now felt that a strike was unavoidable.

_____ 50. **A.** As I pulled myself together, my knees shaking, my mind was in a whirl.

B. Pulling myself together, my knees shaking, my mind was in a whirl.

_____ 51. **A.** Florida, Texas, and California are among the states with the most Spanish-speaking citizens.

B. Florida Texas and California are among the states with the most Spanish-speaking citizens.

_____ 52. **A.** Sometimes making a phone call is better than an email message.

B. Sometimes making a phone call is better than sending an email message.

_____ 53. **A.** My daughter's regular pediatrican, Dr. Bruce, was out of town, so we saw Dr. Janacek instead.

B. My daughter's regular pediatrician Dr. Bruce was out of town, so we saw Dr. Janacek instead.

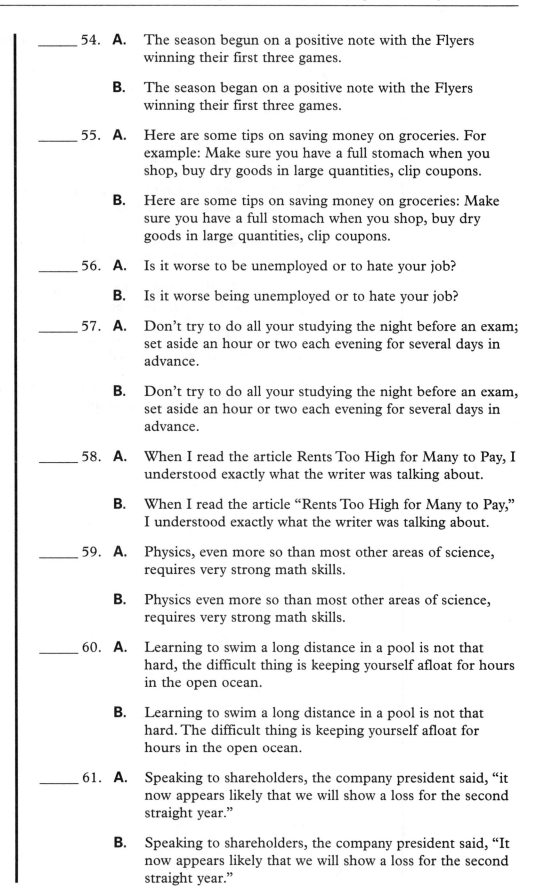

_____ 54. **A.** The season begun on a positive note with the Flyers winning their first three games.

   B. The season began on a positive note with the Flyers winning their first three games.

_____ 55. **A.** Here are some tips on saving money on groceries. For example: Make sure you have a full stomach when you shop, buy dry goods in large quantities, clip coupons.

   B. Here are some tips on saving money on groceries: Make sure you have a full stomach when you shop, buy dry goods in large quantities, clip coupons.

_____ 56. **A.** Is it worse to be unemployed or to hate your job?

   B. Is it worse being unemployed or to hate your job?

_____ 57. **A.** Don't try to do all your studying the night before an exam; set aside an hour or two each evening for several days in advance.

   B. Don't try to do all your studying the night before an exam, set aside an hour or two each evening for several days in advance.

_____ 58. **A.** When I read the article Rents Too High for Many to Pay, I understood exactly what the writer was talking about.

   B. When I read the article "Rents Too High for Many to Pay," I understood exactly what the writer was talking about.

_____ 59. **A.** Physics, even more so than most other areas of science, requires very strong math skills.

   B. Physics even more so than most other areas of science, requires very strong math skills.

_____ 60. **A.** Learning to swim a long distance in a pool is not that hard, the difficult thing is keeping yourself afloat for hours in the open ocean.

   B. Learning to swim a long distance in a pool is not that hard. The difficult thing is keeping yourself afloat for hours in the open ocean.

_____ 61. **A.** Speaking to shareholders, the company president said, "it now appears likely that we will show a loss for the second straight year."

   B. Speaking to shareholders, the company president said, "It now appears likely that we will show a loss for the second straight year."

_____ 62. **A.** Working as a schoolteacher can be both difficult and re-warding.

B. Working as a schoolteacher can be both difficult and it can bring rewards.

_____ 63. **A.** Before I woke up, I had been dreaming about being alone on a beach in Florida.

B. I had been dreaming about being alone on a beach in Florida before I woke up.

_____ 64. **A.** Since Keith started going to bed earlier, his concentration in class has been much better.

B. Since Keith started going to bed earlier; his concentration in class has been much better.

_____ 65. **A.** By the time her boss finally had time to talk with her Kristin's anger had cooled off.

B. By the time her boss finally had time to talk with her, Kristin's anger had cooled off.

Diagnostic Test–D: Answer Key

1. A.	18. B	35. B.	52. B.
2. B.	19. B.	36. A.	53. A.
3. B.	20. C.	37. A.	54. B.
4. B.	21. A.	38. A.	55. B.
5. A.	22. B.	39. B.	56. A.
6. C.	23. A.	40. B.	57. A.
7. B.	24. A.	41. B.	58. B.
8. A.	25. A.	42. B.	59. A.
9. B.	26. A.	43. A.	60. B.
10. A.	27. A.	44. A.	61. B.
11. A.	28. A.	45. B.	62. A.
12. B.	29. A.	46. B.	63. A.
13. B.	30. B.	47. B.	64. A.
14. A.	31. A.	48. A.	65. B.
15. B.	32. B.	49. B.	
16. B.	33. B.	50. A.	
17. A.	34. A.	51. A.	

Diagnostic Test–D

Identification of Problem Areas

The following table will help you to identify your students' strengths and weaknesses in grammar, sentence structure, punctuation, and spelling skills. Use the table to match chapter content in *Real Writing* with individual items from the diagnostic test.

Chapter in **Real Writing**		*Test Items*
22	Fragments	2, 19, 22, 27
23	Run-ons	9, 17, 21, 23, 57, 60
24	Problems with subject-verb agreement	3, 28, 36
25	Verb problems	1, 13, 42, 54
26	Pronouns	7, 15, 33, 41, 47
27	Adjectives and adverbs	34, 45
28	Misplaced and dangling modifiers	46, 50, 63
29	Coordination and subordination	21, 23, 27, 64
30	Parallelism	8, 48, 52, 56, 62
32	ESL	4, 10, 31, 39, 43
33	Word choice	37, 44
34	Commonly confused words	25, 30, 38
35	Spelling	5, 26, 29, 35
36	Commas	14, 24, 51, 53, 59, 65
37	Apostrophes	11, 18, 32, 40
38	Quotation marks	49, 58
39	Other punctuation	16, 19, 22, 55, 57, 64
40	Capitalization	12, 61

Review Tests for Editing Chapters
(*Chapters 21–40*)

Chapter 21: Overview

Chapter Review Test

For each of the following sentences, identify the part of the sentence that is underlined. For verbs, distinguish between action verbs, linking verbs, and helping verbs. Write your answers in the space provided.

EXAMPLE

prepositional phrase <u>After graduating from high school</u>, I needed to think seriously about what kind of career I wanted to pursue.

1. _____ My guidance counselor <u>said</u> that when thinking about a career, I should think about what kinds of things I enjoy doing.

2. _____ My favorite hobby <u>is</u> taking things apart and putting them back together.

3. _____ Mostly, I like to take apart <u>electrical</u> appliances.

4. _____ When I was younger, I <u>secretly</u> took apart my mother's clock radio.

5. _____ I didn't think that <u>she</u> would ever know what I had done.

6. _____ <u>The next morning</u>, the alarm clock did not go off.

7. _____ My mother realized what had happened to her radio, <u>but</u> she didn't get angry with me.

8. _____ Instead, she encouraged me to experiment <u>with</u> old appliances from the junkyard.

9. _____ I <u>was</u> unable to see how I could turn my hobby into a career until I asked my mother for advice.

10. _____ She said that of course she knew the perfect <u>job</u> for me—an electrician—and, as usual, she is right.

Chapter 22: Fragments

Chapter Review Test 1

Circle the fragments in the paragraph, and then edit the paragraph so that there are no fragments.

Charcoal was invented by Henry Ford. The man who also manufactured the first cars. Ford invented a way to convert the wood scraps left over from car manufacturing into charcoal. During the 1920s. His friend, Thomas Edison, designed the factory. That manufactured the pillow-shaped briquets. In 1922, according to the Kingsford Products Company in Oakland, California. Ford turned over the charcoal operation to his relative, E.G. Kingsford. To relieve himself of some responsibilities. Until the 1950s, Kingsford charcoal couldn't be bought just anywhere. Only at Ford dealerships.

Chapter 22: Fragments

Chapter Review Test 2

Read the application letter that follows. Circle the fragments, and then edit the letter so that there are no fragments.

Dear Ms. Brown:

Please consider me as a candidate for the part-time position of administrative assistant in the marketing department. After reading your advertisement in *The San Antonion Daily*. I feel confident that I could make a valuable contribution to the company.

I am a student at San Antonio College. Pursuing a degree in Business Administration. I have completed courses in Principles of Marketing, Introduction to Business, Managerial Finance, and others that give me the skills to qualify for the administrative assistant position. My cumulative grade point average is 3.5.

I also have office and retail experience. Having held positions at Latimer Gifts as secretary to the direct mail manager, sales clerk at The Gap, and sales clerk at PayLess Shoes. Where I was named "Employee of the Month" in September of 1996. These positions have given me an understanding of customer needs, customer service, and direct mail marketing. I believe I can apply what I've learned in your company. While continuing to take courses toward my degree.

(continued)

I have enclosed my résumé. It provides complete information on my education and experience. To help in your selection. I have also enclosed a list of references. On a separate sheet of paper. Also a letter of recommendation. Thank you for your consideration. I will look forward to speaking with you.

Sincerely,

Marcia Perez

Chapter 23: Run-Ons

Chapter Review Test 1

Check each sentence for run-on sentences and comma splices. In the space to the left, write **CS** for a comma splice, **F** for a fused sentence, or **C** for correct. Then edit each sentence by adding words and/or punctuation. Do not use the same method of correction in every sentence.

_____ 1. Living with my parents used to be a drag, however, living on my own can be pretty neat.

_____ 2. Living with my parents was difficult at times, it was especially difficult once I got out of the military.

_____ 3. Dad had his rules for instance we couldn't receive any phone calls after 9 P.M. and had to be in before 10 P.M.

_____ 4. Likewise, Mom had her rules making my bed and cleaning my room before breakfast every morning was my least favorite rule.

_____ 5. And, of course, there were always the chores, I had to mow the yard, clean the bathroom, and clean my closet.

_____ 6. Now my life is a breeze, I don't have any rules to go by but my own.

_____ 7. I'm not on the phone as often as I was at home if I want to call after 9 P.M., I can.

_____ 8. I don't have to be home at a certain time I don't usually, for example, get home from work before 11 P.M.

_____ 9. Although I still have chores, they don't seem as bad since I make them up.

_____ 10. As a result, I think both living situations had their good points I still prefer living on my own.

Chapter 23: Run-Ons

Chapter Review Test 2

Identify the run-ons in the paragraph, and then edit the paragraph so that there are no run-ons.

(1) College admissions officers in large colleges and universities receive thousands of applications every year, many of the applications for fall don't come in until April or May. (2) These dates are well within the deadline there is a good reason to apply earlier. (3) In order for students to be considered for financial aid or scholarship, applications need to be received early in the calendar year. (4) Many transfer students don't realize this they wait too long and can't get money they might have been qualified to receive. (5) Early in the year a student might be awarded a grant later that same student might receive a loan. (6) The difference between the two is significant, the grant is given with no strings attached, the loan must be repaid later.

Chapter 24: Subject-Verb Agreement

Chapter Review Test 1

Read the following sentences carefully for subject-verb agreement problems. If you find a problem, write the correct form of the verb in the space provided. Mark any correct sentences with a **C**.

_____ 1. The United States, land of the free, are rapidly becoming the land of the fat.

_____ 2. Therefore, everyone seem concerned with appearances.

_____ 3. Everywhere you look, people of all ages exercises and watch what they eat.

_____ 4. In my P.E. class, not one of the students like the way he or she looks.

_____ 5. Neither the students nor the teacher has any big weight problem.

_____ 6. There are, believe it or not, one student who weighs only 90 pounds.

_____ 7. However, each of the members of my exercise group want to lose 20 pounds.

_____ 8. Losing those extra pounds are not enough.

_____ 9. Men and women, no matter what their ages, need to concern themselves with staying healthy.

_____ 10. A man or woman who wants to become healthy need to exercise and to plan meals carefully.

_____ 11. My teacher says that everyone in the class have excess body fat that we need to eliminate, even the skinny person.

_____ 12. Aerobic exercise and weight training provide health benefits we need.

_____ 13. Walking, riding a bike, or jogging help improve the cardiovascular system.

_____ 14. Using weights, like ankle weights or the weight machines, build strength and energy.

(continued)

_____ 15. Some of my classmates like to exercise first thing in the morning because there is no jobs or school responsibilities to distract them.

_____ 16. Working out in the afternoon, my favorite time for exercise, increase the energy level so someone can finish the work or school day.

_____ 17. Nighttime exercise have the advantages of more flexible joints, stronger muscles, and more lung capacity.

_____ 18. However, too much exercise before bedtime keep people awake.

_____ 19. How does most people get started?

_____ 20. Everyone have to plan a program that fits into the day's schedule and that allows for good exercise and appropriate rest.

Chapter 24: Subject-Verb Agreement

Chapter Review Test 2

Read the following paragraph for subject-verb agreement problems. If you find an error, write the correct verb in the proper space by the corresponding number at the bottom of the page. If the sentence is correct, write **C** by its corresponding number.

(1) Why do the United States, a country of freedoms, need a rating system for movies? (2) First, the rating system for all major theatrical releases are based on the contents of the movie. (3) There is major differences between R-rated movies and PG-rated movies in today's theaters. (4) An R-rated movie usually have an unbelievable amount of sex and gruesome violence; however, PG-rated movies contain very little, if any, sex or violence. (5) Furthermore, the rating system also issues warnings to the public. (6) For instance, anyone under the age of 17 need a parent along to go to an R-rated movie. (7) A PG movie don't have an age limit, so anyone can see the movie. (8) Also, limited topics and harsher plots appear in R movies since they aim at an adult audience. (9) Thus, anyone going to an R movie expects a graphic look at the grim side of human events. (10) On the other hand, most PG movies provides the audiences with more of a family-value type of thinking. (11) PG movies, the majority of the time, provides more of an unlimited amount of topics for the viewers. (12) Finally, knowing the distinctions between the ratings makes selecting the right movie easier.

1. _____   5. _____   9. _____

2. _____   6. _____   10. _____

3. _____   7. _____   11. _____

4. _____   8. _____   12. _____

Chapter 25: Verb Problems

Chapter Review Test 1

Write the correct form of the verb in parentheses in the space under each sentence.

1. In 1956, Handler and her husband (start) a tiny toy company called Mattel.

   _____

2. In the late 1950s and early 1960s, they (make) baby dolls.

   _____

3. Handler (raise) the idea of a doll that looked older and more realistic, but no one (think) it was a good idea.

   _____

4. Just before she came home from a trip to Europe, Handler (see) a teenaged doll.

   _____

5. She (demand) that Mattel make such a doll.

   _____

6. They (do), and the doll (become) Barbie, named after Handler's daughter.

   _____

7. Barbie (be) the world's most popular doll, and the Mattel toy company (grow) fast.

   _____

8. Today, Barbies (sell) at the rate of two per second.

   _____

9. In 1993, sales (exceed) $1 billion.

   _____

10. Today, the Handler family (live) in Denver, Colorado.

   _____

Chapter 25: **Verb Problems**

Chapter Review Test 2

Circle the errors in verb tense. Write the correct form in the space above the error.

(1) Franklin Delano Roosevelt was the thirty-second president of the United States. (2) Until he was in his early thirties, he was very active and athletic. (3) He sail, ride horses, and play all kinds of sports. He perceived himself as an athlete. (4) However, as a young man, he contracts polio, and for the rest of his life could barely walk. (5) When he does walk, it is with great difficulty and only with the aid of steel crutches. (6) He did not let polio get in his way. (7) Instead, he hold public office. (8) First he become governor of New York, and then he serve three full terms as president. (9) During his terms in office, he has started hundreds of new social and economic programs, work to bring racial equality, and has guided the country through World War II.

(10) People say that if television had exist at that time, Roosevelt would never have became president. (11) They speculate that the American people would not have elected a man in a wheelchair to the highest office in the land. (12) In the 1930s and 1940s, radio is the favorite mass medium. (13) Roosevelt was a powerful speaker, with a confident and vital voice. (14) That were the image that most people had of Roosevelt. (15) Newspapers publish photographs that only showed Roosevelt seated. (16) The average person did not think of Roosevelt as disabled. (17) His will and success prove that a physical disability need not hold one back from great accomplishments.

Chapter 26: Pronouns

Chapter Review Test

The following sentences include one pronoun problem each. Circle the problem and correct it. In some cases it may be necessary to revise the entire sentence.

1. The University Finance Committee put off their decision on whether to raise tuition next year.

2. Considering the costs of tuition, room, board, and books, Joel is no longer sure that he can afford it.

3. The cost of textbooks, it has really increased a lot in recent years.

4. The woman in the financial-aid office said they don't know how much money will be available next year.

5. Can't the government find some way so that they will have more money left over for education?

6. The professor, who Joel had spoken to only once before, was glad that he had come to see her in her office.

7. Anyone who thinks that you can work full-time and take a full load of classes also needs to be prepared to go without much sleep.

8. Students study many different subjects, but they don't all interest them.

9. Ellen likes biology more than me.

10. Me and her both like business administration because it's more closely related to our career plans.

Chapter 27: Adjectives and Adverbs

Chapter Review Test

Circle the correct adjective or adverb in the sentences below.

1. This summer, in an (unusual, unusually) burst of energy, we visited three great American cities: Seattle, St. Louis, and Washington, DC.

2. Although I enjoyed all three, I enjoyed Seattle (more, the most).

3. (Probable, Probably) the reason for my fascination with Seattle is that I had never been to the West Coast.

4. We were prepared for rainy days and cool evenings, but the weather we found was (more good, better, best) than we expected.

5. The sweater I took for cold nights kept me (comfortable, comfortably) in the daytime, and my umbrella never left my suitcase.

6. We began our (excited, exciting) excursion Saturday morning by riding the monorail to Seattle Center, the site of the 1962 World's Fair.

7. From the 520-foot observation deck of the Space Needle, we could see every area of Seattle (easily, easy) and plan our day's sightseeing.

8. Returning to downtown, we toured the Pike Place Market, the oldest (continual, continually) operating farmers' market in the United States.

9. Then we started the steep descent to the Waterfront for a (good, well) lunch of fresh grilled fish.

10. That afternoon found us in Pioneer Square for a tour of Underground Seattle, where we learned how disagreements among early town settlers and the town's (unique, uniquely) plumbing problems led to streets being built ten feet above original streets.

11. Although the day had been (real, really) fun, we were exhausted and ready for a quick dinner and bed.

12. However, our hotel staff insisted our trip wouldn't be complete without a dinner on Redondo Beach, so out we headed for a (relaxed, relaxing) meal with a beautiful view of the water.

13. On Sunday afternoon, we traveled to Snoqualmie Falls, which at 270 feet is 100 feet (higher, more high) than Niagara Falls.

14. The scenery was as (spectacular, spectacularly) breathtaking as it was in the TV show *Twin Peaks*, which was filmed there.

(continued)

15. Then we drove to Mercer Island for Mother's Day dinner with friends and a (rough, roughly) boat ride around Lake Washington.

16. On Monday morning, we toured the Museum of Flight, housed in the Boeing Company's original home—a red barn—and saw a (large, larger) collection of fifty-six planes, including Air Force One.

17. We spent our last afternoon enjoying the sights, sounds, and cuisine of Chinatown with its (dramatic, dramatically) and colorful pagoda donated by the City of Taipei.

18. For our last evening in town, we took a harbor cruise to Blake Island's Tillicum Village for a great smoked salmon dinner, beautiful scenery, and a (most unique, unique) program illustrating the dances and legends of Northwest Coast Indians.

19. The (worse, worst) part of the trip was having to leave the impressive view of Mt. Rainier that we had from our hotel room.

20. Flying out Tuesday morning, we decided we had managed our time (good, well) and had seen more of Seattle than we had imagined possible.

Chapter 28: Misplaced and Dangling Modifiers

Chapter Review Test

Rewrite each sentence to eliminate problems with misplaced and dangling modifiers. In some cases, it may be necessary to add additional words.

1. Arriving at the bookstore, the two books Seung-Yeun needed for her writing class were nowhere to be found.

2. She searched through several stacks and shelves becoming increasingly irritated.

3. At the front desk, Seung-Yeun told the names of the books to the bookstore manager she was unable to find.

4. The manager said that he had almost ordered one hundred additional copies and that they would arrive within a few days.

5. The textbooks still had not been delivered to the bookstore manager's surprise a week later.

6. Anxious not to fall behind in her work, Seung-Yeun's instructor gave her photocopied materials from the textbooks.

7. Difficult to read because the print was too dark, Seung-Yeun finally gave up on the photocopied section and borrowed a classmate's textbook instead.

8. The bookstore manager said the next day that the books finally had arrived, feeling bad about their delay.

9. Being a good businessman, the books were discounted 10 percent for Seung-Yeun.

10. She paid for her purchase and ran off to class with her books showing gratitude with a handshake and a smile.

Chapter 29: Coordination and Subordination

Chapter Review Test

The following paragraph has too many choppy sentences. Join at least three sentences using either coordination or subordination.

There is a building in Washington, DC, with an interesting history. According to some stories, unknown facts about the assassination of Abraham Lincoln are hidden in one of the columns supporting the building. Lincoln's son, Robert, was secretary of war. He learned of documents that showed his father's murder was a conspiracy, not just the act of John Wilkes Booth alone. He got the documents. He was reluctant to reveal them to the country. He concealed them in the columns of a building. It was under construction. Apparently Lincoln intended the documents for posterity. No one knows where the documents are, or if they really exist. Their possible existence is a part of Washington, DC, folklore.

Chapter 30: Parallelism

Chapter Review Test

Read the following paragraph. On a separate piece of paper or on a computer, write the numbers of the sentences that aren't parallel, and then rewrite them in parallel form.

(1) Good relationships require love, respect, and communicating. (2) Avoiding arguments may seem easier than to confront the problem. (3) But over time, avoidance is as destructive to a relationship as constant disagreement is. (4) When couples don't talk to each other, they may not only avoid conflict but also losing the ability to communicate. (5) When this happens, relationships tend either to die or they stagnate. (6) Without communication, relationships can't withstand the pressures of working, taking care of household responsibilities, and parenting. (7) Couples have to talk about both their problems and solving them. (8) If they can discuss things with respect and trust, they can work out problems. (9) Without communicating, love and respect may not be enough.

Chapter 31: Sentence Variety

Chapter Review Test

Create sentence variety in the paragraphs that follow. Edit at least two sentences in each of the paragraphs. Try to use several of the techniques covered in this chapter.

Every country has its own traditions and holiday celebrations. We would expect those traditions and holidays to be very different. Many are. Some are surprisingly similar. New Year's celebrations across the world have one major similarity. The celebrants wish for good luck and wealth as they welcome in the new year.

We are familiar with the United States' traditions. Family and friends dress up and go out to a nice restaurant or club. Others invite friends to a big party at their homes. Everyone drinks champagne, uses noisemakers, and watches the dropping ball in New York's Times Square at midnight on New Year's Eve. No one can leave the table until he or she has eaten black-eyed peas for good luck in the coming year.

Several other countries have food as a big part of the New Year's celebration. Pork is especially popular in many countries such as Brazil. Celebrants in Poland enjoy Pig's Feet Galantine, an aspic-wrapped paté. Italians serve sausage and lentils. They represent the prosperity of a wallet full of money. The Chinese apply a fresh coat of red paint to their front doors for good luck and happiness and serve pork dumplings. The Swedish New Year begins with breakfast in bed. It consists of pork sausage on a bun with an apple. The Austrians are the most elaborate. They serve a suckling pig. They place it on a table of tiny pig-shaped cookies and candy with peppermint ice cream shaped like a four-leaf clover. They eat that for dessert.

(continued)

Other food traditions are found across the world. In the Middle East, people eat pomegranate seeds to ensure fertility. The Japanese serve a dish called *mochi*. *Mochi* is pounded rice cakes. A celebration in Norway would include rice pudding prepared with one whole almond. Tradition says that whoever finds the almond is guaranteed wealth in the new year.

Sicilians eat lasagna. Partygoers in Spain eat twelve grapes at midnight. They eat one at each strike of the clock. The grapes stand for good luck for each month. The Greeks bake a special New Year's bread. It contains a buried coin. The first slice is for the Christ child. The second slice is for the head of the household. Everyone watches when the third slice is cut. If it exposes the coin, it means that an early spring is predicted.

Food is not part of the tradition in England and Scotland. The first person over the threshold after midnight in those two countries is supposed to be a male. The man brings a gift of a piece of coal for the fire. The coal will bring warmth to the house in the new year. The man must enter through the front door and leave through the back door for good luck. People in Wales open the front door to let in the new year, and open and close the back door to let out any bad luck from the old year. The traditions may be different. They all rely on superstitions for good luck.

Chapter 32: ESL Concerns

Chapter Review Test

Edit the following sentences to make the nouns and articles correct.

1. When I moved to Florida, I wanted to go to beach.

2. I never lived near a water and wanted to walk on the sands.

3. I took big umbrella, dog, and Frisbee with me.

4. When waves washed up on shore, I found seashell and clam.

5. For lunch, I bought hot dog and cola from restaurant.

Find and correct any problems with verbs in the sentences below.

6. Coming to this country was one of the most interesting challenges that I experience in my life.

7. First of all, everything is different and strange in my eyes, so to move here was difficult for someone like me from a different cultural background.

8. The opportunity for education and self-improvement will changing my life.

9. After all, I am capable to live with freedom and exposing my mind to new ideas.

10. Overall, this immigration has made me to face all my dreams and wishes.

Edit the following sentences to make sure that prepositions are used correctly.

11. If you want a job, you must first fill up an application form at the company's personnel office.

12. Don't be afraid to going for an interview because the personnel director will be very nice to you.

13. Make sure that you show the employer that you are excited on working for her company.

14. If she hires you, the employer will go to all of the duties of the job and the company's policies.

(continued)

15. If you are confused in the directions, just ask questions.

    For each positive statement below, write one negative statement and one question.

16. All writers experience writer's block.

    _____

    _____

17. You can start writing about a topic that you choose.

    _____

    _____

18. You can pretend to write a letter to a friend.

    _____

    _____

19. Some writers enjoy describing happy memories.

    _____

    _____

20. Other people like to imagine their lives one year from now.

    _____

    _____

Chapter 33: Word Choice

Chapter Review Test

Find and edit any examples of vague and abstract language, slang, wordy language, or clichés in the following paragraphs.

Americans seem to have a fascination with food. Whether it's cooking, eating, shopping, or talking about it, food dominates much of our time and energies. In fact, food can be both good and bad for you. However, whereas food is a life-sustaining necessity, Americans have gone overboard.

In this day and age, fast-food places dominate the highways, and it looks to me like you can't even drive two blocks without seeing a McDonald's or a Taco Bell. If Mom's too dragged out from a hard day at work, she just takes a pass through some drive-through window at the neighborhood chicken shack. In the event that Dad is rushing from here to there during his busy day, he gobbles down a sandwich and chugs down a malted as he drives to his next appointment. Even the family that has spent a leisurely day at home working in the garden or merely enjoying the relative comforts of their home will call for pizza delivery rather than take the time to prepare a nice home-cooked meal.

To the other extreme are the health fanatics. You won't catch a burger and fries sliding over their tongues. No, sir. Their refrigerators look like the produce department at the local grocery store. You won't find any red meat in their homes, but you can find a lot of that green, leafy stuff. Plus, they have an abundant supply of carrots, broccoli, zucchini, and tomatoes. You might as well rename that home "Rabbit Hutch." And forget the sweets. Fruit (with perhaps a fat-free cereal bar thrown in for good measure) is what

(continued)

these people consider dessert. In their opinion, these people believe that vegetables and whole grains are the only way to go.

Probably somewhere in between are the ones who enjoy food but don't take it too seriously. They enjoy a good burger every now and then, but they also count calories and watch their fat intake. Mom and Dad and even the kids will pitch in and produce an evening meal fit for a queen (or king). They carefully itemize the ingredients and try to figure out if all of the food groups are properly included in the family's last meal of the day.

The fact of the matter is that with so many different kinds of eaters, food has become big business. From fancy restaurants to fast-food drive-throughs, Americans have a big choice when it comes to eating out. But even grocery stores are getting into the prepared-food picture. Their deli sections offer fried chicken, lots of salads, cooked vegetables, and desserts. For the person who wants to pretend to have a hand in the food prepara-tion, grocery stores have marinated meats and vegetable dishes that are ready to stick right in the oven as soon as the buyer arrives home. Whatever their tastes and styles, Americans can find what they want. Remember: We are what we eat.

Chapter 34: Commonly Confused Words

Chapter Review Test

In the following sentences, circle the correct word in parentheses.

1. The waiters are paying more attention to the television than to what (their, there, they're) supposed to be doing.

2. The lottery has bigger and more negative aspects (than, then) good ones.

3. I (preceded, proceeded) to tell my four-year-old daughter that she had both of her legs in one pants hole.

4. My hands blistered when I accidentally stuck them (to, too, two) far into the broiler.

5. Alice should not (pass, past) judgment on other people.

6. (Who's, Whose) to say that is the right solution?

7. The children would (loose, lose) the chance to meet new friends, learn leadership skills, and have some fun in their lives.

8. Where is (are, our) money going?

9. Sometimes patients think they (know, no) more than the doctors do.

10. (Weather, Whether) the doctor wants to or not, it is his responsibility to inform patients of their choices.

11. No one in the family wanted my father to go (though, through, threw) with the heart transplant.

12. Tamara was (suppose, supposed) to wash the dishes before going to the movie.

13. Jason answered all of the test questions (accept, except) those dealing with the Hopi Indians.

14. As soon as he saw the chemistry test, Jerry realized that he should (of, have) studied more.

15. If we (by, buy) season tickets to the symphony, we can get better seats for the special shows.

16. Although the patient was (conscience, conscious) when he arrived at the hospital, he soon lapsed into a coma.

(continued)

17. The singer's pants were so (loose, lose) that I thought they would fall off.

18. Because she was angry, Beatriz (set, sit) the glass down so hard that it broke.

19. Moderate to brisk walking can significantly improve (your, you're) fitness level.

20. Before he invested his summer earnings, Syed wanted the (advice, advise) of his stockbroker.

Chapter 35: Spelling

Chapter Review Test

Find and correct any spelling errors in the following paragraphs.

(1) When I first met my college roommate, I was suprized at how much we had in common. (2) For instance, we were both the same hieght and had the same color hair. (3) We also had similiar body shapes. (4) In fact, we were so much alike that our goverment teacher always got us confused. (5) He finally had to seperate us in class when he acidentaly gave Todd my grade.

(6) Both being nonscholarship atheletes, we tried out for the football team. (7) However, the coach thought we weren't strong enough, so he told us to develop muscles and body mass during our freshman year and try again when we were sophomores. (8) Todd and I started a fitness program imediately. (9) We worked out on the Nautilus equitment in the gym three days a week, and on weekends we rode our bicycles fourty miles. (10) Even during the horrable weather in January and Febuary, we managed to keep our training schedule. (11) By the end of the spring term, we had sucessfully reached our goal wieght and proportions. (12) However, by that time, we had joined a fraternity and decided to give up sports, except for fraternity activities.

(13) Todd and I also had the same carrer goals. (14) We both were persuing a degree in bussiness managment. (15) We immersed ourselves totaly in our studies and spent alot of time in the library. (16) We decided that the benifits of studying would definately surpass those of playing football. (17) We were proved right when the personell director of a local firm hired us as interns. (18) Who would have guessed that instead of lonelyness, I would find a life-long friend when I moved away to school?

Chapter 36: Commas

Chapter Review Test

Add any necessary commas in the following sentences. If a sentence is correct, circle the number.

1. The one accomplishment I am most proud of is my car a 1966 Ford Mustang because I have paid for all repairs and improvements with my money.

2. When I first got my car it didn't have a very good paint job.

3. I worked extra hours didn't go to movies asked for money for my birthday and saved every dollar I received.

4. Although expensive, the paint that I selected made the car look ten years newer.

5. Soon after I got my paint job I had to put more hard-earned money into my car.

6. The transmission on the car was old so it went crazy.

7. I had no parking gear and some other gears were gone also.

8. In fact, I had only reverse neutral and one other gear.

9. I was without a car for a couple of weeks while the repair shop rebuilt my transmission but I kept saving as much money as possible during that time.

10. After the transmission was fixed I was satisfied with the car for a little while.

11. Then I decided that I wanted floor mats a new steering wheel a stereo and chrome wheels.

12. Luckily it didn't take long to save enough money for mats and a steering wheel.

13. My next goal was chrome wheels which would make my beautiful car look even better.

14. I soon discovered that the wheels would of course cost more than I had thought.

15. My dad surprised me by saying he would pay for two of the wheels for he wanted to help me out a little bit since I had worked so hard.

(continued)

16. Now the car looks great runs well and is comfortable to drive.

17. You would think wouldn't you that I would be completely happy.

18. Now I want a stereo which will provide additional enjoyment to my driving time.

19. My current goal is to buy an Alpine stereo a CD changer and great speakers by Christmas.

20. Even if I miss that goal I'll know that I have a great car that I paid for myself.

Chapter 37: Apostrophes

Chapter Review Test

Read the following sentences for correct use and placement of apostrophes. Add missing apostrophes, and delete unnecessary apostrophes. Some sentences may have more than one error.

1. Because Pat cant make up his mind, he changes his plan's several times a day.

2. Fiona receives $10 from her parents if she gets all As and Bs on her grade report.

3. After we return from our months vacation, well respond to all the mail and phone messages.

4. Our cat wants it's food in a secluded area, whereas our dogs want their's in the family room.

5. No one want's to live in a vegetative state, unable to eat, walk, or communicate.

6. Therefore, members of the family should be the one's to make the critical medical decision instead of the doctors.

7. The problem is that a doctors word should not be allowed to override the familys decision regarding a loved one.

8. Because Sirkku put too many 0s on the bill, the accounting clerk wrote a check for $100,000 instead of $1,000.

9. Theres never enough time to complete all of the homework assignments in Mr. Buchanans class.

10. Bonnie will buy her shirt in the childrens department because its less expensive than one from the womens department.

Chapter 38: Quotation Marks

Chapter Review Test

Read the following sentences for correct use and placement of quotation marks. Make any necessary corrections. If a sentence is already correct, circle the number.

1. If you want to sell your house more quickly, the realtor advised, paint the interior and keep the yard mowed.

2. She also told us that location is the most important consideration when buying a home.

3. She also suggested that we read How to Sell Your Home for the Best Price, an article in last month's *Consumer Reports*.

4. Do you think we should have the carpets and drapes cleaned? my mother asked.

5. Don't bother to read Chapter 3, class, the teacher announced. You will only be tested over Chapters 2 and 4.

6. One student bravely raised his hand and asked, Can we use our textbooks or notes during the test?

7. I read the chapter titled The Toxicity of Lead three times before I understood it.

8. One of my favorite albums is *Red Hot & Blue*. It is a tribute to Cole Porter by a variety of modern singers, Michelle said.

9. She explained that the album has songs by Sinead O'Connor, the Thompson Twins, Tom Waits, the Fine Young Cannibals, and Debbie Harry.

10. Perhaps we would have heard the doorbell if we had not been listening to k.d. lang singing Cole Porter's song So in Love.

Chapter 39: Other Punctuation

Chapter Review Test

Add colons, semicolons, parentheses, dashes, or hyphens in the following sentences.

1. Health issues ranging from nutrition to exercise to disease have progressively invaded our homes and our everyday lives.

2. Driving in our cars a major part of our daily schedule, we see billboards promoting items that relate to health.

3. While flying down the highway, we might hear on the radio about a two for one special at a health club or maybe a diet cola jingle.

4. Another place for such information would be on restaurant menus, where we might find sections for people with special dietary concerns low fat, low sodium, low cholesterol.

5. Nutrition including the types and amounts of food that we eat plays a big role in one way of staying healthy.

6. More nutritional foods that appeal to a large number of people salads, vegetable platters, diet drinks can now be found on most menus.

7. In addition, most every food product we buy in the grocery store has a list of nutritional facts on the outer label size and number of servings, fat content, calories, carbohydrates, and protein.

8. Television provides the most common source of information there we can see cooking shows that emphasize healthy cooking and paid programs for home exercise equipment.

9. Public service announcements appear on radio and television and in magazines promoting good habits and healthy lifestyles for instance, they warn against drug abuse, heavy smoking, and drinking and driving.

10. With such widespread illustrations, it is easy to conclude that America has become a health conscious nation.

Chapter 40: Capitalization

Chapter Review Test

Read the following sentences and edit for correct capitalization.

1. Vacations offer a wide variety of opportunities whether you are traveling in europe, north or south america, asia, or the united states.

2. between june and august, you can take a week-long cruise between sitka and juneau, alaska, to view humpback whales, otters, seals, and glaciers.

3. If you vacation in denali national park, you can enjoy river rafting, nature hikes, cruises among the glaciers, and minibus tours.

4. my Aunt and Uncle enjoyed their fourteen-day caribbean cruise that included visits to martinique and st. martin and lots of creole food.

5. One of my favorite vacation spots is colorado springs, where i can visit natural wonders such as seven falls and pike's peak.

6. While visiting Washington, dc, you need to see the famous Monuments, the white house, and ford's theater.

7. A short train ride out of boston will take you to the Church that contains the crypts of president john adams and president john quincy adams.

8. If you have children, you might consider a trip to florida for fun times at disney world, sea world, and universal studios.

9. For the person who likes to shop, mall of the americas in minneapolis provides the world's largest selection of shops under one roof, as well as restaurants, a skating rink, a huge Lego display, and an amusement park.

10. You can find great information for travel in publications such as *national geographic* and from organizations such as a local Chamber of Commerce and the American automobile association.

Chapter 21: Overview

Answers to Chapter Review Test

1. action verb

2. helping verb

3. adjective

4. adverb

5. pronoun

6. phrase

7. coordinating conjunction

8. preposition

9. linking verb

10. noun

Chapter 22: Fragments

Answers to Chapter Review Test 1

FRAGMENTS

The man who also manufactured the first cars.

During the 1920s.

That manufactured the pillow-shaped briquets.

In 1922, according to the Kingsford Products Company in Oakland, California.

To relieve himself of some responsibilities.

Only at Ford dealerships.

POSSIBLE REVISIONS

Charcoal was invented by Henry Ford, the man who also manufactured the first cars. Ford invented a way to convert the wood scraps left over from car manufacturing into charcoal during the 1920s. His friend, Thomas Edison, designed the factory that manufactured the pillow-shaped briquets. In 1922, according to the Kingsford Products Company in Oakland, California, Ford turned over the charcoal operation to his relative, E.G. Kingsford in order to relieve himself of some responsibilities. Until the 1950s, Kingsford charcoal couldn't be bought just anywhere, only at Ford dealerships.

Chapter 22: Fragments

Answers to Chapter Review Test 2

FRAGMENTS

After reading your advertisement in *The San Antonion Daily.*

Pursuing a degree in Business Administration.

Having held positions at Latimer Gifts as secretary to the direct mail manager, sales clerk at The Gap, and sales clerk at PayLess Shoes.

Where I was named "Employee of the Month" in September of 1996.

While continuing to take courses toward my degree.

To help in your selection.

On a separate sheet of paper.

Also a letter of recommendation.

POSSIBLE REVISIONS

Dear Ms. Brown:

Please consider me as a candidate for the part-time position of administrative assistant in the marketing department. After reading your advertisement in *The San Antonion Daily,* I feel confident that I could make a valuable contribution to the company.

I am a student at San Antonio College pursuing a degree in Business Administration. I have completed courses in Principles of Marketing, Introduction to Business, Managerial Finance, and others that give me the skills to qualify for the administrative assistant position. My cumulative grade point average is 3.5.

(continued)

I also have office and retail experience, having held positions at Latimer Gifts as secretary to the direct mail manager, sales clerk at The Gap, and sales clerk at PayLess Shoes, where I was named "Employee of the Month" in September of 1996. These positions have given me an understanding of customer needs, customer service, and direct mail marketing. I believe I can apply what I've learned in your company while continuing to take courses toward my degree.

I have enclosed my résumé. It provides complete information on my education and experience. To help in your selection, I have also enclosed a list of references on a separate sheet of paper and a letter of recommendation. Thank you for your consideration. I will look forward to speaking with you.

Sincerely,

Marcia Perez

Chapter 23: Run-Ons

Answers to Chapter Review Test 1

1. CS   2. CS   3. F   4. F   5. CS   6. CS   7. F   8. F   9. C   10. F

POSSIBLE REVISIONS

1. Living with my parents used to be a drag; however, living on my own can be pretty neat.

2. Living with my parents was difficult at times, but it was especially difficult once I got out of the military.

3. Dad had his rules; for instance, we couldn't receive any phone calls after 9 P.M. and had to be in before 10 P.M.

4. Likewise, Mom had her rules. Making my bed and cleaning my room before breakfast every morning was my least favorite rule.

5. And, of course, there were always the chores; I had to mow the yard, clean the bathroom, and clean my closet.

6. Now my life is a breeze because I don't have any rules to go by but my own.

7. I'm not on the phone as often as I was at home, and if I want to call after 9 P.M., I can.

8. I don't have to be home at a certain time. I don't usually, for example, get home from work before 11 P.M.

9. Correct.

10. As a result, I think both living situations had their good points, but I still prefer living on my own.

Chapter 23: Run-Ons

Answers to Chapter Review Test 2

RUN-ONS

Sentences 1, 2, 4, 5, and 6

POSSIBLE REVISIONS

College admissions officers in large colleges and universities receive thousands of applications every year. Many of the applications for fall don't come in until April or May. While these dates are well within the deadline, there is a good reason to apply earlier. In order for students to be considered for financial aid or scholarship, applications need to be received early in the calendar year. Many transfer students don't realize this. They wait too long and can't get money they might have been qualified to receive. Early in the year a student might be awarded a grant, but later that same student might receive a loan. The difference between the two is significant: The grant is given with no strings attached, but the loan must be repaid later.

Chapter 24: Subject-Verb Agreement

Answers to Chapter Review Test 1

1. is   2. seems   3. exercise   4. likes   5. C   6. is   7. wants   8. is   9. C
10. needs   11. has   12. C   13. helps   14. builds   15. are   16. increases
17. has   18. keeps   19. do   20. has

Chapter 24: Subject-Verb Agreement

Answers to Chapter Review Test 2

1. does 2. is 3. are 4. has 5. C 6. needs 7. doesn't 8. C 9. C
10. provide 11. provide 12. C

Chapter 25: Verb Problems

Answers to Chapter Review Test 1

1. started   2. made   3. raised; thought   4. saw   5. demanded
6. did; became   7. was; grew   8. sell   9. exceeded   10. lives

Chapter 25: Verb Problems

Answers to Chapter Review Test 2

1. Correct   2. Correct   3. sailed; rode; played   4. contracted
5. did walk; was   6. Correct   7. held   8. became; served
9. started; worked; guided   10. had existed; have become   11. Correct
12. was   13. Correct   14. was   15. published   16. Correct   17. Correct

Chapter 26: Pronouns

Answers to Chapter Review Test

1. The University Finance Committee put off <u>its</u> decision on whether to raise tuition next year.

2. Considering the costs of tuition, room, board, and books, Joel is no longer sure that he can afford <u>to attend college</u>.

3. The cost of <u>textbooks has</u> really increased a lot in recent years.

4. The woman in the financial-aid office said <u>she doesn't</u> know how much money will be available next year.

5. Can't the government find some way so that <u>it</u> will have more money left over for education?

6. The professor, <u>whom</u> Joel had spoken to only once before, was glad that he had come to see her in her office.

7. Anyone who thinks that <u>he or she</u> can work full-time and take a full load of classes also needs to be prepared to go without much sleep.

8. Students study many different subjects, but <u>not all of the subjects</u> interest them.

9. Ellen likes biology more than <u>I do</u>.

10. <u>She and I</u> both like business administration because it's more closely related to our career plans.

Chapter 27: Adjectives and Adverbs

Answers to Chapter Review Test

1. unusual 2. the most 3. Probably 4. better 5. comfortable 6. exciting 7. easily 8. continually 9. good 10. unique 11. really 12. relaxing 13. higher 14. spectacularly 15. rough 16. large 17. dramatic 18. unique 19. worst 20. well

Chapter 28: Misplaced and Dangling Modifiers

Answers to Chapter Review Test

POSSIBLE REVISIONS

1. When Seung-Yeun arrived at the bookstore, the two books she needed for her writing class were nowhere to be found.

2. Becoming increasingly irritated, she searched through several stacks and shelves.

3. At the front desk, Seung-Yeun told the bookstore manager the names of the books she was unable to find.

4. The manager said that he had ordered almost one hundred additional copies and that they would arrive within a few days.

5. To the bookstore manager's surprise, the textbooks still had not been delivered a week later.

6. Anxious not to fall behind in her work, Seung-Yeun received from her instructor photocopied materials from the textbooks.

7. Finding the photocopied section difficult to read because the print was too dark, Seung-Yeun finally gave up on it and borrowed a classmate's textbook instead.

8. Feeling bad about their delay, the bookstore manager said the next day that the books finally had arrived.

9. Being a good businessman, the bookstore manager discounted the books 10 percent for Seung-Yeun.

10. Showing gratitude with a handshake and a smile, she paid for her purchase and ran off to class with her books.

Chapter 29: Coordination and Subordination

Answers to Chapter Review Test

POSSIBLE REVISIONS

There is a building in Washington, DC, with an interesting history. According to some stories, unknown facts about the assassination of Abraham Lincoln are hidden in one of the columns supporting the building. Lincoln's son, Robert, was secretary of war when he learned of documents that showed his father's murder was a conspiracy, not just the act of John Wilkes Booth alone. He got the documents, but he was reluctant to reveal them to the country. Instead, he concealed them in the columns of a building while it was under construction. Apparently Lincoln intended the documents for posterity, but no one knows where the documents are, or if they really exist. Their possible existence is a part of Washington, DC, folklore.

Chapter 30: Parallelism

Answers to Chapter Review Test

Sentences that are not parallel: 1, 2, 3, 4, 5, 7, 9

POSSIBLE REVISIONS

(1) Good relationships require love, respect, and communication. (2) Avoiding arguments may seem easier than confronting the problem. (3) But over time, avoidance is as destructive to a relationship as constant disagreement. (4) When couples don't talk to each other, they may not only avoid conflict but also lose the ability to communicate. (5) When this happens, relationships tend either to die or to stagnate. (6) Without communication, relationships can't withstand the pressures of working, taking care of household responsibilities, and parenting. (7) Couples have to talk about both their problems and their solutions. (8) If they can discuss things with respect and trust, they can work out problems. (9) Without communication, love and respect may not be enough.

Chapter 31: Sentence Variety

Answers to Chapter Review Test

POSSIBLE REVISIONS

Every country has its own traditions and holiday celebrations, which we would expect to be very different. Many are. Surprisingly, some are similar. Across the world, New Year's celebrations have one major similarity: The celebrants wish for good luck and wealth as they welcome in the new year.

We are familiar with the United States' traditions. Some family and friends dress up and go out to a nice restaurant or club, while others invite friends to a big party at their homes. Drinking champagne, using noisemakers, and watching the dropping ball in New York's Times Square at midnight are standard on New Year's Eve. No one can leave the table until he or she has eaten black-eyed peas for good luck in the coming year.

Several other countries have food as a big part of the New Year's celebration. Pork is especially popular in countries such as Brazil. Celebrants in Poland enjoy Pig's Feet Galantine, an aspic-wrapped paté. Italians serve sausage and lentils, which represent the prosperity of a wallet full of money. The Chinese, who apply a fresh coat of red paint to their front doors for good luck and happiness, serve pork dumplings. The Swedish New Year begins with breakfast in bed, consisting of pork sausage on a bun with an apple. The Austrians, the most elaborate celebrants, serve a suckling pig placed on a table of tiny pig-shaped cookies and candy with peppermint ice cream shaped like a four-leaf clover, which they eat for dessert.

Other food traditions are found across the world. In the Middle East, people eat pomegranate seeds to ensure fertility. The Japanese serve a dish called *mochi*, which is pounded rice cakes. A celebration in Norway would include rice pudding prepared with one whole almond. Finding the almond, tradition says, guarantees wealth in the new year.

Sicilians eat lasagna. Eating one grape at each strike of the clock, partygoers in Spain eat twelve grapes at midnight, one for good luck for each month. The Greeks bake a special New Year's bread containing a buried coin. The first slice is for the Christ child. The second slice is for the head of the household. Everyone watches when the third slice is cut. If it exposes the coin, it means that an early spring is predicted.

Food is not part of the tradition in England and Scotland. In those two countries, the first person over the threshold after midnight is supposed to be a male. The man, who must enter through the front door and leave through the back door for good luck, brings a gift of a piece of coal for the fire. The coal will bring warmth to the house in the new year. Opening the front door to let in the new year, and opening and closing the back door to let out any bad luck from the old year, are customs of Welsh tradition. The traditions, though different, all rely on superstitions for good luck.

Chapter 32: ESL Concerns

Answers to Chapter Review Test

1. When I moved to Florida, I wanted to go to **the** beach.

2. I never lived near water and wanted to walk on the sands.

3. I took **a** big umbrella, **a** dog, and **a** Frisbee with me.

4. When waves washed up on **the** shore, I found **a** seashell and **a** clam.

5. For lunch, I bought **a** hot dog and **a** cola from **the** restaurant.

6. Coming to this country was one of the most interesting challenges that I **had experienced** in my life.

7. First of all, everything **was** different and strange in my eyes, so **moving** here was difficult for someone like me from a different cultural background.

8. The opportunity for education and self-improvement will **change** my life.

9. After all, I am capable **of living** with freedom and exposing my mind to new ideas.

10. Overall, this immigration has made me face all my dreams and wishes.

11. If you want a job, you must first fill **out** an application form at the company's personnel office.

12. Don't be afraid **of** going for an interview because the personnel director will be very nice to you.

13. Make sure that you show the employer that you are excited **to work** for her company.

14. If she hires you, the employer will go **through** all of the duties of the job and the company's policies.

15. If you are confused **by** the directions, just ask questions.

16. Not all writers experience writer's block.
    Do all writers experience writer's block?

17. You can't start writing about a topic that you choose.
    Can you start writing about a topic that you choose?

(continued)

18. You can't pretend to write a letter to a friend.
    Can you pretend to write a letter to a friend?

19. Some writers do not enjoy describing happy memories.
    Do some writers enjoy describing happy memories?

20. Other people do not like to imagine their lives one year from now.
    Do other people like to imagine their lives one year from now?

Chapter 33: Word Choice

Answers to Chapter Review Test

POSSIBLE REVISIONS

Americans seem to have a fascination with food. Whether it's cooking, eating, shopping, or talking about it, food dominates much of our time and energies. In fact, food can be both good and bad for you. <u>Whereas</u> food is a life-sustaining necessity, Americans have <u>become quite obsessed</u>.

<u>Today,</u> fast-food places dominate the highways, and it <u>seems as if</u> you can't even drive two blocks without seeing a McDonald's or a Taco Bell. If Mom's too <u>exhausted</u> from a hard day at work, she just <u>stops at</u> some drive-through window at the neighborhood chicken shack. <u>If Dad is rushing <u>all over</u> during his busy day, he gobbles down a sandwich and <u>gulps</u> a malted as he drives to his next appointment. Even the family that has spent a leisurely day at home working in the garden or enjoying the comforts of their home will call for pizza delivery rather than take the time to prepare a nice home-cooked meal.

To the other extreme are the health fanatics. You won't <u>see them eating hamburgers and french fries</u>. Their refrigerators look like the produce department at the local grocery store. You won't find any red meat in their homes, but you can find a lot of <u>leafy greens</u>. <u>They also</u> have an abundant supply of carrots, broccoli, zucchini, and tomatoes. You might as well rename that home "Rabbit Hutch." And forget the sweets. Fruit (with perhaps a fat-free cereal bar thrown in for good measure) is what these people consider dessert. In their opinion, vegetables and whole grains <u>are the staples of a healthy diet.</u>

Probably somewhere in between are the ones who enjoy food but don't <u>become obsessive about it</u>. They enjoy a good burger every now and then, but they also count calories and watch their fat intake. Mom and Dad and even the kids will <u>help out</u> and produce a <u>delicious</u> evening meal. They carefully itemize the ingredients and <u>make sure that</u> all of the food groups are properly included in the <u>evening meal</u>.

With so many different kinds of eaters, food has become big business. From fancy restaurants to fast-food drive-throughs, Americans have a <u>wide variety of choices</u> when it comes to eating out. But even grocery stores are <u>stocking some prepared foods</u>. Their deli sections offer fried chicken, salads, cooked vegetables, and desserts. For the person who wants to pretend to <u>prepare the meals</u>, grocery stores have marinated meats and vegetable dishes that are ready to stick right in the oven as soon as the buyer arrives home. Whatever their tastes and styles, Americans can find what they want.

Chapter 34: Commonly Confused Words

Answers to Chapter Review Test

1. they're 2. than 3. proceeded 4. too 5. pass 6. Who's 7. lose
8. our 9. know 10. Whether 11. through 12. supposed 13. except
14. have 15. buy 16. conscious 17. loose 18. set 19. your
20. advice

Chapter 35: Spelling

Answers to Chapter Review Test

1. surprised   2. height   3. similar   4. government
5. separate; accidentally   6. athletes   7. Correct   8. immediately
9. equipment; forty   10. horrible; February   11. successfully; weight
12. Correct   13. career   14. pursuing; business; management
15. totally; a lot   16. benefits; definitely   17. personnel   18. loneliness

Chapter 36: Commas

Answers to Chapter Review Test

1. The one accomplishment I am most proud of is my car, a 1966 Ford Mustang, because I have paid for all repairs and improvements with my money.

2. When I first got my car, it didn't have a very good paint job.

3. I worked extra hours, didn't go to movies, asked for money for my birthday, and saved every dollar I received.

4. Correct.

5. Soon after I got my paint job, I had to put more hard-earned money into my car.

6. The transmission on the car was old, so it went crazy.

7. I had no parking gear, and some other gears were gone also.

8. In fact, I had only reverse, neutral, and one other gear.

9. I was without a car for a couple of weeks while the repair shop rebuilt my transmission, but I kept saving as much money as possible during that time.

10. After the transmission was fixed, I was satisfied with the car for a little while.

11. Then I decided that I wanted floor mats, a new steering wheel, a stereo, and chrome wheels.

12. Luckily, it didn't take long to save money for mats and a steering wheel.

13. My next goal was chrome wheels, which would make my beautiful car look even better.

14. I soon discovered that the wheels would, of course, cost more than I had thought.

15. My dad surprised me by saying he would pay for two of the wheels, for he wanted to help me out a little bit since I had worked so hard.

16. Now the car looks great, runs well, and is comfortable to drive.

17. You would think, wouldn't you, that I would be completely happy.

(continued)

18. Now I want a stereo, which will provide additional enjoyment to my driving time.

19. My current goal is to buy an Alpine stereo, a CD changer, and great speakers by Christmas.

20. Even if I miss that goal, I'll know that I have a great car that I paid for myself.

Chapter 37: Apostrophes

Answers to Chapter Review Test

1. Because Pat **can't** make up his mind, he changes his **plans** several times a day.

2. Fiona receives $10 from her parents if she gets all **A's** and **B's** on her grade report.

3. After we return from our **month's** vacation, **we'll** respond to all the mail and phone messages.

4. Our cat wants **its** food in a secluded area, whereas our dogs want **theirs** in the family room.

5. No one **wants** to live in a vegetative state, unable to eat, walk, or communicate.

6. Therefore, members of the family should be the **ones** to make the critical medical decision instead of the doctors.

7. The problem is that a **doctor's** word should not be allowed to override the **family's** decision regarding a loved one.

8. Because Sirkku put too many **0's** on the bill, the accounting clerk wrote a check for $100,000 instead of $1,000.

9. **There's** never enough time to complete all of the homework assignments in Mr. **Buchanan's** class.

10. Bonnie will buy her shirt in the **children's** department because **it's** less expensive than one from the **women's** department.

Chapter 38: Quotation Marks

Answers to Chapter Review Test

1. "If you want to sell your house more quickly," the realtor advised, "paint the interior and keep the yard mowed."

2. Correct.

3. She also suggested that we read "How to Sell Your Home for the Best Price," an article in last month's *Consumer Reports*.

4. "Do you think we should have the carpets and drapes cleaned?" my mother asked.

5. "Don't bother to read Chapter 3, class," the teacher announced. "You will only be tested on Chapters 2 and 4."

6. One student bravely raised his hand and asked, "Can we use our textbooks or notes during the test?"

7. I read the chapter titled "The Toxicity of Lead" three times before I understood it.

8. "One of my favorite albums is *Red Hot & Blue*. It is a tribute album to Cole Porter by a variety of modern singers," Michelle said.

9. Correct.

10. Perhaps we would have heard the doorbell if we had not been listening to k.d. lang singing Cole Porter's song "So in Love."

Chapter 39: Other Punctuation

Answers to Chapter Review Test

1. Health issues—ranging from nutrition to exercise to disease—have progressively invaded our homes and our everyday lives.

2. Driving in our cars (a major part of our daily schedule), we see billboards promoting items that relate to health.

3. While flying down the highway, we might hear on the radio about a two-for-one special at a health club or maybe a diet cola jingle.

4. Another place for such information would be on restaurant menus, where we might find sections for people with special dietary concerns: low fat, low sodium, low cholesterol.

5. Nutrition—including the types and amounts of food that we eat—plays a big role in one way of staying healthy.

6. More nutritional foods that appeal to a large number of people (salads, vegetable platters, diet drinks) can now be found on most menus.

7. In addition, most every food product we buy in the grocery store has a list of nutritional facts on the outer label: size and number of servings, fat content, calories, carbohydrates, and protein.

8. Television provides the most common source of information; there we can see cooking shows that emphasize healthy cooking and paid programs for home exercise equipment.

9. Public service announcements appear on radio and television and in magazines promoting good habits and healthy lifestyles; for instance, they warn against drug abuse, heavy smoking, and drinking and driving.

10. With such widespread illustrations, it is easy to conclude that America has become a health-conscious nation.

Chapter 40: Capitalization

Answers to Chapter Review Test

1. Vacations offer a wide variety of opportunities whether you are traveling in Europe, North or South America, Asia, or the United States.

2. Between June and August, you can take a week-long cruise between Sitka and Juneau, Alaska, to view humpback whales, otters, seals, and glaciers.

3. If you vacation in Denali National Park, you can enjoy river rafting, nature hikes, cruises among the glaciers, and minibus tours.

4. My aunt and uncle enjoyed their fourteen-day Caribbean cruise that included visits to Martinique and St. Martin and lots of Creole food.

5. One of my favorite vacation spots is Colorado Springs, where I can visit natural wonders such as Seven Falls and Pike's Peak.

6. While visiting Washington, DC, you need to see the famous monuments, The White House, and Ford's Theater.

7. A short train ride out of Boston will take you to the church that contains crypts of President John Adams and President John Quincy Adams.

8. If you have children, you might consider a trip to Florida for fun times at Disney World, Sea World, and Universal Studios.

9. For the person who likes to shop, Mall of the Americas in Minneapolis provides the world's largest selection of shops under one roof, as well as restaurants, a skating rink, a huge Lego display, and an amusement park.

10. You can find great information for travel in publications such as *National Geographic* and from organizations such as a local chamber of commerce and the American Automobile Association.

Supplemental Exercises for Editing Chapters
(*Chapters 21–40*)

Chapter 21: Editing Overview—The Basic Concepts

21–1: Identifying Subjects

Underline the subject in each of the following sentences.

EXAMPLE

In the summertime, <u>theaters</u> play lots of movies with expensive special effects.

1. *The Perfect Storm* is a movie starring George Clooney.

2. Before that, it was a best-selling book.

3. The book traces the true story of a fishing boat named the *Andrea Gail*.

4. No one really knows what happened to the *Andrea Gail*.

5. The "perfect storm" was actually three storms that converged at one point.

6. The *Andrea Gail* got caught in the middle of the three storms and never really had a chance.

7. Her sister boat, the *Hannah Boden,* was located sixty miles away from the *Andrea Gail*.

8. Warning messages about the weather were sent from the *Andrea Gail* to the *Hannah Boden.*

9. The crew of the *Hannah Boden* could prepare the boat for the coming storm.

10. The *Andrea Gail* was able to save her sister boat, but not herself.

21–2: Identifying the Verb

In the following sentences, identify each boldfaced verb as an action verb, a linking verb, or a helping + a main verb.

EXAMPLE

action verb
Of all the winter Olympic sports, I **enjoy** downhill skiing the most.

1. The Winter 2002 Olympics **will be** held in Salt Lake City, Utah.

2. Park City, Utah, **is** a popular ski resort town with an Olympic training center for the athletes.

3. The park **provides** a bobsled and luge course and ski jumps for free-style skiers.

4. The Olympics **should bring** much attention to this western state.

5. Few Americans **realize** what a beautiful state Utah is.

6. Utah's landscape **makes** it one of the most geologically interesting places in the United States.

7. The northern part of the state **boasts** many snow-covered mountains that are part of the Rocky Mountain chain.

8. Many people **have skied** at Utah's gorgeous resorts every winter.

9. Southern Utah, on the other hand, **is** desertlike and is home to many canyons and rock formations.

10. In just a two-hour drive, you **can feel** as though you have traveled through completely different but equally amazing climate zones.

21–3: Identifying Complete Thoughts

State whether each item is an incomplete or complete thought by writing "C" for complete and "I" for incomplete after each sentence.

EXAMPLE

To develop an exercise routine that incorporates jogging.   *I*

1. Though it is hard to believe.

2. Jogging has not always been an American sport.

3. Jogging first became popular in the United States in the late 1970s with the birth of Nike shoes.

4. University of Oregon track coach Bill Bowerman.

5. He experimented with his wife's waffle iron to make the memorable soles of his first running shoes.

6. The shoes with waffle patterns on the bottom made running a more comfortable sport for amateur athletes.

7. Thanks to popular young runners like Steve Prefontaine.

8. Nike shoes became well known almost instantly.

9. Prefontaine's determination and ability to withstand the pain that comes with distance running.

10. Steve Prefontaine inspired many Americans to run in his coach Bill Bowerman's shoes.

21–4: Adding Information with Adjectives and Adverbs

Add an adjective or adverb to each of the following sentences to give more information about a noun or verb.

EXAMPLE

Harry Potter and the Goblet of Fire is the fourth book in a series of
seven and is 734 pages long.
          a whopping

1. The Harry Potter books are a series of stories written by J.K. Rowling for children of all ages.

2. The books tell the story of a boy who has magical powers and attends a school for wizards.

3. J.K. Rowling's life story has become as well known as that of the character she writes about, Harry Potter.

4. Rowling was a single mother and a welfare recipient in Edinburgh, Scotland, when she began to write the Harry Potter stories.

5. She wrote the first book while her daughter napped in the afternoons.

6. Her story has been an inspiration to people who think that authors must live a certain kind of lifestyle.

7. She has proven that all you really need are ideas and determination.

8. Recently, bookstores stayed open until midnight on the night that *Harry Potter and the Goblet of Fire* was first sold.

9. Children waited in line for hours to purchase Harry's latest adventures.

10. The book was one of the most anticipated publications in history.

21–5: Identifying Prepositional Phrases and Subjects

Underline the subjects and circle prepositional phrases in each of the following sentences.

EXAMPLE

I would like to get paid (for traveling) (around the world) and seeing exotic places.

1. Travel writing for a newspaper is a job that many people think they would like to have.

2. Even journalists with little experience can venture to faraway places without having to pay for plane fare or hotels.

3. In her first year of writing for the *St. Louis Post-Dispatch,* my friend was sent to Mexico and Peru.

4. The journey across the two countries was exhilarating but at times difficult.

5. Many of the cities that she was required to visit were more difficult to get to than she had expected.

6. Writing in depth about the places she visited often meant taking in many sites per day.

7. The same number of sites that she saw in five days might take ordinary tourists a period of three weeks.

8. On the other hand, some of the finest restaurants in Mexico City and Lima were on her itinerary.

9. Her descriptions of the best these restaurants had to offer were mouth-watering.

10. Her favorite part of the job, though, was getting to write about her experiences upon her return home.

Chapter 22: Sentence Fragments—Incomplete Sentences

22–1: Correcting Fragments That Start with Prepositions

In the following items, correct the fragments by connecting them to the previous or next sentence.

EXAMPLE

I use my computer for just about everything/ ~~F~~rom playing games to paying bills.

1. In 1976, twenty-one-year-old Steven Jobs cofounded Apple Computer, Inc. In his family's garage.

2. In 1984, the team Jobs led created the Apple Macintosh computer. With its user-friendly "point and click" operating system.

3. Yet one year later, Jobs was forced out of his own company. By the board of directors.

4. The Mac revolutionized the computer world. Over the next few years.

5. Apple's rival, the Microsoft Corporation, modeled its Windows operating system. On the Mac.

6. After leaving Apple. Jobs started a computer company called NeXT that developed a cutting-edge new operating system.

7. A British computer programmer created the World Wide Web. On the NeXT system.

8. In 1986, Jobs bought Pixar, a small computer animation studio. From the film director George Lucas.

9. Pixar created the animation. For the 1995 hit movie *Toy Story*.

10. In late 1996, Jobs stunned the computer industry by selling NeXT and its operating system. To his old company, Apple.

22–2: Correcting Fragments That Start with Dependent Words

In the following items, correct the fragments by connecting them to the previous or next sentence.

EXAMPLE

Humans should pay more attention to the natural world, ~~B~~because it can teach us so much about ourselves.

1. The zoologist Frans de Waal has spent the past twenty-five years studying. How apes and monkeys behave in captivity.

2. He is a professor of primate behavior at Emory University in Atlanta. Where he is also a researcher at the Yerkes Regional Primate Research Center.

3. While many scientists have emphasized the role of aggression in animal behavior. De Waal stresses the importance of animal kindness and caring.

4. Although animals clearly have rivals. He believes they also have friends.

5. Each group of chimpanzees has a leader. Though De Waal thinks it is the one who makes the best friendships and alliances rather than the one who is the most aggressive.

6. His research on animal relationships has shown that capuchin monkeys will repeatedly find ways to share food. When they are separated from each other by a mesh screen.

7. This sharing is a deliberate choice. Because the monkeys share only with monkeys they like.

8. De Waal believes that the stereotype of the killer-ape is harmful. Since it suggests that human nature is essentially violent and cruel.

9. He argues that morality is an outgrowth of our natural instincts. Which are automatic responses that all people have.

10. If we want to understand what makes us naturally aggressive. We also have to understand what makes us naturally caring.

22–3: Correcting Fragments That Begin with *-ing* Verbs

In the following items, correct the fragments by connecting them to the previous or next sentence.

EXAMPLE

Facing difficult decisions about medical procedures, Patients and their families are often willing to take risks with new technologies.

1. Sharon Bearor was sitting in a doctor's office at Massachusetts General Hospital. Listening to Dr. Allen Lapey explain her son's options.

2. Suffering from cystic fibrosis. Nineteen-year-old Spencer Bean needed two new lungs.

3. However, the long waiting list for an organ donation meant Spencer might die. Waiting for a pair of lungs to become available.

4. Reaching the top of the list. He might also be too sick to go through with the transplant operation.

5. Explaining that there was another option. Dr. Lapey told Spencer and Sharon about an experimental new medical procedure.

6. Doctors could replace a patient's diseased lungs. Using healthy lung tissue from two living relatives.

7. Realizing that Spencer might die without their help. Sharon and her sister Jean decided to donate part of their lungs.

8. Some people are opposed to living-donor transplants. Believing it's unethical to risk harming a healthy person.

9. They also argue that some people might feel pressured to donate organs. Fearing their family's anger if they say no.

10. Ignoring complicated questions of medical ethics. Sharon and Jean simply did what they thought was right.

22–4: Correcting Fragments Starting with an Example or Explanation

In the following items, correct the fragments by connecting them to the previous sentence.

EXAMPLE

It can be difficult to make decisions sometimes. Especially when your choice will affect another person.

1. Arthur Caplan is a professor of bioethics. The study of ethical issues relating to medicine, health care, and science.

2. He analyzes complex moral questions. Such as whether society should allow doctor-assisted suicide.

3. Bioethical issues are often featured on TV hospital shows. Like *E.R.* and *Chicago Hope*.

4. Caplan thinks these shows do an okay job of exploring certain bioethical issues. Including the question of whether to give an alcoholic a liver transplant.

5. However, he feels they don't pay enough attention to other kinds of issues. Particularly those relating to money.

6. An episode of *Chicago Hope* was based on one of Caplan's actual cases. A heart transplant in which the doctors didn't know if they had to tell the patient they had dropped the heart on the floor.

7. Caplan believes that it is sometimes ethical to lie. Especially if a life is at stake.

8. He thinks a doctor should lie to help a patient who is being pressured by family members. As in the case of someone who is refusing a blood transfusion for religious reasons.

9. A doctor should also give a phony medical excuse to a family member who doesn't want to donate a live organ. Such as a kidney or lung.

10. Here the moral issue is free choice, not saving a life. As in the example of the blood transfusion.

22–5: Correcting Fragments That Begin with *to* + a Verb

In the following sentences, correct the fragments by connecting them to the previous or next sentence or by adding the missing sentence elements.

EXAMPLE

Most parents will reluctantly admit that they have used television as a

babysitter/ To keep their children occupied.

1. Some parents are so fed up with television programming that they want one thing from their families. To kick the TV habit.

2. Producer Linda Ellerbee once threw her TV set out of a second-story window. To get her children's attention when they were watching television.

3. To appease her guilt later in the day. She went out to retrieve the television from her yard. To her amazement, when she plugged it in, it still worked.

4. To study the problem. The Annenberg Public Policy Center has conducted three studies.

5. Parents can use ratings attached to many programs and V-chip technology. To block certain shows they don't want their children to see.

6. Few parents use either method, and most reported they felt powerless. To control their children's viewing habits.

7. According to one researcher, parents have an important role to play. To serve as examples of how much television is acceptable.

8. To give a child his or her own television. Solves many arguments about what to watch, but researchers suggest that this solution means that parents do not know how much television their child is watching.

9. One mother decided to unplug her television one night a week. To show her family that they could survive without television.

10. She reported that everyone struggled, including herself. To keep everyone occupied and busy through the first few weeks. She used all her creative abilities planning activities.

22–6: Sentence Fragments Review (1)

In the following items, correct the fragments by connecting them to the previous or next sentence.

EXAMPLE

Modern technology has revolutionized our society, In ways that influence our daily lives.

1. Have you ever wondered how a microwave oven cooks food? Without heating the plate.

2. A microwave is an electromagnetic wave. Ranging in frequency from around 1,000 to 300,000 megahertz (MHz).

3. An electromagnetic wave is a vibration. Resulting from the motion of positive and negative electrical charges.

4. There are many different kinds of electromagnetic waves. Such as electric waves, radio waves, infrared radiation, visible light, ultraviolet radiation, X-rays, and gamma rays.

5. Microwaves cook food quickly by making the water molecules in the food vibrate. At a rate of 2,450 million times per second.

6. This vibration absorbs energy from the surrounding electromagnetic field. Causing the food to heat up.

7. The plate and utensils don't get hot. Because their materials don't absorb energy from the magnetic field.

8. Since all the energy is absorbed by the food. Microwave cooking is faster than regular cooking.

9. Many different materials are safe to use in a microwave oven. Like china, glass, plastic, and paper.

10. But you should not use items made out of metal or wood when you microwave. To prevent damage to those items.

22–7: Sentence Fragments Review (2)

In the following items, correct the fragments by connecting them to the previous or next sentence.

EXAMPLE

The best inventors are those who are inspired/ ~~B~~y something very simple that no one else sees.

1. Velcro was invented by the Swiss engineer George de Mestral. After he took a walk in the woods with his dog.

2. Arriving back home. He noticed that his socks and his dog were covered with burrs.

3. De Mestral wanted to find out why burrs stick so well. To certain materials. Such as wool and fur.

4. Looking at his socks under the microscope. He discovered that tiny hooks on the ends of the burrs were caught. In the wool's loops.

5. De Mestral figured out a way to copy this natural system. Of hooks and loops.

6. He wove nylon thread into a fabric. Containing densely packed little loops.

7. He cut the loops. On some of the fabric. To make half of each loop a hook.

8. De Mestral called this fabric Velcro. A contraction of the French words *velours* (velvet) and *crochet* (hook).

9. Although Velcro can be peeled apart quite easily. It has extremely high resistance to sideways forces.

10. To prevent equipment, and even astronauts, from floating around. In the space shuttle. Velcro has been used.

Chapter 23: Run-Ons—Two Sentences Joined Incorrectly

23–1: Correcting a Run-On by Adding a Period

In the following items, correct the run-ons by adding a period and capitalizing the first letter of the new sentence. Then indicate whether the run-on is a fused sentence or a comma splice by marking **F** or **CS** in the space provided.

EXAMPLE

Many of the helpful tools we use every day have long histories, the umbrella was invented in China in the fourth century A.D. _CS_

1. Lead pencils don't really contain any lead they're made out of graphite. _____

2. Lead hasn't been used in pencils since the sixteenth century, it's a good thing because lead is poisonous. _____

3. The ancient Egyptians, Greeks, and Romans used small lead discs to make lines on sheets of papyrus, then they wrote on the papyrus with ink and a brush. _____

4. During the fourteenth century European artists made drawings using rods of lead, zinc, or silver the technique was called silverpoint.
_____

5. Wood-encased writing rods were used during the fifteenth century, they were the earliest pencils. _____

6. The modern pencil was developed in 1564 that's when graphite was discovered in Borrowdale, England. _____

7. Graphite is a form of carbon it's greasy and soft with a metallic luster.
_____

8. Pencil "lead" is made by mixing graphite with clay and water, then the mixture is fed into a thin cylinder to create sticks. _____

9. More graphite in the mixture makes the pencil softer and blacker, more clay makes it harder and paler. _____

10. The sticks are cut into pencil-sized lengths then they are fired in a kiln at a temperature of about 2200°F (1200°C). _____

23–2: Correcting a Run-On by Adding a Semicolon

In the following items, correct the run-ons by adding a semicolon.

EXAMPLE

It might be true that being the child of a famous person can be a disadvantage; most of us probably wouldn't mind finding out for ourselves, though.

1. Jakob Dylan is the son of legendary folk-rock star Bob Dylan, he isn't sure if his father's fame has helped or hurt his own musical career.

2. The younger Dylan has finally become famous in his own right, his band, the Wallflowers, is suddenly very hot.

3. Two songs from their second album have become big hits you can't turn on the radio without hearing "6th Avenue Heartache" or "One Headlight."

4. But the Wallflowers are not an overnight success story, they've been struggling to get noticed for seven years.

5. They released their first album in 1992, it didn't sell.

6. One reason is that Dylan's voice was mixed too low in the studio another is that he wasn't willing to promote the album the way the record company wanted.

7. The band got out of its contract with Virgin Records, then they couldn't get signed by another label even though their new demo tape included the songs that eventually became hits.

8. Finally the Wallflowers signed with Interscope Records they began working with producer T-Bone Burnett.

9. Burnett raised Dylan's voice in the sound mix, suddenly you could hear the lyrics.

10. Jakob Dylan's voice is not as distinctive as his father's, it seems to be the decisive factor in his band's recent success, however.

23–3: Correcting a Run-On by Adding a Comma and a Conjunction

In the following items, correct the run-ons by adding a comma if necessary and a coordinating conjunction *(and, but, or, so, for, nor, yet)*.

EXAMPLE

I know that movies can be very unrealistic͵ᵇᵘᵗ I still love to watch them.

1. Don't believe everything you learn about animals from Hollywood movies you might come away misinformed.

2. For example, the 1994 movie *Andre the Seal* is based on a true story about a New England harbor seal, the title character is played by a California sea lion.

3. The real Andre was five feet long and weighed 250 pounds the sea lion actor is twice as big.

4. The decision to cast a solid-brown sea lion as a spotted gray seal may seem ridiculous, the filmmakers had their reasons.

5. Unlike sea lions, harbor seals don't have huge front flippers, they can't scoot around very well.

6. Seals can't do cute tricks on land with human actors, they spend most of their time in the water.

7. In the 1995 movie *Outbreak,* a monkey brings a deadly African virus to America the monkey is actually played by a South American capuchin monkey.

8. That's because capuchins are more readily available than African monkeys, they are easier to train.

9. You might assume that the 1988 movie *Gorillas in the Mist* portrays animals accurately, it was filmed on location in Africa among a band of mountain gorillas.

10. But wild mother gorillas won't let humans touch their young in one scene a baby gorilla is really a chimpanzee in a gorilla suit.

23–4: Correcting a Run-On by Making a Dependent Clause

In the following items, correct the run-ons by adding a dependent word to make a dependent clause. Add a comma if necessary.

EXAMPLE

Being a working mother is difficult, *because* work and school schedules often conflict.

1. Kristin Hersh is a working mother, she has a rather unusual job.

2. Hersh is raising three kids, she is working as the lead singer and guitarist for the band Throwing Muses.

3. Her husband, Billy O'Connell, understands her unconventional career choice he's the band's manager.

4. Hersh has combined rock and roll and motherhood, she had her first child at the age of nineteen.

5. Ten-year-old Dylan now lives with his father most of the year, he spends vacations with his mother and stepfather.

6. The band goes on tour next month, five-year-old Ryder and two-month-old Wyatt will be traveling with their parents.

7. Hersh thinks the rock world is beginning to change it is still uncommon to see children on the tour bus.

8. More women performers are becoming mothers, more kids are being nursed backstage and rocked to sleep in dressing rooms.

9. Hersh and O'Connell only recently allowed Dylan and Ryder to watch their mom perform most shows are so loud and smoky.

10. The boys watched a smoke-free acoustic show Hersh was pregnant with Wyatt.

23–5: Run-Ons Review (1)

In the following items, correct the run-ons by adding a period, a conjunction, a semicolon, or a dependent word. Add a comma if necessary.

EXAMPLE

Although
     's
^Some inventions are created to solve one person's particular problem, they can still be of great benefit to others.

1. Nathan Kane began inventing he was eighteen years old.

2. Kane wanted to create a dust-free environment in their Texas home his father suffered from allergies.

3. Ten years later he won a $30,000 prize for young inventors, the award was presented by the Massachusetts Institute of Technology.

4. Kane is a graduate student at MIT, he is studying mechanical engineering.

5. He thought of the idea for one of his inventions he was refinishing the floors in his parents' house.

6. It was very hot, he was uncomfortable wearing a regular filter mask.

7. Kane invented a mask that supplies fresh air through a flexible hose, the hose is really a lightweight bellows.

8. Bellows have been used for thousands of years, Kane came up with a better design.

9. He and a friend invented a TV remote control that's hard to lose and easy to pass around, it's built inside a foam rubber football.

10. Kane recently served as an adviser to a group of middle-school students, they designed solar-powered model cars.

23–6: Run-Ons Review (2)

In the following items, correct the run-ons by adding a period, a conjunction, a semicolon, or a dependent word. Add a comma if necessary.

EXAMPLE

I don't have a degree in business, ^{but} I want to start my own company someday anyway.

1. Tom Scott and Tom First began selling juice in 1989 they were twenty-four years old.

2. They had been friends since freshman year in college, they moved to the island of Nantucket soon after graduation.

3. Their business began as a floating juice bar in Nantucket Harbor they sold glasses of homemade peach juice off the deck of their boat.

4. Soon Scott and First began bottling their juice by hand, the following summer it was being professionally packaged in New York and distributed throughout Nantucket, Martha's Vineyard, and Cape Cod.

5. Their juice is called Nantucket Nectars, the name of their company is Nantucket Allserve.

6. Sales and production increased dramatically over the next few years, the company was still struggling to survive.

7. In 1993 an investor bought half the company for $500,000, that money allowed Scott and First to expand their markets and product line.

8. Scott and First have no formal business training, today Nantucket Allserve is one of the nation's fastest-growing private companies.

9. Their juice is sold in thirty states their company is worth $30 million.

10. Sales of Snapple and Veryfine juices have been declining, sales of Nantucket Nectars have increased by 6,482 percent in the last four years.

Chapter 24: Problems with Subject-Verb Agreement—When Subjects and Verbs Don't Match

24–1: Correcting Subject-Verb Agreement Problems with the Verbs *Be, Have,* and *Do*

In the following sentences, circle the subject and underline the correct form of the verb in parentheses.

EXAMPLE

The (weather) in New England (<u>is</u>, are) very unpredictable.

1. Believe it or not, the region (was, were) the victim of an amazing April Fool's joke—an enormous blizzard.

2. According to the TV news, it (was, were) the biggest snowstorm to hit Massachusetts since 1978 and the third biggest ever.

3. This blizzard (has, have) to be the worst that I can remember.

4. I (doesn't, don't) know exactly how much snow fell, but in my neighborhood I think we got about two feet.

5. Schools (is, are) closed everywhere today because of the snow in the roads.

6. I (has, have) no idea when our street will be plowed.

7. All my neighbors (is, are) outside shoveling or playing in the snow.

8. My family (has, have) a lot of shoveling to do.

9. Some people (has, have) no electricity or phone service because falling trees knocked down power lines.

10. I (am, is, are) pretty sure school will be canceled tomorrow, too.

24–2: Correcting Subject-Verb Agreement Problems When the Subject and Verb Are Separated by a Prepositional Phrase

In the following sentences, cross out any prepositional phrases between a subject and verb, and then underline the correct form of the verb in parentheses.

EXAMPLE

Although women ~~in this century~~ (<u>face</u>, faces) less discrimination than ever before, they still encounter many obstacles that men do not.

1. Gender discrimination in hiring practices (is, are) often hard to prove.

2. It would be easier to prove if you could compare hiring outcomes when the gender of job applicants (is, are) known and when that gender is unknown.

3. Exactly this type of comparison between hiring outcomes (is, are) now complete for one group of employers—U.S. symphony orchestras.

4. A new study of orchestra hiring practices (finds, find) that women are more likely to get a seat on a major orchestra if they audition anonymously.

5. Orchestras throughout the country (uses, use) "blind" auditions to evaluate musicians and have done so since the early 1970s.

6. For the first and semifinal rounds of auditions, applicants for a position with the orchestra (performs, perform) from behind a thick screen to hide their identity from the judges.

7. Economists Claudia Goldin of Harvard University and Cecilia Rouse of Princeton University analyzed data from the late 1950s to 1996 to determine whether blind auditioning at major orchestras (improves, improve) the chances that a woman will be hired.

8. According to Goldin and Rouse, the percentage of female musicians in the top five American orchestras (is, are) 20 percent higher now than it was in 1970.

9. Their study of orchestras (reports, report) that the use of screens boosts by 25 to 45 percent the odds that a woman will be hired.

10. The authors of the study conclude that the switch to blind auditions (explains, explain) about one-third to one-half of the total increase in the percentage of women hired between 1970 and 1996.

24–3: Correcting Subject-Verb Agreement Problems When the Subject and Verb Are Separated by a Dependent Clause

In the following sentences, cross out any dependent clauses between a subject and verb. Then correct any problems with subject-verb agreement. If there is no problem, write **OK** next to the sentence.

EXAMPLE

have
Often, people ~~who blindly follow fashion~~ has no idea of the original significance of the trendy item they are wearing.

1. Traditionally, the red dot that Indian women wear on their foreheads indicate that they are married Hindus.

2. This dot, which is known as a *bindi* or *pottu*, represent the mystical "third eye" in Hinduism.

3. The *bindi*, which was originally a simple red or maroon powdered circle, have evolved into a stick-on dot available in a variety of shapes, sizes, and colors.

4. These days, some women who wear *bindis* are making more of a fashion statement than a religious one.

5. In fact, the religious symbol that Hindu women have worn for centuries are showing up on the foreheads of hip young Americans, both male and female.

6. The American whose *bindi* first attracted attention among trendy, pierced people are probably Gwen Stefani.

7. Stefani, who is the lead singer of the band No Doubt, wear a stick-on *bindi*.

8. This California rock star, whom many people have compared to Madonna, like to wear a shiny, teardrop-shaped *bindi*.

9. The style that is a favorite among southern Indian women look a bit strange with Stefani's platinum-blonde hair and skintight wardrobe.

10. The *bindi*, which was once a meaningful religious symbol, is now just another cool fad.

24–4: Correcting Subject-Verb Agreement Problems with Compound Subjects

In the following sentences, circle the compound subject and then underline the correct form of the verb in parentheses.

EXAMPLE

Although (a human and a cat) (doesn't, <u>don't</u>) seem to have much in common, there are animals with great similarities to humans.

1. The orangutan, gorilla, chimpanzee, and bonobo (is, are) the four species of great apes.

2. Although obviously the chimp and the gorilla (looks, look) more alike, chimpanzees are in fact genetically more similar to humans than to gorillas.

3. In fact, the chimpanzee and the bonobo (shares, share) about 98 percent of the genetic material, or DNA, found in humans.

4. Chimpanzees and humans (is, are) the only two species that deliberately seek out and kill members of their own species.

5. Murder, rape, torture, gang warfare, and territorial raiding (occurs, occur) frequently among chimpanzees.

6. The chimpanzee and the bonobo (is, are) even more closely related to one another than chimps and humans (is, are), yet the bonobo is one of the most peaceful species of mammal.

7. The male and female bonobo (has, have) equal power because the females form alliances that prevent the males from taking control.

8. If a mother bonobo or her son (is, are) attacked, the mother's female allies will chase off the male aggressor.

9. The status or power of a male bonobo usually (depends, depend) on his mother's rank within the group.

10. Today, many scientists disagree over whether the chimpanzee or the bonobo (is, are) more human in its behavior.

24–5: Correcting Subject-Verb Agreement Problems When the Subject Is an Indefinite Pronoun

In the following sentences, circle the subject and cross out any prepositional phrases or dependent clauses that separate it from the verb in parentheses. Then underline the correct form of that verb.

EXAMPLE

(Anyone) ~~who speaks another language~~ (<u>understands</u>, understand) how difficult it can be to learn a new one.

1. Everyone in my college writing class (speaks, speak) English better than I do.

2. A few of the students (is, are) native speakers of English, but everybody else is learning English as a second language.

3. Many of the students (is, are) from Spanish-speaking places, particularly the Dominican Republic.

4. Several of the best students in the class (is, are) from Haiti, where they grew up speaking a dialect of French called Creole.

5. One of my closest friends in the class (comes, come) from Korea and moved here just six months ago.

6. Both of us (lives, live) with our parents, and we commute to school on the same bus.

7. No one who is in my class (speaks, speak) English the way you hear it spoken on television and in the movies.

8. Each of us (studies, study) hard, but I think that I work the hardest.

9. Unfortunately, none of my hard work (seems, seem) to have paid off yet.

10. Neither of my parents (speaks, speak) much English, so maybe that's why I'm having such a hard time.

24–6: Correcting Subject-Verb Agreement Problems When the Verb Comes before the Subject

In the following sentences, correct any problems with subject-verb agreement. If there is no problem, write **OK** next to the sentence.

EXAMPLE

Included in the course requirements ~~are~~ *is* a research paper.

1. Here is the first two pages of the essay that you promised to look over for me.

2. There are two more pages that I'm not ready to show you yet.

3. Has you helped other students with their papers before?

4. There is probably lots of mistakes in grammar, punctuation, and spelling.

5. Is this the worst paper you have ever seen?

6. In your opinion, what is my paper's biggest problems?

7. Is papers like this always difficult for freshmen like me?

8. Does other students go to the Writing Center for help?

9. I heard there is computers that we can use in the Center.

10. There is a friend of mine who might also need your help, if that's all right with you.

24–7: Subject-Verb Agreement Review

In each of the following sentences, underline the subject and circle the correct form of the verb in parentheses.

1. Commuting (is, are) a hassle for just about everyone.

2. Many (has, have) to race against time and traffic to make it to work or to school on time.

3. Travel within cities (has become, have become) easier with increased public transportation.

4. However, commuting in the snow or the rain (remain, remains) a problem even for those who take a train, bus, or subway.

5. Businesses around the country (continue, continues) to experiment with telecommuting as an option for their employees.

6. Telecommuters, who set up an office equipped with a computer, fax machine, second telephone line, and email, (works, work) productively without having to leave home.

7. Companies that have spent time and money rethinking "the office" (reports, report) that telecommuters are no less productive than their in-office counterparts.

8. Collaboration and feedback (happen, happens) electronically through employee email accounts and networking technology.

9. Community colleges and universities (is, are) taking their cue from business and offering classes by distance learning.

10. (Has, Have) you heard about some of these alternative ways of commuting?

Chapter 25: Verb Problems—Mistakes in Verb Form and Verb Tense

25-1: Using the Correct Verb Form for Regular Verbs in the Present Tense

For each of the sentences below, fill in the blank with the correct present-tense form of the verb in parentheses.

EXAMPLE

I _____*want*_____ (to want) to learn how to live a long, healthy life.

1. Doctors _____ (to explain) that exercise plays an important part in staying healthy.

2. Some days, I _____ (to stop) at the gym to work out.

3. When I am there, I usually _____ (to use) the Stairmaster and the rowing machine.

4. My gym also _____ (to offer) classes in kickboxing, yoga, and aerobics.

5. Many people _____ (to take) these classes because they prefer to exercise in groups.

6. I suppose that they _____ (to feel) it's easier to stay motivated when there is an instructor telling them what to do.

7. My friend Karen _____ (to love) taking karate classes.

8. On nice days in the spring and fall, I _____ (to prefer) to run or ride my bicycle outside for exercise.

9. Lots of people who do not exercise much _____ (to think) that people who do so are just worried about their weight.

10. However, exercising several times a week _____ (to keep) me feeling energetic and strong.

25–2: Using the Correct Verb Form for Regular Verbs in the Past Tense

For each of the sentences below, fill in the blank with the correct past-tense form of the verb in parentheses.

EXAMPLE

Rhodesian Ridgebacks, a playful and sociable breed, ___*hunted*___ (to hunt) lions alongside their masters on the plains of Africa and were once called African Lion Hounds.

1. The dogs that we know today as house pets once _____ (to specialize) in certain tasks that made them invaluable to humans.

2. For example, Saint Bernards _____ (to rescue) avalanche victims in the Alps.

3. Similarly, the Alaskan malamute _____ (to pull) sleds in freezing weather.

4. The Doberman pinscher's strength, speed, and courage _____ (to result) in their use as police dogs.

5. Irish wolfhounds, also strong and fast, _____ (to use) their powerful jaws to hold wolves by the neck and shake them until they died.

6. Even breeds such as the terriers and spaniels _____ (to help) humans.

7. The Scottish terrier _____ (to chase) rats and badgers away from people's homes.

8. Little cocker spaniels _____ (to scare) birds out of bushes and trees so that they could be hunted.

9. The ever-popular Labrador retriever not only _____ (to retrieve) hunted animals on land but could also swim in icy waters.

10. Their tireless assistance and love for their masters _____ (to earn) dogs the well-known title of "man's best friend."

25–3: Using the Correct Verb Form for Regular Verbs in the Present Tense and Past Tense

In the following sentences, fill in the correct form and tense of the verb in parentheses.

EXAMPLE

I _____*wish*_____ (to wish) that finding a job were easier to do.

1. Recently, I _____ (to apply) for a job as an administrative assistant at an insurance company.

2. I _____ (to hope) to hear something soon because I really need a job.

3. Before I found this job notice, I _____ (to search) everywhere I could think of.

4. I _____ (to check) all the help wanted ads in the newspaper.

5. My sister _____ (to show) me how to look for jobs on the Internet.

6. She still _____ (to help) me find a new Internet site to check every day.

7. I _____ (to want) to have a job before the end of the summer.

8. My tuition _____ (to increase) a lot last semester.

9. I _____ (to need) to make enough money to pay it.

10. My books _____ (to cost) a lot, too.

25–4: Using the Correct Forms for *Be* and *Have* in the Present Tense

In the following sentences, fill in the correct present-tense form of the verb in parentheses.

EXAMPLE

A well-written cover letter _____ *is* _____ (to be) an important part of a job application.

1. I _____ (to be) interested in applying for the part-time sales position you advertised in last Sunday's *Gazette*.

2. As you can see from my résumé, I _____ (to have) two years' experience working in retail sales.

3. Last year I worked as a sales associate at Jeans R Us, and I _____ (to be) now the assistant weekend store manager at Clothes to the Bone.

4. As you know, both stores _____ (to have) excellent reputations for customer satisfaction.

5. In addition to my professional experience in sales, I _____ (to be) currently a student at Green Valley Community College.

6. Because I _____ (to be) a marketing major, I feel that my academic work helps qualify me for a sales position at your store.

7. I _____ (to have) a 3.2 grade point average and have been on the Dean's List for the past two semesters.

8. I would particularly like to work at your store because it _____ (to have) such a strong commitment to environmental and social issues.

9. I hope that if the job _____ (to be) still open, you will consider me a serious candidate.

10. I will call you next week to see if you _____ (to be) interested in arranging an interview.

25–5: Using the Correct Forms for Irregular Verbs in the Past Tense

In the following sentences, fill in the correct past-tense form of the verb in parentheses.

EXAMPLE

Sports heroes _____*had*_____ (to have) a strong influence on me when I was a child.

1. Tiger Woods, the most successful young golfer in the history of the sport, _____ (to grow) up in Cypress, California.

2. He _____ (to begin) learning golf when he was only six months old, watching his father practice swings in the garage.

3. Four months later Tiger _____ (to take) his own first swing with a sawed-off club.

4. When he _____ (to be) a year and a half old, Tiger would practice hitting at the driving range.

5. While other toddlers played in sandboxes, Tiger _____ (to hit) chip shots out of sand traps.

6. His parents _____ (to bring) him up strictly, yet they never pushed him into stardom.

7. Beginning when Tiger was very young, his father _____ (to teach) him to take responsibility for his own actions and to live by the rules.

8. As a teenager, Tiger tried playing baseball, basketball, football, and track, but he _____ (to quit) these other sports because they interfered with golf.

9. Growing up in a family of mixed racial heritage—Native American, African American, Chinese, Thai, and white—he _____ (to know) about the racism his father had experienced in college and the military.

10. In one of his first ads for Nike, Tiger _____ (to say) that there are still twenty-three golf courses in the United States where he is not allowed to play because of the color of his skin.

25–6: Using the Correct Forms for Irregular Verbs in the Past Tense

For each of the following sentences, fill in the blank with the correct past-tense form of the irregular verb in parentheses.

EXAMPLE

My grandmother _____*was*_____ (to be) a great baker and an even better cook.

1. When I was growing up, I _____ (to eat) differently than I do now.

2. My mother _____ (to make) fried chicken with mashed potatoes and gravy every Saturday.

3. We never _____ (to think) about cholesterol or calories.

4. Then, ten years ago my older brother John _____ (to have) a heart attack.

5. His wife _____ (to bring) him to the hospital immediately, and luckily the doctors were able to save his life.

6. The surgeon _____ (to say) that if John had arrived at the hospital five minutes later than he did, he probably wouldn't be alive today.

7. John _____ (to know) that he had to lose weight and change his diet dramatically.

8. He _____ (to lose) eighty pounds in seven months, bringing him to a healthy weight.

9. He _____ (to tell) me that I should begin to eat a healthier diet and lose weight, too.

10. I _____ (to quit) eating a lot of the foods I was used to, but I have found many new favorites.

25–7: Using the Correct Forms for the Past Participles of Regular Verbs

For each of the following sentences, fill in the blank with the correct past participle form of the verb in parentheses.

EXAMPLE

Having a college degree has ____*benefited*____ (to benefit) me immensely in my job search.

1. These days, many people have _____ (to try) a few different job options before they settle on a profession.

2. Those people who have _____ (to work) part time in high school or college have gotten a taste of working life.

3. I have _____ (to wait) on tables at my neighborhood restaurant, Taco Loco, for the past year.

4. This work has _____ (to help) me to see that I do not like working with difficult customers.

5. In addition to working as a waitress, I also have _____ (to park) cars at a fancy hotel.

6. Part-time jobs have _____ (to prepare) me to join the full-time workforce.

7. They have _____ (to allow) me to see what I am good at and what I most enjoy.

8. I have _____ (to realize) that I might prefer machines to people.

9. As a result, I have _____ (to register) for classes in computer technology.

10. This field has _____ (to expand) enormously in the last decade and should be both lucrative and enjoyable for me.

25–8: Using the Correct Forms for the Past Participles of Irregular Verbs

For each of the following sentences, fill in the blank with the correct past participle form of the irregular verb in parentheses.

EXAMPLE

Many people have _____*seen*_____ (to see) movies or TV shows about gangsters.

1. I have _____ (to begin) to see why everyone is raving about the TV show *The Sopranos*.

2. The show has _____ (to become) extremely popular over the last year or so.

3. People all over the country have _____ (to catch) on to the show that is changing the nature of the gangster story.

4. In addition, *The Sopranos* has _____ (to win) several Emmy awards.

5. In the past, I have _____ (to find) many gangster movies to be unrealistic.

6. The writers of *The Sopranos* have _____ (to do) a wonderful job of creating believable and interesting characters.

7. They have _____ (to write) a script in which dialogue is more important than action.

8. The actors have _____ (to show) the ability to mimic a certain kind of New Jersey accent.

9. I have _____ (to fall) into a routine of watching the show every Sunday night with friends.

10. People like us have _____ (to make) *The Sopranos* as popular as many shows on regular network television.

25–9: Using the Present Perfect Tense

In the following sentences, underline the correct tense of the verb in parentheses. Choose between the past tense and present perfect tense.

EXAMPLE

Over the course of my life, I (changed, <u>have changed</u>) direction more than once.

1. When I graduated from high school back in 1979, I (was, have been) not interested in going to college.

2. Instead, I got married and (became, have become) a mother right away.

3. For the past eighteen years, I (stayed, have stayed) home to raise my three children.

4. When my youngest child entered high school last September, I (began, have begun) thinking about what it would be like to have my own career.

5. Until recently, my family (got, has gotten) by on my husband's paycheck.

6. Then Tom (lost, has lost) his job after sixteen years with the same company.

7. Since the layoff, he (applied, has applied) for more than one hundred jobs but can find only part-time work that doesn't pay very well.

8. After much discussion, we finally (decided, have decided) that I should go back to school to become a paralegal.

9. For the past semester I (attended, have attended) Mt. Ida College.

10. Though I enjoy my classes, at first it (felt, have felt) strange to be a student again.

25–10: Using the Present Perfect Tense

For each of the following sentences, fill in the blank with the correct present perfect form of the verb in parentheses.

EXAMPLE

Current events *have reinforced* (to reinforce) my fear of flying.

1. A number of recent crashes _____ (to raise) questions about the risks of letting new pilots fly at night.

2. The National Transportation Safety Board _____ (to investigate) the circumstances surrounding these fatal crashes.

3. The Board _____ (to state) that approximately eighty people die each year in crashes of privately flown planes.

4. Evidence _____ (to show) that disorientation is a major risk for inexperienced pilots.

5. Nevertheless, the Federal Aviation Administration _____ (to announce) that the current rules for new pilots are adequate.

6. Some experts _____ (to argue) that these types of crashes have decreased in number over the last twenty years.

7. Other countries, such as Great Britain, _____ (to create) laws that require new pilots to have special instruments for flying at night.

8. In many cases, these instruments _____ (to help) disoriented pilots distinguish the earth from the sky.

9. As a result, the instruments _____ (to prevent) pilots from crashing into the earth.

10. Many Americans _____ (to write) to their representatives and senators to try to get similar legislation passed in the United States.

25–11: Using the Past Perfect Tense (1)

In the following sentences, underline the correct tense of the verb in parentheses. Choose between the past tense and the past perfect tense.

EXAMPLE

Just when I thought I had it all figured out, life (<u>threw</u>, had thrown) me another curve ball.

1. Before I (became, had become) a student at Hudson Valley Community College this fall, I had been a stay-at-home mother for nine years.

2. I (thought, had thought) about going back to school ever since my sister got her degree in 1992.

3. Yet until my husband and I split up two years ago, I (saw, had seen) no way to make such a dramatic change in my life.

4. I (was, had been) divorced for six months before I even began to apply to colleges.

5. At first I (tried, had tried) to get a job without going back to school, but that plan gradually fell apart.

6. The only jobs I (found, had found) didn't even pay enough to cover my childcare expenses.

7. I (worked, had worked) as a secretary before I quit to have kids.

8. When I (stopped, had stopped) working in 1982, I had never even used a computer.

9. If I (knew, had known) that I would one day be a single mother, I would never have left the workforce.

10. On the other hand, I guess that if I (kept, had kept) working, I would never have gone to college.

25–12: Using the Past Perfect Tense (2)

For each of the following sentences, fill in the blank with the correct past perfect form of the verb in parentheses.

EXAMPLE

When I asked my grandfather about his career, I _had guessed_ (to guess) correctly that he would have a long and interesting story to tell.

1. When my grandfather retired at the age of seventy, he _____ (to hold) many different jobs.

2. By the time he was fifteen years old, he _____ (to drop out) of school and was working full time at a pizzeria.

3. Before he was a chef at the pizzeria, though, he _____ (to be) a tailor at the shop across the street.

4. When he married my grandmother at the age of eighteen, he _____ (to work) at four different restaurants and bakeries.

5. He left each job after a short time because he _____ (to figure out) that there would be a better wage at another one.

6. Before my uncle was born, my grandfather _____ (to realize) that he was going to have to try something else yet again in order to support his rapidly growing family.

7. His own father _____ (to manage) grocery stores for a living, and he decided to give that kind of job a try.

8. The grocery store business was very good to him, and by the time he moved to Florida forty years later he _____ (to receive) more than twenty-five promotions and raises.

9. My grandfather always says that what he wishes he _____ (to learn) earlier is that there is often more to gain sticking with one job than bouncing around.

10. I'm not sure that this is always true, though, and I might not have found the great job I have now if I _____ (not to try) a couple of other ones first.

25–13: Identifying Active and Passive Voice

In each of the following sentences, underline the subject once and the verb twice, and indicate whether the sentence is active or passive by writing **A** or **P** in the space provided.

EXAMPLE

_P_ I <u>was asked</u> by my former teacher to talk to her class about how I began my career as a computer technician.

1. _____ I completed a certificate program in computer science one year ago.

2. _____ A lot was taught by my teacher about different computer platforms, software, and networks.

3. _____ It was suggested to me by my teacher that I start looking for a job before I finished the program.

4. _____ Letters were sent out to the technical support departments of several companies asking about job openings.

5. _____ In the letters, I mentioned that I would soon finish the certificate program and that I had also done extra research about the computer industry on my own.

6. _____ Form letters were sent by a few companies that had no job openings.

7. _____ Several companies called me to come in for interviews.

8. _____ A part-time job was offered by one company until I finished school and could start full-time.

9. _____ Of course, I accepted the company's offer.

10. _____ Skilled and motivated technical support workers are needed by practically every company these days.

25–14: Using Active Voice

Revise each of the following sentences to change passive voice to active voice.

EXAMPLE

It has been decided by the students that the increase in parking rates is unfair.

The students have decided that the increase in parking rates is unfair.

1. A poll was taken by several student organizations that are working together to oppose the increase in parking rates.

2. It was voted by 90 percent of the students who drive to school that the increase is too high.

3. "The rates were already high, and now they have more than doubled," was remarked by one student.

4. That the state has given the college less money this year is recognized by the students.

5. Students who drive to school should not be forced by the college to make up the entire amount of money cut by the state.

6. In most cases, driving to school is resorted to only by students who don't live near public transportation.

7. Paying the increased rate will be found impossible by some of these students.

8. Not enough time is had by students who come to class after work to drive to a subway station and then take the subway to school.

9. Some people may be discouraged from applying to the college at all by the expensive parking rates.

10. Funds should be raised by the college in a way that is fair to all students.

25–15: Using the Passive Voice

Rewrite each of the following sentences using the passive voice.

EXAMPLE

The library is enforcing a new policy.

A new policy is being enforced by the library.

1. We should not bring drinks or food into the library.

2. I brought a drink into the library the other day.

3. My friend spilled the drink on a book.

4. Someone found the ruined book on Tuesday.

5. This person reported my friend and me to the librarians.

6. The authorities revoked our library cards the following day.

7. They denied us the chance to plead our case.

8. A professor who heard about our case told the dean how unfair it was.

9. No one actually saw us spill the drink on the book.

10. The law states that rights and privileges cannot be revoked based on circumstantial evidence.

25–16: Correcting Problems with Consistency of Verb Tense

In the following sentences, select the proper form of the verb to maintain consistency of tense throughout the set of sentences. Remember that sometimes shifts in tense are logical.

EXAMPLE

Bicycle racers seldom (<u>achieve</u>, achieved) fame in the United States, but today there (<u>is</u>, was) an exception.

1. Texan Lance Armstrong (is, was) definitely a hero in many eyes.

2. In July 2000 he (wins, won) his second consecutive Tour de France.

3. The twenty-three-day, 2,276-mile bicycle race (is, was) grueling for most athletes, but Armstrong (is, was) not a typical athlete.

4. In 1996, two months after he competed in the 1996 Olympics, his doctor (tells, told) him that he (has, had) testicular cancer that (has, had) spread to his lungs, abdomen, and brain.

5. Doctors (give, gave) him a 40 percent chance of survival, but he (refuses, refused) to accept those odds.

6. He (endures, endured) chemotherapy, brain surgery, and the removal of the testicle.

7. He (survives, survived) and (improves, improved) his upper body for racing.

8. His success (is, was) not only evident in his athletic achievements.

9. In 1998 Armstrong (marries, married) and (is, was) now a father.

10. To help people like himself manage and survive cancer, he (has, had) started the Lance Armstrong Foundation, which (has, had) raised over $3 million.

25–17: Using Consistent Verb Tense

For each of the following sentences, fill in the blank with the form of the verb in parentheses that is consistent with the other verbs in the sentence.

EXAMPLE

As Internet access has expanded, the number of Internet users <u>*has increased*</u> (to increase) dramatically during the last few years.

1. The Internet has become increasingly popular in the last several years and _____ (to change) the way many people conduct their daily lives.

2. Many people shop over the Internet and _____ (to read) about topics that interest them.

3. One woman who had been set up on a blind date ran an Internet search on her beau and _____ (to find) that he had been described in an online article as one of the ten worst dates of all time.

4. People are becoming concerned about privacy on the Internet and _____ (to ask) questions about its benefits.

5. The Internet has made knowledge more available but also _____ (to raise) new questions about the boundaries between private and public information.

6. A recent article in the *New York Times* argued that we are losing our privacy and _____ (to give) examples of what average people do on the Internet.

7. People order books or _____ (to listen) to music online and reveal potentially important information about themselves to corporations.

8. Many companies have offered discounts or _____ (to give) away free products to consumers who supply information for marketing research.

9. Some people _____ (to erase) their Internet transactions with special software that costs a great deal of money.

10. But most of us do not buy this software and _____ (to be) at risk of having our personal preferences and interests becoming public information.

25–18: Verb Problems Review

In the following sentences, fill in the correct form and tense of the verb in parentheses.

EXAMPLE

Many great works of art _____*are*_____ (to be) in danger of being destroyed by time.

1. Leonardo da Vinci _____ (to be) probably the world's most famous artist.

2. His reputation as an inventor, scientist, and engineer _____ (to grow) tremendously over the years.

3. You may _____ (to see) a copy of his painting the *Mona Lisa.*

4. The original painting at the Louvre Museum in Paris _____ (to lie) behind a thick sheet of bulletproof glass.

5. Da Vinci _____ (to paint) another of his famous works, the *Last Supper,* on the wall of a church in Milan, Italy, in 1497.

6. Unfortunately, this great painting _____ (to decay) badly over time.

7. In fact, the *Last Supper* _____ (to begin) to fall apart almost immediately after Leonardo _____ (to finish) it.

8. He _____ (to use) an experimental technique that _____ (to give) him more time to work but _____ (to make) the painting crack and peel.

9. Since 1726 there _____ (to be) many disastrous attempts to restore the *Last Supper.*

10. Luckily, a conservation effort that _____ (to begin) in 1977 _____ (to reverse) some of the damage.

Chapter 26: Pronouns—Using Substitutes for Nouns

26–1: Identifying Pronouns

Underline the pronoun or pronouns in each of the following sentences.

EXAMPLE

"Take This Job and Shove It" was a popular country song by Johnny Paycheck.

1. Today, nearly a quarter of all Americans stay at their jobs for one year or less.

2. Workers consider themselves more valuable now than they did in the past because of a tighter labor market.

3. Employees know that they are in demand and have more choices than ever before.

4. One grocery store employee recently said she wanted a merit raise and would not hesitate to quit if she did not receive one.

5. Workers like her know that they can easily find jobs elsewhere.

6. For the last three years, American workers have averaged three years of working at their place of business.

7. Industries such as food services currently are seeing their worst employee turnover rates ever.

8. The food services industries often provide dead-end, boring, or dangerous jobs that leave their workers dissatisfied.

9. Industry leaders are beginning to realize that such turnover is costing them a great deal of money.

10. Customers will soon begin to see these costs passed on to them.

26–2: Making Pronouns Agree with Indefinite Pronouns and Collective Nouns

In the following sentences, underline the correct pronoun or pronouns from the choices in parentheses.

EXAMPLE

If a student group is really dedicated to a particular cause, (<u>it</u>, they) can help bring about change.

1. My college just announced that (it, they) will be raising tuition next year.

2. This is terrible news for anyone who has to pay (his or her, their) own way.

3. Someone wrote a letter to the editor of the school paper saying that (she, they) would have to drop out of college if tuition went up.

4. Several other letter-writers said that (he or she, they) had no idea how to come up with the extra money.

5. "Society needs to turn (its, their) attention to the fact that ordinary people can no longer afford a college education," wrote one angry student.

6. A group calling (itself, themselves) Students Against Soaring Tuition (SAST) held a protest rally outside the president's office, and the crowd chanted slogans for three hours.

7. Both my parents work hard at (his or her job, their jobs), but neither of them can afford to pay so much money for my education.

8. My family does all (it, they) can to pay the rent and grocery bill each month.

9. The financial aid office said that (it, they) won't be able to increase my loan for next year.

10. Luckily, however, the jewelry company where I worked part-time last summer promised that (it, they) would give me more hours this summer.

26–3: Making Pronouns Agree with Indefinite Pronouns

Fill in the blank with the correct pronoun in each of the following sentences.

EXAMPLE

Someone who puts ___*his or her*___ life at risk for others is a hero.

1. Everyone remembers where _____ was the day that the *Challenger* space shuttle exploded and killed all the passengers on board.

2. At my school, several of the teachers turned on the television sets in _____ classrooms.

3. Everybody put _____ things away in a locker and crowded into a room with a television.

4. No one could believe _____ eyes when the shuttle blew up after less than a minute in the air.

5. Each student sat with _____ mouth open.

6. Many could not leave _____ seats even after the news broadcast was over.

7. One teacher had applied for Christa McAuliffe's position, and everyone at Belvedere had crossed _____ fingers hoping he would get the position.

8. Few could forget how close _____ came to losing a beloved teacher.

9. The day after the explosion, many of us said _____ could not sleep that night.

10. The newspapers and television news both made the *Challenger* explosion _____ lead story for over a week.

26–4: Making Pronouns Agree with Collective Nouns

For each of the following sentences, fill in the blank with the correct pronoun.

EXAMPLE

A company on the Internet will let people search _____*its*_____ records for information about their ancestors.

1. My mother's family has had _____ history recorded in several different books because her descendants were slaves of one of the wealthiest plantations in Mississippi.

2. Our local historical society asked if _____ could have permission to research and write about our family.

3. The college in the town where my great-grandfather was born holds much information about my family in _____ library.

4. The government of Mississippi kept records of all of _____ citizens and their property.

5. Because slaves were considered property, the group of authors and researchers from the historical society was able to find the information _____ needed in those records.

6. A committee that helps to retrieve historical information about slaves offered _____ assistance to the authors in gathering data.

7. When the books were published, the publishing company asked if _____ could host a meeting with the authors to lecture about their findings.

8. When we got to the meeting, the audience was enormous and had lined _____ up outside the meeting hall waiting to get in.

9. A team of journalists waited _____ turn to take pictures of our family.

10. The crowd got to hear what _____ had come for—my mother's moving speech about her family and the authors' recounting of what they found about her descendants.

26–5: Avoiding Ambiguous, Vague, or Repetitious Pronoun References

Edit each sentence to eliminate any ambiguous, vague, or repetitious pronoun references. Some sentences may be revised in more than one way.

EXAMPLE

insurance companies

Insurance policies can be difficult to understand, especially when ~~they~~ don't offer good customer service.

1. Yesterday I got a letter from my doctor informing me that they were no longer accepting my insurance plan.

2. Dr. Reuter and her partner, Dr. Spingarn, they have decided not to go along with the insurance company's new way of paying doctors.

3. According to the letter, my insurance company is now forcing doctors to accept capitation, a payment method that it describes as "unethical."

4. With this payment method, every month the doctor gets a fixed fee for each patient, no matter how much treatment he or she provides.

5. In other words, doctors are paid the same amount whether they need six office visits a month or none.

6. With the traditional fee-for-service method of reimbursing doctors, insurance companies pay every time they treat a patient.

7. My doctor and her partner believe that capitation is bad because they reward doctors for providing less medical care and penalize them for providing more.

8. They think it creates a conflict of interest between doctors and patients because they have a financial incentive to withhold treatment.

9. Dr. Reuter and Dr. Spingarn decided that they could not accept the capitation plan even if it meant losing patients who could not switch to a different insurance company.

10. When I called my insurance company to complain about capitation, they told me that they were simply trying to keep my premiums down by controlling medical costs.

26–6: Using the Right Type of Pronoun with Compound Subjects and Objects

Edit the following sentences to ensure that the proper type of pronoun is used. If a sentence is already correct, write **OK** next to it.

EXAMPLE

Sometimes day-to-day problems can put stress on a marriage, but my husband and ~~me~~ *I* always talk over a problem until it is solved.

1. Last March my friend Elena and me both had babies, five days apart.

2. Everyone in the neighborhood gave Elena and I a double baby shower, with matching outfits for our two kids.

3. During the summer Elena and I used to spend a lot of time together, pushing Max and Lucy in their strollers and sitting in the park.

4. Unfortunately, now that I'm in school and Elena is back at her job, me and her don't see each other as much as we used to.

5. Sometimes me and Max run into her and Lucy at the playground or the library.

6. When we saw Lucy and her the other day, Elena was complaining that her and her husband, Danny, never spend any time together anymore.

7. They're always so tired and stressed out from working and taking care of Lucy that when her and Danny do see each other, they just end up arguing.

8. Elena thinks it would be a good idea for her and Danny to go away for a long weekend without the baby.

9. The other day she said, "If things don't get better between he and I, Danny and me are going to end up getting a divorce."

10. I told her that me and David had struggled with the same issue and that I thought they would work things out if they could just spend more time together.

26–7: Using the Right Type of Pronoun in Comparisons

Edit the following sentences to ensure that the proper type of pronoun is used. If a sentence is already correct, write **OK** next to it. Some sentences may have more than one error.

EXAMPLE

I try not to be too competitive with my brother because I already know that I can do everything better than ~~him~~ *he*.

1. My older sister, Nadine, always seems to get her schoolwork done faster than me.

2. Nadine does better on tests, but I write better papers than her.

3. As a result, she usually gets about the same grades as me.

4. However, I don't think she tries as hard as I or cares as much about school.

5. The whole time we were growing up, teachers always seemed to like her better than I.

6. It drove me crazy that they didn't treat me the same as her.

7. Nadine is eighteen months older than me, but people always ask us if we're twins.

8. Now that we're both in college, I keep wondering if I'm doing as well as she.

9. I guess deep down inside I'm worried that people will respect her more than me or think she's smarter than me.

10. I don't understand why I'm so competitive with Nadine, since I don't know any sisters who are closer friends than us.

26–8: Choosing between *Who* and *Whom*

In the following sentences, underline the correct pronoun, choosing between *who* and *whom* or *whoever* and *whomever.*

EXAMPLE

When a company is interviewing candidates for a job, it looks for the person (who, whom) will best fulfill the job requirements.

1. I had a job interview last week with a woman (who, whom) is the editor of a nutrition newsletter called *You Are What You Eat.*

2. I also met with her assistant, (who, whom) I had spoken to on the phone when I set up the interview.

3. The editor, (who, whom) talked with me for about twenty minutes, described the newsletter and asked me about my interest in working there.

4. She explained that the newsletter had been started four years ago by her boss, (who, whom) used to be a writer for a health and fitness magazine.

5. Her boss, (who, whom) I did not get a chance to meet, is also planning to start a nutrition Web site.

6. The editor said that she is looking for someone (who, whom) has excellent computer skills as well as some experience with desktop publishing software.

7. She said that (whoever, whomever) she decides to hire will help lay out the newsletter and may have some involvement with designing the new Web site.

8. During the interview, I said that I had become interested in nutrition because of my mother, (who, whom) is a dietitian for a hospital.

9. The editor said that she was going to be interviewing several other people, some of (who, whom) have more experience than I do.

10. She asked me to give her the names and phone numbers of two people (who, whom) she could call as references.

26–9: Making Pronouns Consistent in Person

Edit each sentence to ensure that the pronouns are consistent in person.

EXAMPLE

People who set goals for themselves find that ~~you~~ *they* achieve what ~~you~~ *they* set out to do.

1. Many students and professionals do not realize that writing can provide you with a means of achieving goals.

2. They need to understand that writing down your goals is better than just thinking about them.

3. When someone writes down a goal, one part of his or her brain starts collecting pertinent information and sends it to the conscious part of your mind.

4. Thus, the person starts to recognize opportunities you never would have noticed otherwise.

5. When you put your goals on paper, people need to include both short- and long-term goals.

6. People who try this technique should not worry about your spelling or edit your ideas.

7. If students have trouble writing goals, you might want to write down on another sheet what is keeping you from reaching your goals.

8. By being specific rather than vague, people can more easily decide how to meet your goals.

9. To help you focus on the outcome, a person may want to include smaller goals that are steps to the final goal.

10. People who follow this technique have learned that the fears that could keep them from succeeding become more manageable if you write those fears down.

Chapter 27: Adjectives and Adverbs—Describing *Which One?* or *How?*

27–1: Choosing between Adjectives and Adverbs

In the following sentences, underline the correct adjective or adverb in parentheses, and then circle the word it describes, or modifies, in the sentence.

EXAMPLE

Many ancient societies had strong (<u>oral</u>, orally) (traditions), meaning that stories were passed on by word of mouth.

1. Every culture tells folktales about a (mischievous, mischievously) character known as the trickster.

2. He is a (greedy, greedily) troublemaker who is always doing something he was told not to do or poking his nose where it doesn't belong.

3. The trickster is (usual, usually) a small animal who has to rely on his wits to survive.

4. His (foolish, foolishly) pranks often backfire, and we learn through his example how we should *not* behave.

5. However, though we reject the trickster's dishonesty, we (secret, secretly) admire his cleverness.

6. We enjoy watching him outsmart his (powerful, powerfully) opponents.

7. In some folktales, the trickster is a hero because his thefts and deceptions turn out to help his people in (unexpected, unexpectedly) ways.

8. The world's most (popular, popularly) tricksters are Reynard the Fox in European folktales, Anansi the spider in West African tales, Brer Rabbit in African American tales, and Coyote in Native American tales.

9. In a story told by the Zuni people of the American Southwest, Coyote persuades his (sensible, sensibly) friend Eagle to help him steal the sun and the moon so that they will have light to hunt by.

10. (Uncontrollable, Uncontrollably) curious, Coyote opens a box containing the sun and the moon and allows them to escape, thus bringing winter into the world.

27–2: Using Comparative and Superlative Forms

In the following sentences, write the correct form of the adjective or adverb in parentheses.

EXAMPLE

Folktales often offer explanations for the *most intriguing* (intriguing) aspects of the natural world, such as why the sky is blue.

1. Coyote is the _____ (famous) trickster character in Native American folklore, appearing in stories told throughout California, the Southwest, and the Central Plains.

2. He is _____ (famous) than Mink, Raven, or Bluejay, who are the trickster characters among the tribes of the Pacific Northwest.

3. Coyote is the _____ (important) animal of the mythical pre-human animal age, when animals were believed to be able to talk.

4. In many tales he is simply a comical bad guy who thinks he can outsmart all the _____ (strong) animals because he is so much _____ (clever) than the other animals.

5. Even though he is a troublemaker, Coyote sometimes makes life _____ (easy) for people by getting them things they need, such as fire and light.

6. In the Zuni folktale "Coyote Steals the Sun and Moon," Coyote does help people, but he also makes things _____ (hard) for them by introducing winter into the world.

7. Coyote and his friend Eagle encounter the Kachinas, friendly spirits who get their light by opening up two boxes; the _____ (small) one contains the moon, and the _____ (big) one contains the sun.

8. Coyote convinces Eagle that they should steal the sun and the moon, and after the Kachinas fall asleep, Coyote and Eagle add the moon to the _____ (large) box and fly away with it.

9. When Coyote peeks inside the box, the moon immediately escapes into the sky, and the sun flies up even _____ (high).

10. Coyote makes life _____ (difficult) for people because it's his fault that cold and winter come into the world, but he is also responsible for two good things: the coming of light and the natural cycle of the seasons.

27–3: Using *Good, Well, Bad,* and *Badly*

In the following sentences, underline the correct word in parentheses, choosing between *good* and *well* or between the comparative or superlative forms of *good* and *bad*.

EXAMPLE

Some people think that stealing is not wrong if it is done for a (<u>good</u>, well) reason.

1. Coyote, a famous trickster character in Native American folklore, is always up to no (good, well).

2. The Zuni folktale "Coyote Steals the Sun and Moon" tells how Coyote makes life (worse, worst) for people by introducing winter into the world.

3. Because Coyote hunts (bad, badly), he decides to team up with Eagle, who is an excellent hunter.

4. Coyote tells Eagle that it would be (better, best) if the world were not dark because then it would be easier to hunt.

5. When Coyote and Eagle encounter some friendly spirits, the Kachinas, the pair notice that the Kachinas get their light from two boxes—one containing the sun and one containing the moon—and Coyote convinces Eagle that the (better, best) thing to do is to steal the sun and the moon.

6. Eagle then decides that a (good, well) plan is to put the sun and the moon into one box.

7. After Eagle moves the moon into the box with the sun and flies away with it, he refuses to let Coyote carry the box because he knows that things always turn out (bad, badly) when Coyote gets his way.

8. Because Coyote keeps begging to carry the box, Eagle finally gives in, hoping things will turn out (better, best) than he thinks they will.

9. Eagle then fears that the (worse, worst) will happen when Coyote peeks inside the box and the moon and the sun escape into the sky.

10. Although Coyote causes winter to come into the world, the effects of his actions aren't all (bad, badly) because he also brings light to people.

Chapter 28: Misplaced and Dangling Modifiers—Avoiding Confusing Descriptions

28–1: Correcting Misplaced Modifiers

Edit the following sentences to correct any misplaced modifiers.

EXAMPLE

Doing something yourself can ~~both~~ be *both* rewarding and educational.

1. We have been building for the past four months an addition onto our house.

2. The addition will be a sunroom that will be entirely lit with almost natural light.

3. Surrounded by windows, I have wanted a room like this one for a long time.

4. We are building the addition using materials recycled from the garage we are tearing down fairly inexpensively.

5. The cedar planks will look charmingly rustic in our new room that once served as the garage siding.

6. We have taken skylights that were once over the bedroom closet and also moved them to the sunroom's roof.

7. We found an old glass door that we can use in our attic for the doorway between the sunroom and the backyard in our attic.

8. Without hesitation, to do the floor ourselves seemed like an impossible job, so we hired a contractor.

9. When we are done with nearly sheetrocking the walls, he can come in and begin laying out the frame for the floor.

10. Soon-to-be-finished, I can't wait until we can begin eating dinner in our new room.

28–2: Correcting Dangling Modifiers

Edit the following sentences to correct any dangling modifiers.

EXAMPLE

Expecting a relaxing day on the water, the *passengers on the* boat set sail without worries.

1. Armed and well trained, a yacht where four people were being held hostage yesterday was raided by five elite coast guard divers.

2. A woman and her three children, no one was harmed.

3. Scared of the hijacker, the yacht began to sail off its original course.

4. Wanting to go to Greece, the yacht began heading east.

5. Bravely, the hijacker's plans were foiled by a secret message sent to the coast guard.

6. Picking up the signal, the action was swift and effective.

7. Distracted by three coast guard boats surrounding the front of the yacht, the divers climbed aboard the back of the yacht.

8. Motioning to the hostages to keep quiet, the boats outside kept the hijacker distracted as the ambush started.

9. Unwilling to give in, the firing began.

10. Trained to fire back when necessary, the hijacker was shot.

28–3: Avoiding Misplaced and Dangling Modifiers (1)

Edit the following sentences to eliminate problems with misplaced and dangling modifiers. It may be necessary to add or change words.

EXAMPLE

I find
Not having a car, public transportation is very convenient.
^

1. Getting to work from my house by subway only takes about twenty minutes.

2. While riding the subway, the time passes quickly if you have something to read.

3. I used to take the bus to work instead of the subway, which is slower.

4. The bus nearly takes twice as long as the subway because of all the traffic.

5. Also, the bus almost stops at every corner.

6. Having taken the bus for years, it had never occurred to me to try the subway.

7. Though rather noisy, I prefer the subway because I can read without getting a headache.

8. Riding the subway for a year, I haven't even gotten a headache once.

9. Reading on the bus, my head would start throbbing after five minutes.

10. Unable to read, I only could stare out the window.

28–4: Avoiding Misplaced and Dangling Modifiers (2)

Edit the following sentences to eliminate problems with misplaced and dangling modifiers. It may be necessary to add or change words. Some sentences may have more than one error.

EXAMPLE

While gardening in my yard,
I found a kitten that had been abandoned by its mother. ~~gardening in my yard.~~

1. Painting our living room, our black cat pushed open the door and rubbed up against the wet molding.

2. Looking like a skunk, we found Lucy hiding under the bed.

3. We had used oil-based paint on the molding, which was now on her fur.

4. We decided to clean her fur with paint thinner after considering our other options.

5. Now covered with paint thinner, we needed to wash and rinse Lucy with soap and water.

6. We realized that we had made a terrible mistake in the basement an hour later cleaning our brushes.

7. Usually so gentle and affectionate, we found Lucy hissing and arching her back at us.

8. Rushing Lucy to the emergency animal hospital, the vet told us that you should never use paint thinner on an animal.

9. We learned that we should have just used soap and water or a lanolin hand cleaner during our conversation with the vet.

10. After being sedated and thoroughly bathed, we took Lucy home, grateful that she was okay.

Chapter 29: Coordination and Subordination—Joining Ideas

29–1: Coordinating Ideas with Coordinating Conjunctions

Fill in the blank in each sentence with the correct coordinating conjunction.

EXAMPLE

America's landscape is very varied, _____*and*_____ one of the best ways to see it all is to drive across the country.

1. Americans have built dams and rerouted rivers, _____ they have made even the driest parts of the West inhabitable.

2. The Southwest is naturally arid and rocky, _____ we have tried to make it lush and green like the East.

3. The Southwest has a very hot and dry climate, _____ water used for irrigation purposes evaporates and is lost almost as quickly as it is sprayed out of hoses.

4. This means that water is being taken out of streams and rivers without being put back in, _____ the result of such irrigation can be disastrous to natural bodies of water.

5. Damming waterways has effects in the Northwest as well, _____ rivers as far north as Washington State are also artificially rerouted.

6. When rivers are dammed, the salmon that live in them cannot survive, _____ can the bears that depend on the salmon for food.

7. Indian tribes with national rights to the salmon also lose out, _____ the fish that they have depended on for hundreds of years are now becoming extinct.

8. Sport fishermen, environmental groups, and many Indian tribes have asked the government to reconsider its policies about damming waterways, _____ the groups in favor of reallocating rivers and streams have often proved to be more powerful.

9. Many environmentalists have pointed out that we must take better care of our natural waterways, _____ we will lose them and the wildlife dependent on them forever.

10. The author Wallace Stegner has written many essays about this subject, _____ in one of them he writes, "You have to get over the color green; you have to quit associating beauty with gardens and lawns; you have to get used to an inhuman scale."

29–2: Coordinating Sentences with Semicolons

Combine each of the following pairs of sentences into a single sentence by using a semicolon.

EXAMPLE

Women athletes are demanding the same respect as their male

counterparts; They are making their mark in soccer, basketball, and

other traditionally male sports.

1. Sports that have historically been considered off-limits to women are changing. Women are beginning to participate in professional athletics in areas where they have never competed before.

2. One example is weightlifting. Seventeen-year-old Cheryl Haworth has quickly become the most well-known female weightlifter.

3. Haworth is five feet nine inches tall and weighs 300 pounds. She has the ideal build for a weightlifter.

4. She can lift over 300 pounds. This power made her the medal favorite at the 2000 Olympics.

5. She lifts as much as 25 tons in the course of her daily workout. Every day she lifts the equivalent of five elephants or one F-15 fighter jet.

6. Haworth is also something of a practical jokester. She has been known to lift her friend's car and move it to a different location.

7. Haworth's thighs measure 32 inches in circumference. She can bench press 500 pounds.

8. She began lifting weights when she was twelve years old and already weighed 240 pounds. She could lift over 110 pounds.

9. She also has the speed and flexibility needed by a great weightlifter. She can run a 40-yard dash in five seconds.

10. Women like Haworth are calling for significant changes now and in the future in women's sports. The inclusion of female weightlifting for the first time in the 2000 Olympics is proof of these changes.

29–3: Coordinating Ideas with Semicolons and Connecting Words

Combine each of the following pairs of sentences into a single sentence by using a semicolon and a connecting word.

EXAMPLE

however,

A college degree can sometimes seem like an unattainable goal; It is something worth striving for.

1. My friend Simone became pregnant when she was a junior in college. She could not go back to finish her senior year.

2. She could not afford child care. She had to stay home after Danny, her son, was born.

3. Danny is five now and is beginning kindergarten next month. Simone will have five hours free every day.

4. Simone has signed up for two morning classes in nursing at her community college. She has applied for a part-time job at a nursing home.

5. It won't be easy fitting work and classes into her busy parenting schedule. Simone feels that Danny will be better off when they are financially secure.

6. There are things she would like to buy for Danny that she cannot afford. Simone wants to show Danny that she can beat the odds.

7. Simone would like to eventually be a nurse. Through caring for Danny, she's already had some practice as one.

8. The three-year course to become a nurse is too much for Simone. She could take fewer classes and become a nurse practitioner.

9. Either way, she would be working with patients. She would be making good use of her naturally caring personality.

10. Simone says she feels more dedicated now than she did five years ago, and so she is glad her schooling was put on hold. She has a wonderful son in her life.

29–4: Using Coordination to Join Two Sentences

Combine each of the following pairs of sentences into a single sentence by using one of the methods of coordination discussed in the chapter: using a comma and a coordinating conjunction, using a semicolon, or using a semicolon and a connecting word or phrase.

EXAMPLE

Owning a car can be convenient and fun, *but* It can also be a big hassle.

1. My car started making a funny noise. I took it to the repair shop down the street.

2. The mechanic told me the car needed a new water pump. He thought it would cost about $300, including labor.

3. My car isn't worth a lot of money. It's probably not worth much more than $300.

4. It's a 1987 Nissan Sentra hatchback with about 130,000 miles. Up until last week it had been driving just fine.

5. Over the years I've had good luck with this car. I've grown quite attached to it.

6. My brother thinks I should get the car repaired. My sister thinks I'd be foolishly throwing good money after bad.

7. My sister is probably right. I'm unhappy about abandoning my car.

8. I could buy my neighbor's 1994 Toyota Tercel wagon. I could go to the used-car dealer my parents recommended.

9. I'm just not sure it makes sense for me to take out a car loan right now. I don't have any money for a down payment.

10. Maybe I should get the car repaired. I could buy a new car after I've saved some money over the summer.

29–5: Using Subordination to Join Two Sentences

Combine each of the following pairs of sentences into a single sentence by turning one of them into a subordinate clause. Use a subordinating conjunction that makes sense with the two sentences. Add a comma if the subordinate clause is at the beginning of the sentence.

EXAMPLE

Although
ᴬDoctors can attempt to predict a pregnant woman's delivery date/,
          b
B̸abies keep their own schedules.

1. On May 21, 1997, Jahmal Haney delivered his first baby. He was only eight years old.

2. Jahmal's mother, Donna Murray, wasn't due for another month. She started having contractions in the middle of the night.

3. Two hours later she called 911. She realized she wasn't going to make it to the hospital.

4. The 911 operator, Sean Stentiford, asked Murray if there was anyone else at home. She handed the phone to her son.

5. His mother went to lie down in the bedroom. Jahmal listened carefully to Stentiford's instructions.

6. Stentiford told Jahmal to make sure his mother was lying in the middle of the bed. They didn't want the baby to fall on the floor.

7. Jahmal returned from the bedroom. He told Stentiford he could see the baby's head.

8. Stentiford instructed Jahmal to put his hands under the head. His mother pushed the baby out.

9. Jahmal had to run back and forth between his mother in the bedroom and the phone in the living room. He helped deliver his new baby sister, Samantha Elise Murray.

10. The ambulance arrived. The baby had already been born.

Chapter 30: Parallelism—Balancing Ideas

30–1: Correcting Errors in Parallelism (1)

Edit the following sentences to make them parallel.

EXAMPLE

and performance

Consumers should get information on the price of a product ~~and how well it performs~~ before making a purchase.

1. Among college students, halogen lamps have become more popular than using a traditional incandescent lamp.

2. Halogen lamps are more popular because they are cheaper and the light they produce is brighter.

3. However, there are two problems with halogen lamps: They not only cause fires but also lots of energy is used.

4. A 300-watt halogen bulb gets almost three times as hot as to use a 150-watt incandescent bulb.

5. A Harvard engineering professor discovered that halogen lamps—not toasters, hair dryers, stereos, refrigerators, or the use of computers—were responsible for rising energy consumption in residence halls.

6. Some colleges are considering both banning halogen lamps in dormitories and to offer students low-energy fluorescent lamps.

7. The new lamps would be provided either free or they would be at a discount.

8. These energy-efficient lamps cost about four to five times more than the price of halogen lamps.

9. Unfortunately, most consumers would rather save money when they buy an item than when using it.

10. To figure out a lamp's lifetime cost, you have to consider the cost of the lamp itself, of replacement bulbs, and the price of using electricity.

30–2: Correcting Errors in Parallelism (2)

Edit the following sentences to make them parallel.

EXAMPLE

What people who suffer from chronic medical problems need most

from family, friends, and ~~those they work with~~ are compassion and

support.

coworkers

1. A migraine is an intense headache characterized by pulsing pain, nausea, dizziness, double vision, and by being sensitive to light and sound.

2. Migraines are often triggered by red wine, chocolate, aged cheese, and by cured meats.

3. These terrible headaches can also be triggered by certain medicines and when you eat certain food additives.

4. Migraines are three times more common in women than men have them.

5. Women's migraines are often hormonal, related to the fluctuation of both estrogen and of progesterone during their menstrual cycles.

6. Birth control pills or taking estrogen replacement therapy can make hormonal migraines much worse.

7. Throughout history, there have been many failed remedies for migraines, such as purging, bleeding, encircling the head with a hangman's noose, and to drill a hole in the skull.

8. In a famous essay entitled "In Bed," the writer Joan Didion argues that people with migraines not only suffer from the headaches themselves but also the common belief that they are somehow causing their own sickness.

9. Despite what some people think, migraines are caused neither by having a bad attitude nor because you have a certain personality trait.

10. An international team of scientists has not only isolated the gene that causes one severe type of migraine, but also they expect to find genes for more common forms.

Chapter 31: Sentence Variety—Putting Rhythm in Your Writing

31–1: Starting Sentences with an Adverb

Edit the following sentences to begin with an adverb. You may need to add an adverb if an appropriate adverb is not already in the sentence.

EXAMPLE

Usually, it
~~It usually~~ takes people a long time to grieve the loss of a loved one.
^

1. My friend recently has had problems concentrating and finishing the projects she starts.

2. Very thorough, Karen says she has felt distracted since her brother died of cancer last spring.

3. This has gotten in her way at work, where she is expected to complete assignments on time.

4. Her boss is very understanding and told Karen that she would like to support her through this difficult time.

5. Karen went to a psychologist to see if there was anything that Karen could do about her concentration problems.

6. The psychologist explained that the overwhelming emotions Karen was experiencing were completely normal after the loss of a loved one.

7. "These feelings do not last forever," the psychologist explained, "and the grief will eventually become less consuming."

8. After talking with the psychologist, Karen began to attend a support group for people who have lost relatives to cancer.

9. Karen said she began to feel a little better very soon after joining the group.

10. She is getting back on her feet.

31–2: Joining Ideas Using an *-ing* Verb Form

Edit the following pairs of sentences by joining them with an *-ing* verb form.

EXAMPLE

Knowing

~~Television networks know~~ that gymnastics is one of the most popular

^

television networks

summer Olympic events/, ~~They~~ schedule coverage of this sport during

prime time.

1. Kerri Strug led the 1996 U.S. Olympics gymnastics team. Her injured ankle didn't stop her from nailing a perfect landing in her last event.

2. Several of the 1996 women gymnasts have continued training. They hope to be on the 2000 team in Sydney.

3. Dominique Moceanu wants to go to Sydney. Her routines have been altered to accommodate her nine-inch, forty-pound growth spurt.

4. The 2000 women's gymnastics team may not be recognizable to television viewers. It will contain mostly new athletes.

5. Elite gymnastics coaches turn their protégés into champions. These coaches are sometimes criticized for exploiting young children.

6. Young girls can lose their childhoods to constant work in the gym. They can suffer serious injuries as well.

7. Men's gymnastics is dominating the spotlight this Olympic year. Traditionally, men's gymnastics has held less interest for the public than women's gymnastics.

8. Blaine Wilson appeared to be the one to watch. He has won the last five national titles.

9. Blaine wears three earrings. He also dyes his hair and sports numerous tattoos.

10. Blaine has challenged the stereotypes of the male gymnast. He tends to his image both outside and inside the gym.

31–3: Joining Ideas Using an *-ed* Verb Form

Join the following pairs of sentences by using an *-ed* verb.

EXAMPLE

~~The great novel *Moby Dick* was~~ b^B^ased partly on the true story of the
Moby Dick
Essex, ~~It~~ is a tale of a man's obsession with a white whale.

1. The *Essex* was an old whaling ship by the time it sailed its last voyage in 1820. It was regarded as particularly lucky.

2. The *Essex* inspired the final scene of Herman Melville's *Moby Dick*. The *Essex* was attacked by a sperm whale.

3. The larger story actually began after the ship was sunk. It was passed down over the years through town lore.

4. Nantucket, home of the *Essex*, was a prosperous whaling town. It was considered enlightened and a good place for free blacks to live during the era of slavery.

5. Many of the sailors on the *Essex* were only fifteen years old. They were orphaned and desperate for work.

6. Thomas Nickerson was a fourteen-year-old cabin boy. He was determined to record what happened during the attack and in the ninety days that followed.

7. Nickerson's narrative recorded starvation, madness, and desperation. It was discovered in 1981.

8. Twenty crew members were stranded on small boats for ninety days after the *Essex* was sunk. They were forced to resort to desperate measures to stay alive.

9. Melville's narrator, Ishmael, was troubled by his captain's obsession. His story ends when the boat sinks.

10. The crew of the *Essex* may have wished for that fate by the end of their ordeal. They were starved and driven to desperate measures.

31–4: Joining Ideas Using an Appositive

Join the following pairs of sentences by using an appositive.

EXAMPLE

Health-care professionals have high-stress jobs. ~~They are a brave group of people.~~ *, a brave group of people,* ^

1. My brother has some very interesting stories from his work. He is a paramedic.

2. Rush hour afforded him a particularly good story last week. Rush hour is a tense and hectic time for ambulance workers.

3. A pregnant woman called from her car phone. The woman was a rush hour victim.

4. The woman had started to go into labor. Labor is one of the most intense experiences a person can have.

5. The woman hoped that an ambulance could rescue her from the traffic jam. She was a first-time mother.

6. Jake was working with my brother that day. Jake is one of the best ambulance drivers in the area.

7. They found the woman about an eighth of a mile down the highway from where she had called. The woman was a model of courage despite her pain and fear.

8. They left her car at the side of the road. Her car was a 1997 red Lexus.

9. They lifted her into the ambulance and sped away. The ambulance was a godsend to the woman and her unborn child.

10. The woman gave birth to her child seven minutes after arriving at the hospital. Her child was a healthy little girl.

31–5: Joining Ideas with an Adjective Clause

Combine the following pairs of sentences by using an adjective clause that begins with *who, which,* or *that.*

EXAMPLE

Hummus is a healthful food made from chick peas. ~~It~~ *that* can be used as a spread for pita bread.

1. Alice Waters is a well-known chef. She has helped bring attention to organic produce and locally grown foods.

2. Waters has a restaurant named Chez Panisse. It is located in Berkeley, California.

3. Chez Panisse uses only locally grown foods. These foods are pesticide- and chemical-free.

4. In recent years many people have become much more aware of the quality of the foods they eat. They have heard or read about the organic farm movement.

5. They have come to realize that the nutritional value of food involves many factors. It is usually associated only with vitamin content.

6. Organic produce has to be sold more quickly and is therefore fresher. It often has a higher vitamin content.

7. In addition, organic produce is free of pesticides and chemicals. Pesticides and chemicals can be carcinogenic.

8. Chemicals can have other effects. These effects may be less dangerous but are still undesirable.

9. For example, sulfites can produce an allergic reaction in many people. Sulfites are often added to fruits and vegetables to prevent discoloration.

10. Adding sulfites to fruits and vegetables also makes them appear fresher for longer. This allows fruits and vegetables to be sold several weeks after they have been picked.

31–6: Improving Sentence Variety (1)

Edit the following sentences or pairs of sentences to create better sentence variety. Use the techniques covered in this chapter: starting a sentence with an *-ly* adverb, or joining sentences by using an *-ing* word, *-ed* word, appositive, or adjective clause that begins with *who, which,* or *that*. In many cases, there is more than one way to combine the sentences.

EXAMPLE

, who grow up in the public eye,
Child television and movie stars often have difficult teenage years.
~~They grow up in the public eye.~~

1. Everyone obviously knows that Disney is the biggest name in children's home entertainment.

2. Unless you have a daughter between the ages of eight and twelve, you probably don't realize that the second-biggest name is Olsen.

3. Mary-Kate and Ashley Olsen dominate the live-action children's video market. This market is incredibly profitable.

4. The Olsen twins entered show business when they were only four months old. They starred for eight seasons in the hit TV sitcom *Full House.*

5. They both played the part of Michelle. She is the youngest daughter in the Tanner family.

6. Mary-Kate and Ashley are now ten-year-old millionaires. They have made three TV movies, a feature film, two home video series, a music video, and two music CDs.

7. The movie *It Takes Two* earned a modest $19.5 million at the box office but a whopping $75 million in home video sales. It costars Kirstie Alley and Steve Guttenberg.

8. Altogether, the fourteen titles in their two video series have sold more than six million copies. The two series are called *The Adventures of Mary-Kate and Ashley* and *You're Invited to Mary-Kate and Ashley's.*

9. In the *Adventures* videos, the twins play cute detectives. They promise to "solve any crime by dinnertime."

10. These videos are aimed at preteen girls. The videos face virtually no competition in the home entertainment market.

31–7: Improving Sentence Variety (2)

Edit the following sentences or pairs of sentences to create better sentence variety. Use the techniques covered in this chapter: starting a sentence with an *-ly* adverb or joining sentences by using an *-ing* word, *-ed* word, appositive, or adjective clause that begins with *who, which,* or *that.* In many cases, there is more than one way to combine the sentences.

EXAMPLE

Frequently, p

Pregnant women who smoke in public are ~~frequently~~ criticized by
^
complete strangers.

1. A group of scientists recently discovered that babies whose mothers smoked during pregnancy have the same levels of nicotine in their bodies as adult smokers.

2. The results of their study strongly suggest that these newborns go through withdrawal. The study was presented at a meeting of the American College of Cardiology.

3. Dr. Claude Hanet said that the baby of a smoking mother should be considered an ex-smoker. Dr. Hanet spoke at the conference.

4. The study examined the urine of 273 babies and toddlers. The study was conducted by a team of Belgian researchers.

5. Of these children, 139 were newborns. These newborns were one to three days old.

6. Researchers checked the children's urine for cotinine. Cotinine is the substance that remains in the body for several days after nicotine breaks down.

7. Some of the mothers had smoked during pregnancy. They had newborns with cotinine levels that were about the same as their own.

8. In toddlers with smoking mothers, cotinine levels were significantly higher than in certain adult nonsmokers. These adults were exposed to secondhand smoke at home.

9. Pregnant women should not only quit smoking but also avoid secondhand smoke. Secondhand smoke is smoke inhaled from other people's cigarettes.

10. A 1996 study found that even nonsmoking pregnant women can pass cancer-causing chemicals to their fetuses. These nonsmokers have inhaled secondhand smoke.

Chapter 32: ESL Concerns—Areas of Special Interest to Nonnative Speakers

32–1: Using Nouns and Articles

Edit the following sentences by adding articles as needed and by making sure that nouns are used correctly. Keep in mind that in some places more than one answer may be acceptable.

EXAMPLE

Whenever I get ^*a* party invitation, I get nervous because I am ^*a* shy person.

1. Last Saturday I went to party at my sociology professor's house.

2. Since I don't own car, I got ride to party with friend of mine.

3. Professor Zelinsky lives in big house on lake, along with his wife (who is artist) and enormous dog named McDuff.

4. Dog is Scottish deerhound, unusual breed that is almost as big as pony.

5. Food at party was delicious: two huge platters of cheese, fruit, raw vegetables, bread, and crackers, plus barbecued chicken, salad, and sesame noodles.

6. Woman who was petting dog spilled plate of chicken wings on living room couch and glass of wine on chair.

7. I hope Professor Zelinsky wasn't too upset about furniture; I thought woman showed lots of courage in telling him about spills right away.

8. Professor Zelinsky and his wife had hired rock and roll band, and lead singer was classmate of mine.

9. Everyone danced for hours on wooden platform that had been set up on lawn.

10. I went down to beach to watch sun set over lake, and I sat on sand until mosquitoes started to bite.

32–2: Using the *-ing* Form or the *to* Form after Verbs

Edit the following sentences to make sure that verbs are used correctly. Keep in mind that in some places more than one answer may be acceptable. If a sentence is already correct, write **OK** next to it.

EXAMPLE

You should choose ~~working~~ *to work* in a field you enjoy.

1. Because I enjoy to work with children, when I graduate from college I hope getting a job as a teacher in a day-care center.

2. I decided to become a day-care teacher because I enjoyed to be a nanny last summer.

3. I miss to take care of those two little children, Anna and Ethan; I loved spending time with them.

4. In September I discussed to change my major with my college adviser, and I began studying early childhood education that semester.

5. After student-teaching at my college day-care center during the spring semester, I decided that I prefer working with three- and four-year-olds, rather than infants.

6. People keep to ask me why I would choose to work in such a low-paying profession.

7. I am knowing that childcare jobs do not pay well, but I consider to work with children a great privilege and an enormous responsibility.

8. I fail to understand why in this country it is costing so much to send a child to day care, yet the teachers get paid so poorly.

9. A beginning day-care teacher can expect earning about $7 an hour and often cannot hope receiving medical benefits.

10. We as a society need starting to treat early childhood education with more respect—and to stop to pretend that it requires no special skill or training.

32–3: Using Prepositions after Adjectives and Verbs

Fill in the blank with the correct preposition.

EXAMPLE

During the summer, I am usually not interested _____*in*_____ anything on TV.

1. In the summer of 2000, the CBS network was proud _____ *Survivor,* the number one TV show in America.

2. The producers of *Survivor* picked _____ an interesting, diverse group of contestants.

3. The contestants lived on an island full _____ rats and snakes for thirty-nine days.

4. A host dropped _____ on the *Survivor* group from time to time and made them compete in bizarre contests.

5. The contestants dreaded the tribal council, where they were responsible _____ voting one person off the island.

6. The remaining contestants would pick _____ their torches and go on.

7. In the end, the last contestant won a million-dollar prize; needless to say, he was happy _____ his reward.

8. Don't feel sorry _____ the other contestants, though; many of them were offered contracts to write books and star in other shows.

9. The TV networks are trying to fill _____ their schedules by creating other reality shows like *Survivor.*

10. These shows usually have Web sites that people who are excited _____ the show can check to see the status of their favorite reality TV stars.

32–4: Using Prepositions after Adjectives and Verbs

Edit the following sentences to make sure that the prepositions are used correctly. Keep in mind that in some places more than one answer may be acceptable. If a sentence is already correct, write **OK** next to it.

EXAMPLE

You will be satisfied ~~in~~ *with* your decision to follow the career you enjoy.

1. I am writing to let you know that I am very excited on the prospect of working as an assistant teacher in the Preschool 1 classroom at the Kenwood Children's Center.

2. At that age, children are suddenly so aware to the world around them—full of curiosity and eager to try everything they see.

3. When I visited the classroom yesterday, I was impressed about the way all the children were helping around at cleanup time.

4. At circle time I was glad that the teacher called to the girls just as often as the boys.

5. One little girl was so proud on having become a big sister over the weekend that she couldn't wait to share her news.

6. She was waving her arm so hard that I thought it was going to fall off.

7. I have to admit that I couldn't quite understand what one of the younger boys was trying to say, but the teacher didn't give off until she finally understood him.

8. Before nap time, each child chose a book to look to quietly for a few minutes, and then the teacher read *Make Way for Ducklings* to the whole class.

9. After the story, a few of the children couldn't settle down until the teacher turned out some quiet music and pulled down the shades.

10. Some of the kids were so worn off from their busy morning that I don't think they could have stayed awake one second longer.

32–5: Using Negatives and Questions

For each of the following positive statements, write one negative statement and one question. Keep in mind that in some places more than one answer may be acceptable.

EXAMPLE

Studying abroad teaches you a lot about another culture.

Negative: *Studying abroad does not teach you a lot about another culture.*

Question: *Does studying abroad teach you a lot about another culture?*

1. I came to this country two years ago to attend college.

   Negative: _____

   Question: _____

2. My family lives in Argentina.

   Negative: _____

   Question: _____

3. I had a job as a camp counselor this summer.

   Negative: _____

   Question: _____

4. The camp is located on a lake in New Hampshire.

   Negative: _____

   Question: _____

5. It has been around for thirty years.

   Negative: _____

   Question: _____

6. I taught horseback riding and soccer.

   Negative: _____

   Question: _____

(continued)

7. I also directed the camp musical.

   Negative: _____

   Question: _____

8. My English has improved a lot over the summer.

   Negative: _____

   Question: _____

9. I am going to work at the camp again next summer.

   Negative: _____

   Question: _____

10. It was a wonderful experience for me.

    Negative: _____

    Question: _____

32–6: Placing Adjectives in the Correct Order

In the following sentences, place the adjectives in parentheses in the correct order. (Commas have been provided where they are necessary.)

EXAMPLE

I once lost my backpack, and it had all my ___valuable___
___personal___ (personal, valuable) things in it.

1. Yesterday I found a _____ _____ (nylon, purple)
   backpack on the bus.

2. Inside the backpack was a _____ _____ (beat-up,
   paper) notebook.

3. I looked inside it for some information that would help me find the
   owner, but all I found were a few pages covered with _____ ,
   _____ (neat, round) handwriting in a foreign language.

4. Then I noticed that the backpack had a _____
   _____ (outer, small) pocket.

5. Inside there was a _____ _____ _____
   (black, thick, vinyl) address book.

6. On the front page I found a name, address, and phone number circled
   in _____ _____ (felt-tipped, red) pen.

7. I called the number and spoke to a _____ _____
   _____ (cheerful, Italian, young) woman who said that the
   backpack was hers.

8. We agreed to meet at the _____ _____
   _____ (gray, marble, old) fountain in Washington Park.

9. We decided that it would be easier to find each other there than at the
   _____ _____ _____ (enormous, new,
   wooden) playground at the other end of the park.

10. As I approached the fountain, I saw a woman wearing a
    _____ _____ _____ (blue, bright, cotton)
    dress.

Chapter 33: Word Choice—Avoiding Language Pitfalls

33–1: Improving Word Choice

Rewrite the following sentences to eliminate the four language pitfalls covered in Chapter 33: vague and abstract words, slang, wordiness, and clichés.

EXAMPLE

Graphic design is a way cool thing to do because it's fun and you can earn a lot of dough performing it because it pays great.

Graphic design is an excellent career; it's fun, and it also pays well.

1. I am writing you this letter to let you know how totally awesome it was to meet you the other day at the interview I had with you.

2. I also wanted to take this opportunity to thank you after the fact for taking the time out of your busy day to interview me for the job at your company.

3. As far as I'm concerned, Nadler & Lattimore seems like a wicked cool place to work, and the job seems truly mint and right up my alley.

4. I have to say that I think I have good qualifications for the job in question, due to the fact that I have taken some courses in graphic design and advertising.

5. Based on the description you were kind enough to give me pertaining to the position, I know that I could perform at an unbelievable level as a summer intern, leaving no stone unturned in the performance of my duties and responsibilities.

6. I think it is fair to say that for me, the job would be nothing less than the opportunity of a lifetime, a dream come true—which is what I told you already at the interview.

(continued)

7. I also wanted to inform you that I have made phone contact with all the folks I gave you as references, just to let them know that you might be calling them sometime in the foreseeable future to check me out, so to speak.

_____

8. Please do not wait to let me know if it turns out that you have any other questions pertaining to my experience and background.

_____

9. As for me, I'll just be chillin' as I wait to hear from you about whether or not you decided that I'm your man.

_____

10. Once again, it was nice of you to interview me, and I thank you for your time from the bottom of my heart.

_____

Chapter 34: Commonly Confused Words—Avoiding Mistakes with Sound-Alikes

34–1: Using the Right Word (1)

In the following sentences, underline the correct word from the choices in parentheses.

EXAMPLE

Parents have to decide what is (<u>right</u>, write) for their children because adults know better (<u>than</u>, then) kids do.

1. I need some good (advice, advise), so I thought I would (right, write) you this letter.

2. When I'm feeling confused, (its, it's) often helpful for me to put my thoughts down on a (peace, piece) of paper.

3. I really don't have anyone else I can turn to (accept, except) my sister, (who's, whose) children (are, our) much older (than, then) mine.

4. But in the (passed, past), she and I have often disagreed on how to raise (are, our) kids, so I don't think she's the (right, write) person to (advice, advise) me this time.

5. My problem is that (their, there, they're) is a girl in my daughter's first-grade class (who's, whose) always inviting Anna over (to, too, two) play.

6. Anna (use, used) to play with Kate, but (than, then) she told me that she really didn't want to anymore, either at (are, our) apartment or at (their, there, they're) house.

7. I believe in the (principal, principle) that you should (of, have) the (right, write) to decide who (your, you're) friends (are, our)—even if (your, you're) only seven.

8. So I don't think (its, it's) fair to force my daughter to play with Kate, whether or not I understand or approve (of, have) Anna's reasons for disliking her.

9. However, my (conscience, conscious) is bothered by deception, (to, too), particularly when I'm the one (who's, whose) doing the deceiving.

10. I (know, no) I'll never (have, of) any (piece, peace) (have, of) mind until I (quiet, quit, quite) lying (to, too) Kate's mother, Diane.

(continued)

11. Well, maybe (its, it's) not (quite, quiet) lying, but I (use, used) to make up phony excuses for Anna whenever Diane called.

12. I kept saying Anna was busy or sick, instead (have, of) just sitting down with Diane (an, and) telling her the unpleasant truth.

13. At first, I wasn't really (conscience, conscious) that I was misleading her, because the situation was so (knew, new).

14. I guess I was simply trying to (by, buy) some time, hoping I could persuade Anna (to, too, two) change her (mine, mind).

15. (Than, Then) I'd find myself getting annoyed with Diane for not taking the hint, even (though, through) I (knew, new) I was giving her mixed signals.

16. I was trying (to, too, two) avoid having (a, an) awkward conversation vaguely agreeing that the (to, too, two) girls would get together some other time.

17. When Diane calls again, I definitely don't want to (accept, except) another invitation, but I also don't want to hurt her feelings or (loose, lose) her friendship.

18. I should (have, of) just been honest with her from the very beginning, but I guess I was afraid (have, of) how the truth would (affect, effect) her—(an, and) Kate (to, too).

19. I thought it would be kinder to tell (a, an) little white lie (than, then) to come (right, write) out (an, and) say, "My daughter doesn't like (your, you're) daughter."

20. I (suppose, supposed) that I should try to (fine, find) a good time to (set, sit) down with Diane (an, and) tell her the truth.

34–2: Using the Right Word (2)

In the following sentences, correct any words that are used incorrectly. Some sentences may contain more than one error.

EXAMPLE

Sometimes ~~their~~ *there* are things about ~~you're~~ *your* friends that you have to simply ~~except.~~ *accept*

1. Do you no anyone whose always giving you advise whether your asking for it or not?

2. I use to be friends with someone like that, an I just accepted the situation.

3. Elena thought she had the write to tell me what to do about everything, and that was the basis of are relationship.

4. We would be talking about something going on in my life, but than she would interrupt me too start talking about her own supposedly similar experience.

5. One time when we were on the phone, I counted twenty-to times that Elena cut me off before I was threw with my sentence.

6. She probably wasn't conscience of what she was doing, or of the affect her behavior was having on me, but buy the end of the conversation, I could of screamed.

7. I suddenly realized that Elena wasn't listening to me; she was simply waiting to talk about herself or to offer me her next peace of unwelcome advice.

8. Their is only so much of that kind of "friendship" I can except—it's just not worth the trouble.

9. Though eventually I quit talking to Elena about anything except her new boyfriend, she never even noticed how quite I had become during are conversations.

10. Then I started thinking about how it would feel to loose Elena's friendship, and I suddenly new that I wouldn't mine at all.

Chapter 35: Spelling—Using the Right Letters

35–1: Using the Six Spelling Rules (1)

In the following sentences, choose the correct spelling from the choices in parentheses. You may want to refer to the six spelling rules explained in Chapter 35.

EXAMPLE

Sometimes I have trouble in school because I act a little too (<u>conceited</u>, concieted) in class.

1. I (believe, beleive) I did well on the English paper I wrote last week.

2. I'm (assumeing, assuming) that I didn't make any spelling mistakes, even though I was (hurrying, hurriing) to turn it in on time.

3. (Luckily, Luckyly), my girlfriend proofread a rough draft and caught a few errors that I then (corrected, correctted) in my final version.

4. I had (omited, omitted) the letter *e* in forming the plural of the word *potato*, and I had (flipped, fliped) the letters *e* and *i* in the word (*acheive*, *achieve*).

5. Until I started checking everything in the dictionary, I (useed, used) to be so (worried, worryed) whenever I (submited, submitted) an assignment.

6. My papers always came back from the teacher with comments (saing, saying) that (sloppyness, sloppiness) was my main problem.

7. My teacher, Professor Bauer, grades us based on our writing (portfolios, portfolioes), and she expects to see a lot of (improvment, improvement) during the semester.

8. She doesn't care if you wear a nose ring or are covered with (tattoos, tatooes)—she just can't stand (laziness, lazyness).

9. I can't (concieve, conceive) of a more (encourageing, encouraging) teacher than Professor Bauer, and I'm (hopeful, hopful) that I'll be able to take another class with her.

10. This year at graduation, she (clapped, claped) and (cheerred, cheered) when two of her former students gave (speeches, speechs).

35–2: Using the Six Spelling Rules (2)

In the following sentences, correct any misspelled words. You may want to refer to the six spelling rules in Chapter 35.

EXAMPLE

When my sister got her own apartment and moved out of the house, I
begged
~~beged~~ my mother to let me get a cat.
^

1. My sister is allergic to cats and to dogs, so we definitly could not get a cat while she lived at home.

2. Since she moved out, I've been convinceing my mother that we should get a cat.

3. When I first brought up the subject, my mother said that she prefered dogs to cats.

4. Since I don't like dogs very much, I couldn't beleive my ears.

5. Dogs are far more troublsome than cats, I told her.

6. Cats are also much cleanner animals than dogs.

7. I tried to persuade my mother that she would be much happyer if she didn't have to get up early every day to walk a dog.

8. When I get home from class and then have to go right to work, I know that I won't feel like offerring to walk a dog.

9. I reminded her of how our nieghbor's dog barks every night and keeps everyone awake.

10. Eventually, my mother said that we didn't really need to have an arguement—she wanted a cat all along!

35–3: Using the Six Spelling Rules (3)

In the following sentences, correct any misspelled words. You may refer to the six spelling rules in Chapter 35.

EXAMPLE

My mother and I decided to get a cat, but ~~niether~~ *neither* of us wanted to buy one from a pet store.

1. Both my mother and I had heard storys about pet stores mistreating animals.

2. Besides, we both knew that we could not afford thier prices.

3. There are lots of animal shelteres that rescue abandoned and unwanted animals.

4. By making a donation to the shelter, you can adopt one of these animals, which might otherwise be put to sleep.

5. My mother and I scheduleed a time to visit the shelters together.

6. We both were hopeing to find a kitten.

7. As soon as we entered the first shelter, however, I spoted a big, fluffy, adult gray cat.

8. I don't know what happenned, but I just knew that he was the cat I wanted.

9. We were able to take him out of his cage, and we found that he was very freindly.

10. My mother admited that she too had immediately chosen that cat, so we adopted him and brought him home.

35–4: Correcting Spelling Mistakes (1)

In the following sentences, find and correct any spelling mistakes. You may want to refer to the list of commonly misspelled words in Chapter 35.

EXAMPLE

My parents ~~usualy~~ *usually* mind ~~there~~ *their* own ~~busness~~ *business* and let me make my own decisions—but not always.

1. During my sophmore year in college, I decided that I wanted to become a high school mathematics teacher.

2. My carreer choice definately came as a great surprize to my parents and freinds, and it has caused alot of arguements.

3. My father was incredibly dissappointed that I didn't want to go into the family busness—a jewlry store.

4. My mother probly assumed that I would become a secretery or work in a conveneince store untill I got marryed and had kids.

5. In my opinion, my parents have never shown much confidence in my inteligence or judgment.

6. As a child, I never recieved any encouragment for my schoolwork, since I was percieved as a good athleet but a poor student.

7. I was especialy aweful at arithemetic, and by the second grade, I allready felt anxious and embarassed every time I had to anser a question in class.

8. By the eighth grade, I was convinced that I would never acheive anything in life—that I was just not maent to suceed.

9. All that changed when I got to college and finally began to analize my strengths and intrests in a supportive envirment.

10. My adviser doesn't think it's wierd that I want to pursue a job in teaching; in fact, she sincerely believes that I will be an excellant role model for kids who have had similar school experiences.

35–5: Correcting Spelling Mistakes (2)

In the following sentences, correct any misspelled words. You may want to refer to the six spelling rules and the list of commonly misspelled words in Chapter 35.

EXAMPLE

My mother and I were both happy with our new cat, but we were ~~sur-prized~~ *surprised* to find that we could not stop thinking about the other animals we had seen in the shelter.

1. Untill we had gone to the shelter to adopt a cat, niether of us had thought much about how many abandoned and stray animals there are in the city.

2. I tryed to discribe to my sister how sad some of the animals in the shelter looked that day.

3. I am sure that animals can feel sadness and lonelyness the same way people do.

4. As soon as we saw how quickly and happyly our cat, Fluffy Gus, made himself at home, I regreted that we hadn't adopted another animal as well.

5. I didn't want my mother to think I was disapointed with our new cat, so I didn't mention my feelings to her.

6. About a week after we got the cat, my mother told me that it was neccessary for us too go back to the shelter.

7. I became worryed thinking that somthing was wrong with Fluffy Gus.

8. The cat was fine, but my mother had allready decided that we should adopt a dog from the shelter, too.

9. So we went back to the shelter, and we came home with the prettyest little black and white mutt.

10. The dog and the cat imediately became friends—but know my mother and I have to agree on a name for the dog.

Chapter 36: Commas

36–1: Using Commas in a Series

In the following sentences, add commas where they are needed in the series. If a sentence is already correct, write **OK** next to it.

EXAMPLE

Babysitting a newborn can be fun, enlightening, and exhausting.

1. Studies show that newborn babies immediately begin to explore their environment by using their senses of sight hearing touch smell and taste.

2. Yet, it is difficult to tell what newborns can perceive because they are often sleeping dozing or crying.

3. Researchers test what newborns can see by showing them objects or pictures and then observing their responses.

4. They film their eye movements and measure changes in their heart rates sucking and sweating.

5. Research has shown that newborns can see large objects that are close to them but not small objects that are far away.

6. A newborn sees poorly because its brain eyes and nerves have not yet fully developed.

7. At first infants can focus only on lines corners and the edges of objects.

8. Patterns with large shapes clear outlines and high contrast are what they see best.

9. Every parent grandparent or babysitter knows that infants love to look at people's faces.

10. In one study babies as young as an hour old could tell the difference between a simple drawing of a face and several other patterns.

36–2: Using Commas in a Compound Sentence

In the following compound sentences, add commas where they are needed.

EXAMPLE

A strong desire to succeed can take you far, but it can also cause you a lot of stress.

1. Some people are more motivated to achieve excellence than other people so psychologists are interested in understanding why.

2. People with high achievement motivation have a strong desire to master tasks and they experience great satisfaction when they achieve success.

3. In one experiment, researchers gave children a test designed to measure their need for achievement and then they asked these children to play a ring-toss game.

4. Those children who had scored low on the test stood so close to the target that they always scored or they stood so far away that they always missed.

5. In other words, they succeeded at an unchallenging task or they failed at an impossible one.

6. In contrast, the children who had scored well on the test stood far enough away from the target to make the game challenging but they did not stand so far away as to guarantee their own failure.

7. Psychologists believe that people with high achievement motivation tend to set challenging but realistic goals for themselves and they are willing to take risks to achieve those goals.

8. They experience intense satisfaction from success but they are not discouraged by failure if they feel they have tried their best.

9. People with low achievement motivation also prefer success to failure but they usually experience relief at *not* having failed rather than pleasure or pride at having succeeded.

10. They do not tend to seek out feedback from critics nor do they struggle with a problem instead of quitting in the face of failure.

36–3: Using Commas after Introductory Word Groups

In the following sentences, add commas where they are needed after introductory words or word groups.

EXAMPLE

Within the past few years,the issue of violence on television has come to be recognized as a serious problem.

1. According to a recent study children can unlearn violent behavior in less than six months.

2. Published in *The Journal of the American Medical Association* the study helps disprove the idea that nothing can be done to stop violence among America's youth.

3. For Americans between the ages of fifteen and twenty-four violence is one of the leading causes of death.

4. Financed by the Centers for Disease Control and Prevention the study involved 790 second- and third-graders at twelve schools in the state of Washington.

5. Over a period of sixteen to twenty weeks about half of these students were taught a violence-prevention curriculum.

6. During the study the behavior of this group of students was compared with the behavior of the students who did not take the course.

7. Six months after the program ended students who had taken the course engaged in about thirty fewer aggressive acts per day at school than the students in the other group.

8. Significantly aggressive behavior (such as hitting, kicking, and shoving) increased in those children who did not take the course.

9. Developed in 1986 by a Seattle educator the Second Step antiviolence program consists of weekly or twice-weekly sessions lasting about half an hour each.

10. Widely used in American and Canadian schools the program is designed to teach empathy, problem-solving, and anger management to preschool through ninth-grade students.

36–4: Using Commas to Set Off Appositives and Interrupters

In the following sentences, add commas where they are needed to set off appositives and interrupters.

EXAMPLE

The exploration of outer space, once strongly supported by the public, is now less important to the average person.

1. Thousands of "snowballs" from outer space are hitting Earth's atmosphere every day according to scientists at the 1997 meeting of the American Geophysical Union in Baltimore.

2. Over billions of years they reported this bombardment of cosmic slush has added vast amounts of water to Earth's atmosphere and oceans.

3. These extraterrestrial snowballs made up of ice and cosmic dust may have played a key role in nurturing life on this planet and perhaps elsewhere in the solar system.

4. They are about forty feet in diameter the size of a small house.

5. These small, cometlike objects unlike large comets are extremely hard to see because they break up into fragments and then vaporize.

6. Astronomers and physicists however have speculated about their existence since 1986.

7. Dr. Louis A. Frank a physicist at the University of Iowa first theorized about them to explain the dark spots he observed in images of Earth's sunlit atmosphere.

8. Dr. Frank noticed these spots or atmospheric holes while analyzing data from NASA's *Dynamics Explorer 1* satellite.

9. NASA's *Polar* satellite launched in February 1996 produced more detailed images of these atmospheric holes.

10. Many scientists now believe that these snowballs are hitting Earth's outer atmosphere at an incredible rate of five to thirty a minute or up to 43,000 a day.

36–5: Using Commas with Adjective Clauses

In the following sentences, add commas around or before adjective clauses where they are needed. Remember that if the adjective clause is essential to the meaning of the sentence, you should not use commas. Some sentences may contain more than one adjective clause. If a sentence is already correct, write **OK** next to it.

EXAMPLE

Many writers use their own experiences as the basis for their works, which can then reveal a lot about the author's life.

1. Bernard Malamud who was born in Brooklyn in 1914 wrote novels and short stories about Jewish immigrant life.

2. His parents who were Russian immigrants owned a struggling neighborhood grocery store.

3. In fact, the grocer character who appears in several of Malamud's works was modeled after his own father.

4. A baseball player who is endowed with supernatural abilities is the hero of Malamud's first novel.

5. *The Natural* which was made into a movie starring Robert Redford is considered one of the greatest baseball novels of all time.

6. Malamud's first short-story collection which won the National Book Award is called *The Magic Barrel*.

7. In the title story, a young man who is studying to become a rabbi falls in love with a woman who turns out to be his marriage broker's daughter.

8. The novel that earned Malamud both the National Book Award and the Pulitzer Prize is *The Fixer*.

9. This novel which is set in Russia is about a Jewish handyman who is falsely accused of ritual murder.

10. Malamud who died in 1986 is considered one of the greatest contemporary American fiction writers.

36–6: Using Commas in Other Situations

In the following sentences, add commas where they are needed. If a sentence is already correct, write **OK** next to it.

EXAMPLE

Even when I think one of my relatives is making the wrong choice, I often say, "It's your decision," because none of them ever listens to me.

1. Two years ago, my parents decided to sell their house in St. Paul Minnesota and retire to Florida.

2. During a vacation they had stopped in Lake Worth, Florida to visit my father's cousin Lila, and they decided they liked the area.

3. On December 29 1995 my mother called to tell me that they had put down a deposit on a house that was going to be built in a new development near Lila's condominium.

4. When I heard the news, I said "Mom have you and Dad gone out of your minds? Isn't this kind of sudden?"

5. "Yes it is" she replied "but I think your father and I have made a wise decision."

6. Both my parents have always insisted that they would never retire to a place like Florida or Phoenix Arizona, because they enjoy the winter.

7. My father grew up in Madison Wisconsin and moved to St. Paul in 1952.

8. My mother grew up in Minneapolis and moved to St. Paul when she married my father in June 1958.

9. "Peter we're putting the Carter Avenue house on the market this May," my mother calmly informed me, "and we expect to be moving to Florida by September or October 1996."

10. On October 3 1996 my parents moved to a small stucco house at 61 Rosewood Lane Green Acres Florida 33463.

Chapter 37: Apostrophes

37–1: Using Apostrophes to Show Ownership

Edit the following sentences by adding apostrophes where they are needed to show ownership and by crossing out any apostrophes that are used incorrectly or positioned incorrectly in the word.

EXAMPLE

Animal rights is a big issue among students in my state's high school's.

1. There is a growing rebellion in the nations high school's against dissecting animals in biology class.

2. More and more students' feel that dissection is inhumane and unnecessary.

3. Until recently, a students' refusal to dissect has usually resulted in a lower grade or other academic penalty.

4. However, California, Florida, Maryland, New York, and Pennsylvania have passed laws' that allow students to complete alternative science assignments if they oppose dissection.

5. Other states' are considering legislation modeled on these states laws.

6. It was fifteen-year-old Jennifer Grahams refusal to dissect a frog in 1987 that caused her state's lawmakers to debate the issue.

7. When Grahams school would not allow her to complete an alternative assignment, she sued the school district over it's policy.

8. The California courts ruling stated that schools could require students to dissect a frog, but only if it's death was from natural causes.

9. Grahams lawsuit led state lawmakers in California to pass the nations first laws protecting students who oppose dissection.

10. Because Jasmine Dixons reasons for opposing dissection are environmental as well as humanitarian, her Indianapolis high school is allowing her to fulfill her' science requirement by taking an environmental class instead of biology.

37–2: Using Apostrophes in Contractions and with Letters, Numbers, and Time

Edit the following sentences by adding apostrophes where they are needed and by crossing out any apostrophes that are used incorrectly or positioned incorrectly in the word.

EXAMPLE

My older sister said she'll try to come to my graduation ceremony, but I'm not sure if she can really make it in time.

1. At last years graduation ceremony, I could'nt believe how long it took to hand out all the diplomas.

2. I wasnt surprised that the president of the college called the graduating students' up to the stage according to the first letter of their last names.

3. But I would'nt have guessed that it would take half an hour' for just the *A*s, *B*s, *C*s, and *D*s to get their diplomas.

4. Sitting in the hot sun, I started to realize that it would take about two hour's time to get through the rest of the alphabet.

5. For some letters, student's were filing up to the stage by the 20s and 30s, but for the *Q*s, *X*s, and *Z*s, students were going up in 2s and 3s.

6. I think its going to take even longer to hand out diplomas to this years' graduating class, but well find out in a weeks' time.

7. Im pretty sure that the Class of 1998 has about fifty more students than the Class of 1997, and it's members are more diverse in age and ethnic background.

8. Ive heard that lots of students are planning to wear 98s' all over their caps and gowns.

9. My parents sent me an enormous graduation card covered with *X*s and *O*s; my boyfriend didnt know that its customary to use those letters to stand for kisses and hugs.

10. Its hard to believe that in a few month's time, I'll be a college graduate starting my new job as a teachers aide.

Chapter 38: Quotation Marks

38–1: Punctuating Direct and Indirect Quotations

Edit the following sentences by adding quotation marks and commas where they are needed and by crossing out quotation marks and commas that are used incorrectly. Also correct any other punctuation mistakes you notice. If a sentence is already correct, write **OK** next to it.

EXAMPLE

"They are too dangerous," I said when my brother told me that he wants to get a motorcycle.

1. Darryl called his parents from the hospital emergency room to tell them that, "he had just been in an accident."

2. I was riding my bike down New Scotland Avenue, he explained when his mother picked up the phone. A guy who had just parked his van in front of the Bagel Baron opened his door.

3. Darryl told his mother that he had hit the door of the van and gone flying off his bicycle.

4. "Luckily, I was wearing a helmet, he said or I'd probably be dead."

5. Are you all right"? interrupted Darryl's mother. "What hospital are you at"?

6. "I hurt my shoulder, but I'm not sure how badly because I haven't seen a doctor yet." replied Darryl. "I'm at St. Peter's.

7. "George" his mother called to his father, pick up the phone in the kitchen. Darryl hurt his shoulder in a bicycle accident."

8. Darryl said, he had to get off the phone because the doctor was ready to examine him.

9. "Okay, honey," said his mother. She assured him that they would be at the hospital in ten minutes.

10. Don't let them do anything to you until we get there and talk to the doctor! insisted Darryl's father.

38–2: Using Quotation Marks for Direct Quotations and Certain Titles

Edit the following sentences by adding quotation marks and commas where they are needed around direct quotations and titles and by crossing out quotation marks and commas that are used incorrectly.

EXAMPLE

Whenever someone asks me which poets I like, I tell them that "Anne Sexton is my favorite."

1. I think you would enjoy reading some poems by Martín Espada, my English teacher told me during our conference.

2. I'm going to lend you a book called *City of Coughing and Dead Radiators* she said.

3. "I'll take a look," I replied but I really don't like poetry very much."

4. I had a student last year who announced, I hate poetry, but he changed his mind after reading this book, replied my teacher.

5. A week later I told Professor Macarrulla that "I too had changed my mind about poetry after reading Espada's book."

6. Which poems did you like the best? Professor Macarrulla asked me.

7. I told her that my favorites were, Borofels and Day of the Dead on Wortman Avenue.

8. I explained that "Borofels reminded me of my own experience growing up in Brooklyn with Puerto Rican parents who spoke very little English."

9. Professor Macarrulla said that her favorite poem in the book was, Who Burns for the Perfection of Paper.

10. "I like that poem, she explained because it reminds me that no matter how much success you achieve in life, you should never forget your working-class roots.

Chapter 39: Other Punctuation

39–1: Using Colons, Semicolons, Parentheses, Dashes, and Hyphens (1)

Edit the following sentences by adding colons, semicolons, parentheses, dashes, and hyphens where needed. You may also need to change some commas to semicolons.

EXAMPLE

Chemistry‾ the subject I almost failed in high school‾ has always fascinated me.

1. Scientists at Cornell University have discovered something that seems too good to be true a strain of bacteria that can break down some of the most toxic chemicals in polluted water.

2. Dr. Stephen H. Zinder and his colleagues have found this pollution fighting organism in sewage sludge the solid matter produced during sewage treatment.

3. This strain of bacteria breaks down two of the most common pollutants of groundwater the chemical compounds trichloroethene and tetrachloroethene.

4. Both chlorinated compounds are solvents that are used in such products as glue, paint remover, and cleaning solutions for clothing, machinery, brakes, engines, and electronic parts.

5. These two water polluting solvents can damage the human nervous system they are also suspected carcinogens cancer causing substances.

6. They are major groundwater pollutants because for years they were handled carelessly spilled on the ground, poured down drains, and dumped into landfills before their danger was clearly understood.

7. These solvents seep hundreds of feet into the earth and then dissolve gradually as groundwater the main source of drinking water for half the U.S. population flows by.

8. Scientists have known for about fifteen years that bacteria can sometimes change these chlorinated compounds into ethylene the harmless gas that causes fruit to ripen.

9. However, the exact chemical process as well as the conditions necessary for it to occur have been poorly understood until now.

10. The Cornell scientists have figured out that these bacteria break down the solvents by using them the way people use oxygen for the cycle of biochemical reactions known as respiration breathing.

39–2: Using Colons, Semicolons, Parentheses, Dashes, and Hyphens (2)

Edit the following sentences by adding colons, semicolons, parentheses, dashes, and hyphens or by correcting errors in their usage. If a sentence is already correct, write **OK** next to it.

EXAMPLE

There have recently been many movies adapted from classic works of literature: *Sense and Sensibility*, *The Scarlet Letter*, *The Crucible*, and *Portrait of a Lady*.

1. The 1993 movie *Schindler's List* directed by Steven Spielberg won the Academy Award for Best Picture in 1994.

2. The movie tells the true story of an unlikely hero of the Holocaust; a German factory owner from Czechoslovakia who saved thousands of Jews from almost certain death at the hands of the Nazis.

3. This unlikely hero was: Oskar Schindler, drinker, gambler, womanizer, and black market profiteer.

4. The movie features an extraordinary cast Liam Neeson as Schindler, Ben Kingsley as Itzhak Stern, Schindler's Jewish business adviser and friend, and Ralph Fiennes as Amon Goeth, the brutal and corrupt commander of a slave labor camp in Nazi-occupied Poland.

5. This Oscar winning-movie was shown—on television—in February 1997 without commercial interruption; only a few minutes of the original three and a half hour film were cut by Spielberg himself for the Ford sponsored broadcast on NBC.

6. The TV broadcast of *Schindler's List* was viewed by sixty five million people; more than twice the number who saw the big screen version in movie theaters.

7. Many viewers probably did not realize that the movie was based on a 1982 book (originally published in England as: *Schindler's Ark*) by the Australian writer Thomas Keneally.

8. Keneally first heard about Oskar Schindler when he was shopping at a Beverly Hills luggage store owned by one of the Jews whom Schindler saved: Leopold Pfefferberg.

9. Keneally's book won England's 1982 Booker Prize for Fiction the nation's best known literary award.

10. Keneally's victory generated a huge controversy in England; because in the preface the author insists that his book is not a work of fiction he describes it instead as a "documentary novel" that tells a true story.

Chapter 40: Capitalization—Using Capital Letters

40-1: Capitalizing (1)

Edit the following sentences by capitalizing as needed.

EXAMPLE

$\underset{I}{\text{I}}$n $\underset{N}{\text{n}}$ew $\underset{Y}{\text{y}}$ork $\underset{C}{\text{c}}$ity you can probably find people from almost every

region of the world—$\underset{E}{\text{e}}$urope, the $\underset{M}{\text{m}}$iddle $\underset{E}{\text{e}}$ast, $\underset{A}{\text{a}}$sia, $\underset{A}{\text{a}}$frica—and plenty

of native $\underset{N}{\text{n}}$ew $\underset{Y}{\text{y}}$orkers, too.

1. according to an article in *the new york times magazine*, more and more americans are rejecting their parents' religion.

2. in an article entitled "choosing my religion," stephen j. dubner analyzes a trend that affects him on a personal level.

3. dubner, who is an editor at the magazine, grew up in a large catholic family.

4. his parents, however, both grew up jewish and converted to catholicism when they were in their twenties.

5. his mother, florence greenglass, and his father, solomon dubner, were both born in brooklyn, the children of russian and polish immigrants.

6. when florence greenglass was baptized a roman catholic, she chose "veronica" as her baptismal name; solomon chose the name "paul."

7. they were married on march 2, 1946, at st. brigid's catholic church in brooklyn; none of their families attended the wedding.

8. stephen dubner, the youngest of eight children, grew up on a farm in upstate new york, near the town of duanesburg.

9. his family was devoutly catholic, but by the time dubner left home for college, he had become uncomfortable with his religion.

10. under the guidance of his friend ivan, dubner began exploring judaism and learning hebrew while he was in graduate school.

40–2: Capitalizing (2)

Edit the following sentences by correcting errors in capitalization.

EXAMPLE

I appreciate the architecture of all different *r*Religions' places of worship, such as Jewish *t*Temples, *C*Christian churches, and Islamic mosques.

1. According to Dean Hoge, a Sociology Professor at Catholic university in washington, D.C., switching religions is more common in America today than it has ever been in history.

2. In their book *One nation under God,* Barry a. kosmin and seymour p. Lachman estimate that 30 percent of Americans switch religions or denominations during their lifetimes.

3. Most of these people switch from one Protestant Denomination to another, but some changes are more dramatic.

4. Kosmin and lachman, who surveyed 113,000 people for their book, concluded that the most common reason for switching religions is intermarriage—marrying someone of a different Faith.

5. In his *New york times magazine* article "Choosing my Religion" (march 31, 1996), Stephen J. dubner explores his own switch from catholicism to judaism, but he also spotlights several other young americans who have changed religions.

6. Daniel Dunn grew up a congregationalist but became a catholic after he almost died in a serious water-skiing accident.

7. Judith Anderson grew up in a jewish family in Teaneck, New jersey, but she is now a buddhist.

8. Like many jews who practice buddhism, Anderson has not renounced her Judaism; instead, she feels that she has added another Spiritual layer to her life.

9. Fatima shama is the Daughter of a devoutly Catholic brazilian mother and a muslim palestinian father who isn't very religious.

10. She grew up Catholic in the bronx but began practicing a liberal form of islam during College.

Answers to 21–1

1. *The Perfect Storm.*
2. it.
3. book.
4. one.
5. "perfect storm".
6. *Andrea Gail.*
7. boat.
8. messages.
9. crew.
10. *Andrea Gail.*

Answers to 21–2

1. helping + main verb.
2. linking verb.
3. action verb.
4. helping + main verb.
5. action verb.
6. action verb.
7. action verb.
8. helping + main verb.
9. linking verb.
10. helping + main verb.

Answers to 21–3

1. I. 2. C. 3. C. 4. I. 5. C. 6. C. 7. I.
8. C. 9. I. 10. C.

Answers to 21–4

POSSIBLE REVISIONS

1. The wonderful Harry Potter books are a series of stories written by J.K. Rowling for children of all ages.
2. The books tell the mysterious story of a boy who has magical powers and attends a school for wizards.
3. Interestingly, J.K. Rowling's life story has become as well known as that of the character she writes about, Harry Potter.
4. Rowling was a struggling single mother and a welfare recipient in Edinburgh, Scotland, when she began to write the Harry Potter stories.
5. She wrote the first book while her daughter napped soundly in the afternoons.
6. Her dramatic story has been an inspiration to people who mistakenly think that authors must live a certain kind of lifestyle.
7. She has proven that all you really need are great ideas and determination.
8. Recently, bookstores eagerly stayed open until midnight on the night that *Harry Potter and the Goblet of Fire* was first sold.
9. Children waited in line for hours to gleefully purchase Harry's latest adventures.
10. The hefty book was one of the most anticipated publications in history.

Answers to 21–5

1. Subject: travel writing. Prepositional phrase: for a newspaper.
2. Subject: journalists. Prepositional phrases: with little experience; without having to pay; for plane fare or hotels.
3. Subject: friend. Prepositional phrases: in her first year, of writing; for the *St. Louis Post-Dispatch;* to Mexico and Peru.
4. Subject: journey. Prepositional phrases: across the two countries; at times.
5. Subject: many. Prepositional phrase: of the cities.
6. Subject: assignments. Prepositional phrases: in depth; about the places.
7. Subject: number. Prepositional phrases: of sites; in five days; of three weeks.
8. Subject: some. Prepositional phrases: on the other hand; of the finest restaurants; in Mexico City and Lima; on her itinerary.
9. Subject: descriptions. Prepositional phrase: of the best.
10. Subject: part. Prepositional phrase: of the job; about her experiences; upon her return home.

Answers to 22–1

1. In 1976, twenty-one-year-old Steven Jobs cofounded Apple Computer, Inc., in his family's garage.
2. In 1984, the team Jobs led created the Apple Macintosh computer, with its user-friendly "point and click" operating system.

3. Yet one year later, Jobs was forced out of his own company by the board of directors.
4. Over the next few years, the Mac revolutionized the computer world.
5. Apple's rival, the Microsoft Corporation, modeled its Windows operating system on the Mac.
6. After leaving Apple, Jobs started a computer company called NeXT that developed a cutting-edge new operating system.
7. A British computer programmer created the World Wide Web on the NeXT system.
8. In 1986, Jobs bought Pixar, a small computer animation studio, from the film director George Lucas.
9. Pixar created the animation for the 1995 hit movie *Toy Story*.
10. In late 1996, Jobs stunned the computer industry by selling NeXT and its operating system to his old company, Apple.

Answers to 22–2

1. The zoologist Frans de Waal has spent the past twenty-five years studying how apes and monkeys behave in captivity.
2. He is a professor of primate behavior at Emory University in Atlanta, where he is also a researcher at the Yerkes Regional Primate Research Center.
3. While many scientists have emphasized the role of aggression in animal behavior, de Waal stresses the importance of animal kindness and caring.
4. Although animals clearly have rivals, he believes they also have friends.
5. Each group of chimpanzees has a leader, though de Waal thinks it is the one who makes the best friendships and alliances rather than the one who is the most aggressive.
6. His research on animal relationships has shown that capuchin monkeys will repeatedly find ways to share food when they are separated from each other by a mesh screen.
7. This sharing is a deliberate choice because the monkeys share only with monkeys they like.

8. De Waal believes that the stereotype of the killer-ape is harmful, since it suggests that human nature is essentially violent and cruel.
9. He argues that morality is an outgrowth of our natural instincts, which are automatic responses that all people have.
10. If we want to understand what makes us naturally aggressive, we also have to understand what makes us naturally caring.

Answers to 22–3

1. Sharon Bearor was sitting in a doctor's office at Massachusetts General Hospital listening to Dr. Allen Lapey explain her son's options.
2. Suffering from cystic fibrosis, nineteen-year-old Spencer Bean needed two new lungs.
3. However, the long waiting list for an organ donation meant Spencer might die waiting for a pair of lungs to become available.
4. Reaching the top of the list, he might also be too sick to go through with the transplant operation.
5. Explaining that there was another option, Dr. Lapey told Spencer and Sharon about an experimental new medical procedure.
6. Doctors could replace a patient's diseased lungs using healthy lung tissue from two living relatives.
7. Realizing that Spencer might die without their help, Sharon and her sister Jean decided to donate part of their lungs.
8. Some people are opposed to living-donor transplants, believing it's unethical to risk harming a healthy person.
9. They also argue that some people might feel pressured to donate organs, fearing their family's anger if they say no.
10. Ignoring complicated questions of medical ethics, Sharon and Jean simply did what they thought was right.

Answers to 22–4

1. Arthur Caplan is a professor of bioethics, the study of ethical issues relating to medicine, health care, and science.

2. He analyzes complex moral questions, such as whether society should allow doctor-assisted suicide.

3. Bioethical issues are often featured on TV hospital shows like *E.R.* and *Chicago Hope.*

4. Caplan thinks these shows do an okay job of exploring certain bioethical issues, including the question of whether to give an alcoholic a liver transplant.

5. However, he feels they don't pay enough attention to other kinds of issues, particularly those relating to money.

6. An episode of *Chicago Hope* was based on one of Caplan's actual cases, a heart transplant in which the doctors didn't know if they had to tell the patient they had dropped the heart on the floor.

7. Caplan believes that it is sometimes ethical to lie, especially if a life is at stake.

8. He thinks a doctor should lie to help a patient who is being pressured by family members, as in the case of someone who is refusing a blood transfusion for religious reasons.

9. A doctor should also give a phony medical excuse to a family member who doesn't want to donate a live organ, such as a kidney or lung.

10. Here the moral issue is free choice, not saving a life, as in the example of the blood transfusion.

Answers to 22–5

POSSIBLE REVISIONS

1. Some parents are so fed up with television programming that they want one thing from their families: They long for them to kick the TV habit.

2. Producer Linda Ellerbee once threw her TV set out of a second-story window to get her children's attention when they were watching television.

3. To appease her guilt later in the day, she went out to retrieve the television from her yard. To her amazement, when she plugged it in, it still worked.

4. To study the problem, the Annenberg Public Policy Center has conducted three studies.

5. Parents can use ratings attached to many programs and V-chip technology to block certain shows they don't want their children to see.

6. Few parents use either method, and most reported they felt powerless to control their children's viewing habits.

7. According to one researcher, parents have an important role to play. They should serve as examples of how much television is acceptable.

8. To give a child his or her own television solves many arguments about what to watch, but researchers suggest that this solution means that parents do not know how much television their child is watching.

9. One mother decided to unplug her television one night a week. She intended to show her family that they could survive without television.

10. She reported that everyone struggled, including herself. To keep everyone occupied and busy through the first few weeks, she used all her creative abilities planning activities.

Answers to 22–6

1. Have you ever wondered how a microwave oven cooks food without heating the plate?

2. A microwave is an electromagnetic wave ranging in frequency from around 1,000 to 300,000 megahertz (MHz).

3. An electromagnetic wave is a vibration resulting from the motion of positive and negative electrical charges.

4. There are many different kinds of electromagnetic waves, such as electric waves, radio waves, infrared radiation, visible light, ultraviolet radiation, X-rays, and gamma rays.

5. Microwaves cook food quickly by making the water molecules in the food vibrate at a rate of 2,450 million times per second.

6. This vibration absorbs energy from the surrounding electromagnetic field, causing the food to heat up.
7. The plate and utensils don't get hot because their materials don't absorb energy from the magnetic field.
8. Since all the energy is absorbed by the food, microwave cooking is faster than regular cooking.
9. Many different materials are safe to use in a microwave oven, like china, glass, plastic, and paper.
10. But you should not use items made out of metal or wood when you microwave, to prevent damage to those items.

Answers to 22–7

1. Velcro was invented by the Swiss engineer George de Mestral after he took a walk in the woods with his dog.
2. Arriving back home, he noticed that his socks and his dog were covered with burrs.
3. De Mestral wanted to find out why burrs stick so well to certain materials, such as wool and fur.
4. Looking at his socks under the microscope, he discovered that tiny hooks on the ends of the burrs were caught in the wool's loops.
5. De Mestral figured out a way to copy this natural system of hooks and loops.
6. He wove nylon thread into a fabric containing densely packed little loops.
7. He cut the loops on some of the fabric to make half of each loop a hook.
8. De Mestral called this fabric Velcro, a contraction of the French words *velours* (velvet) and *crochet* (hook).
9. Although Velcro can be peeled apart quite easily, it has extremely high resistance to sideways forces.
10. Velcro has been used to prevent equipment, and even astronauts, from floating around in the space shuttle.

Answers to 23–1

1. Lead pencils don't really contain any lead. They're made out of graphite. **F**

2. Lead hasn't been used in pencils since the sixteenth century. It's a good thing because lead is poisonous. **CS**
3. The ancient Egyptians, Greeks, and Romans used small lead discs to make lines on sheets of papyrus. Then they wrote on the papyrus with ink and a brush. **CS**
4. During the fourteenth century European artists made drawings using rods of lead, zinc, or silver. The technique was called silverpoint. **F**
5. Wood-encased writing rods were used during the fifteenth century. They were the earliest pencils. **CS**
6. The modern pencil was developed in 1564. That's when graphite was discovered in Borrowdale, England. **F**
7. Graphite is a form of carbon. It's greasy and soft with a metallic luster. **F**
8. Pencil "lead" is made by mixing graphite with clay and water. Then the mixture is fed into a thin cylinder to create sticks. **CS**
9. More graphite in the mixture makes the pencil softer and blacker. More clay makes it harder and paler. **CS**
10. The sticks are cut into pencil-sized lengths. Then they are fired in a kiln at a temperature of about 2200°F (1200°C). **F**

Answers to 23–2

1. Jakob Dylan is the son of legendary folk-rock star Bob Dylan; he isn't sure if his father's fame has helped or hurt his own musical career.
2. The younger Dylan has finally become famous in his own right; his band, the Wallflowers, is suddenly very hot.
3. Two songs from their second album have become big hits; you can't turn on the radio without hearing "6th Avenue Heartache" or "One Headlight."
4. But the Wallflowers are not an overnight success story; they've been struggling to get noticed for seven years.
5. They released their first album in 1992; it didn't sell.

6. One reason is that Dylan's voice was mixed too low in the studio; another is that he wasn't willing to promote the album the way the record company wanted.
7. The band got out of its contract with Virgin Records; then they couldn't get signed by another label even though their new demo tape included the songs that eventually became hits.
8. Finally the Wallflowers signed with Interscope Records; they began working with producer T-Bone Burnett.
9. Burnett raised Dylan's voice in the sound mix; suddenly you could hear the lyrics.
10. Jakob Dylan's voice is not as distinctive as his father's; it seems to be the decisive factor in his band's recent success, however.

Answers to 23–3

POSSIBLE REVISIONS

1. Don't believe everything you learn about animals from Hollywood movies, or you might come away misinformed.
2. For example, the 1994 movie *Andre the Seal* is based on a true story about a New England harbor seal, but the title character is played by a California sea lion.
3. The real Andre was five feet long and weighed 250 pounds, but the sea lion actor is twice as big.
4. The decision to cast a solid-brown sea lion as a spotted gray seal may seem ridiculous, yet the filmmakers had their reasons.
5. Unlike sea lions, harbor seals don't have huge front flippers, so they can't scoot around very well.
6. Seals can't do cute tricks on land with human actors, for they spend most of their time in the water.
7. In the 1995 movie *Outbreak,* a monkey brings a deadly African virus to America, yet the monkey is actually played by a South American capuchin monkey.
8. That's because capuchins are more readily available than African monkeys, and they are easier to train.

9. You might assume that the 1988 movie *Gorillas in the Mist* portrays animals accurately, for it was filmed on location in Africa among a band of mountain gorillas.
10. But wild mother gorillas won't let humans touch their young, so in one scene a baby gorilla is really a chimpanzee in a gorilla suit.

Answers to 23–4

POSSIBLE REVISIONS

1. Kristin Hersh is a working mother, although she has a rather unusual job.
2. While Hersh is raising three kids, she is working as the lead singer and guitarist for the band Throwing Muses.
3. Her husband, Billy O'Connell, understands her unconventional career choice because he's the band's manager.
4. Hersh has combined rock and roll and motherhood since she had her first child at the age of nineteen.
5. Ten-year-old Dylan now lives with his father most of the year, though he spends vacations with his mother and stepfather.
6. When the band goes on tour next month, five-year-old Ryder and two-month-old Wyatt will be traveling with their parents.
7. Hersh thinks the rock world is beginning to change, although it is still uncommon to see children on the tour bus.
8. As more women performers are becoming mothers, more kids are being nursed backstage and rocked to sleep in dressing rooms.
9. Hersh and O'Connell only recently allowed Dylan and Ryder to watch their mom perform, since most shows are so loud and smoky.
10. The boys watched a smoke-free acoustic show when Hersh was pregnant with Wyatt.

Answers to 23–5

POSSIBLE REVISIONS

1. Nathan Kane began inventing when he was eighteen years old.

2. Kane wanted to create a dust-free environment in their Texas home because his father suffered from allergies.
3. Ten years later he won a $30,000 prize for young inventors. The award was presented by the Massachusetts Institute of Technology.
4. Kane is a graduate student at MIT; he is studying mechanical engineering.
5. He thought of the idea for one of his inventions while he was refinishing the floors in his parents' house.
6. It was very hot, so he was uncomfortable wearing a regular filter mask.
7. Kane invented a mask that supplies fresh air through a flexible hose. The hose is really a lightweight bellows.
8. Though bellows have been used for thousands of years, Kane came up with a better design.
9. He and a friend invented a TV remote control that's hard to lose and easy to pass around; it's built inside a foam rubber football.
10. Kane recently served as an adviser to a group of middle-school students as they designed solar-powered model cars.

Answers to 23–6

POSSIBLE REVISIONS

1. Tom Scott and Tom First began selling juice in 1989 when they were twenty-four years old.
2. They had been friends since freshman year in college, and they moved to the island of Nantucket soon after graduation.
3. Their business began as a floating juice bar in Nantucket Harbor; they sold glasses of homemade peach juice off the deck of their boat.
4. Soon Scott and First began bottling their juice by hand. The following summer it was being professionally packaged in New York and distributed throughout Nantucket, Martha's Vineyard, and Cape Cod.
5. Their juice is called Nantucket Nectars, but the name of their company is Nantucket Allserve.
6. Sales and production increased dramatically over the next few years, yet the company was still struggling to survive.
7. In 1993 an investor bought half the company for $500,000; that money allowed Scott and First to expand their markets and product line.
8. Although Scott and First have no formal business training, today Nantucket Allserve is one of the nation's fastest-growing private companies.
9. Their juice is sold in 30 states, and their company is worth $30 million.
10. While sales of Snapple and Veryfine juices have been declining, sales of Nantucket Nectars have increased by 6,482 percent in the last four years.

Answers to 24–1

1. Subject: region; verb: was. 2. Subject: it; verb: was. 3. Subject: blizzard; verb: has. 4. Subject: I; verb: don't. 5. Subject: schools; verb: are. 6. Subject: I; verb: have. 7. Subject: neighbors; verb: are. 8. Subject: family; verb: has. 9. Subject: people; verb: have. 10. Subject: I; verb: am.

Answers to 24–2

1. Prepositional phrase: in hiring practices; verb: is. 2. Prepositional phrase: of job applicants; verb: is. 3. Prepositional phrase: of comparison between hiring outcomes; verb: is. 4. Prepositional phrase: of orchestra hiring practices; verb: finds. 5. Prepositional phrase: throughout the country; verb: use. 6. Prepositional phrase: for a position with the orchestra; verb: perform. 7. Prepositional phrase: at major orchestras; verb: improves. 8. Prepositional phrase: of female musicians in the top five American orchestras; verb: is. 9. Prepositional phrase: of orchestras; verb: reports. 10. Prepositional phrase: to blind auditions; verb: explains.

Answers to 24–3

1. Dependent clause: that Indian women wear on their foreheads; verb: indicates. 2. Depen-

dent clause: which is known as a *bindi* or *pottu;* verb: represents.   3. Dependent clause: which was originally a simple red or maroon powdered circle; verb: has evolved.   4. Dependent clause: who wear *bindis;* verb: are. **OK**   5. Dependent clause: that Hindu women have worn for centuries; verb: is.   6. Dependent clause: whose *bindi* first attracted attention among trendy, pierced people; verb: is.   7. Dependent clause: who is the lead singer of the band No Doubt; verb: wears.   8. Dependent clause: whom many people have compared to Madonna; verb: likes.   9. Dependent clause: that is a favorite among southern Indian women; verb: looks.   10. Dependent clause: which was once a meaningful religious symbol; verb: is. **OK**

Answers to 24–4

1. Compound subject: The orangutan, gorilla, chimpanzee, and bonobo; verb: are.   2. Compound subject: the chimp and the gorilla; verb: look.   3. Compound subject: the chimpanzee and the bonobo; verb: share.   4. Compound subject: Chimpanzees and humans; verb: are.   5. Compound subject: Murder, rape, torture, gang warfare, and territorial raiding; verb: occur.   6. Compound subject: The chimpanzee and the bonobo; verb: are; compound subject: chimps and humans; verb: are.   7. Compound subject: The male and female bonobo; verb: have.   8. Compound subject: a mother bonobo or her son; verb: is.   9. Compound subject: The status or power; verb: depends.   10. Compound subject: the chimpanzee or the bonobo; verb: is.

Answers to 24–5

1. Subject: Everyone; prepositional phrase: in my college writing class; verb: speaks.   2. Subject: few; prepositional phrase: of the students; verb: are.   3. Subject: Many; prepositional phrase: of the students; verb: are.   4. Subject: Several; prepositional phrase: of the best students in the class; verb: are.   5. Subject: One; prepositional phrase: of my closest friends in the class; verb: comes.   6. Subject: Both; prepositional phrase: of us; verb: live.   7. Subject: No one; prepositional phrase: in my class;

verb: speaks.   8. Subject: Each; prepositional phrase: of us; verb: studies.   9. Subject: none; prepositional phrase: of my hard work; verb: seems.   10. Subject: Neither; prepositional phrase: of my parents; verb: speaks.

Answers to 24–6

1. are.   2. **OK.**   3. Have.   4. are.   5. **OK.** 6. are.   7. Are.   8. Do.   9. are.   10. **OK.**

Answers to 24–7

1. Subject: Commuting; verb: is
2. Subject: Many; verb: have
3. Subject: Travel; verb: has become
4. Subject: commuting; verb: remains
5. Subject: Businesses; verb: continue
6. Subject: Telecommuters; verb: work
7. Subject: Companies; verb: report
8. Subject: Collaboration and feedback; verb: happen
9. Subject: Community colleges and universities; verb: are
10. Subject: you; verb: have

Answers to 25–1

1. explain.
2. stop.
3. use.
4. offers.
5. take.
6. feel.
7. loves.
8. prefer.
9. think.
10. keeps.

Answers to 25–2

1. specialized.
2. rescued.
3. pulled.
4. resulted.
5. used.
6. helped.
7. chased.
8. scared.
9. retrieved.
10. earned.

Answers to 25–3

1. applied. 2. hope. 3. searched.
4. checked. 5. showed. 6. helps. 7. want.
8. increased. 9. need. 10. cost.

Answers to 25–4

1. am. 2. have. 3. am. 4. have. 5. am.
6. am. 7. have. 8. has. 9. is. 10. are.

Answers to 25–5

1. grew. 2. began. 3. took. 4. was. 5. hit.
6. brought. 7. taught. 8. quit. 9. knew.
10. said.

Answers to 25–6

1. ate.
2. made.
3. thought.
4. had.
5. brought.
6. said.
7. knew.
8. lost.
9. told.
10. quit.

Answers to 25–7

1. tried.
2. worked.
3. waited.
4. helped.
5. parked.
6. prepared.
7. allowed.
8. realized.
9. registered.
10. expanded.

Answers to 25–8

1. begun.
2. become.
3. caught.
4. won.
5. found.
6. done.
7. written.
8. shown.
9. fallen.
10. made.

Answers to 25–9

1. was. 2. became. 3. have stayed.
4. began. 5. has gotten. 6. lost.
7. has applied. 8. decided. 9. have attended.
10. felt.

Answers to 25–10

1. have raised.
2. has investigated.
3. has stated.
4. has shown.
5. has announced.
6. have argued.
7. have created.
8. have helped.
9. have prevented.
10. have written.

Answers to 25–11

1. became. 2. had thought. 3. had seen.
4. had been. 5. had tried. 6. found.
7. had worked. 8. stopped. 9. had known.
10. had kept.

Answers to 25–12

1. had held.
2. had dropped out.
3. had been.
4. had worked.
5. had figured out.
6. had realized.
7. had managed.
8. had received.
9. had learned.
10. had not tried.

Answers to 25–13

1. **A;** subject: I; verb: completed. 2. **P;** subject: a lot; verb: was taught. 3. **P;** subject: it; verb: was suggested. 4. **P;** subject: letters; verb: were sent. 5. **A;** subject: I; verb: mentioned. 6. **P;** subject: letters; verb: were sent.

7. **A;** subject: companies; verb: called.   8. **P;** subject: job; verb: was offered.   9. **A;** subject: I; verb: accepted.   10. **P;** subject: workers; verb: are needed.

Answers to 25–14

POSSIBLE REVISIONS

1. Several student organizations that are working together to oppose the increase in parking rates took a poll.
2. Ninety percent of the students who drive to school voted that the increase is too high.
3. "The rates were already high, and now they have more than doubled," one student remarked.
4. The students recognize that the state has given the college less money this year.
5. The college should not force students who drive to school to make up the entire amount of money cut by the state.
6. In most cases, only students who don't live near public transportation resort to driving to school.
7. Some of these students will find paying the increased rate impossible.
8. Students who come to class after work don't have enough time to drive to a subway station and then take the subway to school.
9. The expensive parking rates may discourage some people from applying to the college at all.
10. The college should raise funds in a way that is fair to all students.

Answers to 25–15

POSSIBLE REVISIONS

1. No drinks or food should be brought into the library.
2. A drink was brought into the library the other day.
3. A drink was spilled on a book.
4. The ruined book was found on Tuesday.
5. My friend and I were reported to the librarians.
6. Our library cards were revoked the following day.

7. We were denied the chance to plead our case.
8. The dean was told by a professor how unfair our case was.
9. We were not seen spilling the drink on the book.
10. It is stated by the law that rights and privileges cannot be revoked based on circumstantial evidence.

Answers to 25–16

1. is.   2. won.   3. is; is.   4. told; had; had. 5. gave; refused.   6. endured.   7. survived; improved.   8. is.   9. married; is.   10. has, has.

Answers to 25–17

1. has changed.   2. read.   3. found. 4. are asking.   5. has raised.   6. gave. 7. listen.   8. have given.   9. erase.   10. are.

Answers to 25–18

1. is.   2. has grown.   3. have seen.   4. lies. 5. painted.   6. has decayed.   7. began; finished.   8. used; gave; made.   9. have been. 10. began; has reversed.

Answers to 26–1

1. their.
2. themselves; they.
3. they.
4. she; she.
5. her; they.
6. their.
7. their.
8. their.
9. them.
10. them.

Answers to 26–2

1. it.   2. his or her.   3. she.   4. they.   5. its. 6. itself.   7. their jobs.   8. it.   9. it.   10. it.

Answers to 26–3

1. he or she.
2. their.

3. his or her.
4. his or her.
5. his or her.
6. their.
7. his or her.
8. they.
9. we.
10. their.

Answers to 26–4

1. its.
2. it.
3. its.
4. its.
5. it.
6. its.
7. it.
8. itself.
9. its.
10. it.

Answers to 26–5

POSSIBLE REVISIONS

1. Yesterday I got a letter from my doctor informing me that she and her partner were no longer accepting my insurance plan.
2. Dr. Reuter and her partner, Dr. Spingarn, have decided not to go along with the insurance company's new way of paying doctors.
3. According to the letter, my insurance company is now forcing doctors to accept capitation, a payment method that my doctor describes as "unethical."
4. With this payment method, every month the doctor gets a fixed fee for each patient, no matter how much treatment the doctor provides.
5. In other words, doctors are paid the same amount whether a patient needs six office visits a month or none.
6. With the traditional fee-for-service method of reimbursement, insurance companies pay doctors every time they treat a patient.
7. My doctor and her partner believe that capitation is bad because it rewards doctors for providing less medical care and penalizes them for providing more.
8. They think it creates a conflict of interest between doctors and patients because doctors have a financial incentive to withhold treatment.
9. Dr. Reuter and Dr. Spingarn decided that they could not accept the capitation plan even if rejecting it meant losing patients who could not switch to a different insurance company.
10. When I called my insurance company to complain about capitation, the customer service representative told me that the company was simply trying to keep my premiums down by controlling medical costs.

Answers to 26–6

1. Last March my friend Elena and I both had babies, five days apart.
2. Everyone in the neighborhood gave Elena and me a double baby shower, with matching outfits for our two kids.
3. **OK**
4. Unfortunately, now that I'm in school and Elena is back at her job, she and I don't see each other as much as we used to.
5. Sometimes Max and I run into her and Lucy at the playground or the library.
6. When we saw Lucy and her the other day, Elena was complaining that she and her husband, Danny, never spend any time together anymore.
7. They're always so tired and stressed out from working and taking care of Lucy that when she and Danny do see each other, they just end up arguing.
8. **OK**
9. The other day she said, "If things don't get better between him and me, Danny and I are going to end up getting a divorce."
10. I told her that David and I had struggled with the same issue and that I thought they would work things out if they could just spend more time together.

Answers to 26–7

1. My older sister, Nadine, always seems to get her schoolwork done faster than I.
2. Nadine does better on tests, but I write better papers than she.
3. As a result, she usually gets about the same grades as I.
4. **OK**
5. The whole time we were growing up, teachers always seemed to like her better than me.
6. **OK**
7. Nadine is eighteen months older than I, but people always ask us if we're twins.
8. **OK**
9. I guess deep down inside I'm worried that people will respect her more than me or think she's smarter than I.
10. I don't understand why I'm so competitive with Nadine, since I don't know any sisters who are closer friends than we.

Answers to 26–8

1. who. 2. whom. 3. who. 4. who.
5. whom. 6. who. 7. whoever. 8. who.
9. whom. 10. whom.

Answers for 26–9

1. Many students and professionals do not realize that writing can provide **them** with a means of achieving goals.
2. They need to understand that writing down **their** goals is better than just thinking about them.
3. When someone writes down a goal, one part of his or her brain starts collecting pertinent information and sends it to the conscious part of **his or her** mind.
4. Thus, the person starts to recognize opportunities **he or she** never would have noticed otherwise.
5. When **they** put **their** goals on paper, people need to include both short- and long-term goals.
6. People who try this technique should not worry about **their** spelling or edit **their** ideas.

7. If students have trouble writing goals, **they** might want to write down on another sheet what is keeping **them** from reaching **their** goals.
8. By being specific rather than vague, people can more easily decide how to meet **their** goals.
9. To help focus on the outcome, a person may want to include smaller goals that are steps to the final goal.
10. People who follow this technique have learned that the fears that could keep them from succeeding become more manageable if **they** write those fears down.

Answers to 27–1

1. mischievous **character.** 2. greedy **troublemaker.** 3. **is** usually. 4. foolish **pranks.** 5. secretly **admire.** 6. powerful **opponents.** 7. unexpected **ways.**
8. popular **tricksters.** 9. sensible **friend.**
10. Uncontrollably **curious.**

Answers to 27–2

1. most famous. 2. more famous.
3. most important. 4. stronger; more clever.
5. easier. 6. harder. 7. smaller; bigger.
8. larger. 9. higher. 10. more difficult.

Answers to 27–3

1. good. 2. worse. 3. badly. 4. better.
5. best. 6. good. 7. badly. 8. better.
9. worst. 10. bad.

Answers to 28–1

POSSIBLE REVISIONS

1. We have been building an addition onto our house for the past four months.
2. The addition will be a sunroom that will be lit almost entirely with natural light.
3. I have wanted a room surrounded by windows, like this one, for a long time.
4. Using material recycled from the garage we are tearing down, we are building the addition fairly inexpensively.

5. The cedar planks that once served as garage siding will look charmingly rustic in our new room.
6. We have also taken skylights that were once over the bedroom closet and moved them to the sunroom's roof.
7. We found an old glass door in our attic that we can use for the doorway between the sunroom and the backyard.
8. To do the floor ourselves, though, seemed like an impossible job, so without hesitation we hired a contractor.
9. When we are nearly done with sheetrocking the walls, he can come in and begin laying out the frame for the floor.
10. I can't wait until we can begin eating in our soon-to-be-finished new room.

Answers to 28–2

POSSIBLE REVISIONS

1. Armed and well trained, five elite coast guard divers raided a yacht yesterday where four people were being held hostage.
2. The hostages, a woman and her three children, were unharmed.
3. Scared of the hijacker, the captain began to sail the yacht off its original course.
4. Wanting to go to Greece, the hijacker demanded that the yacht begin heading east.
5. Bravely, the captain sent a secret message to the coast guard and foiled the hijacker's plans.
6. Picking up the signal, the coast guard acted swiftly and effectively.
7. Distracted by three coast guard boats surrounding the front of the yacht, the hijacker did not even notice the divers climbing aboard the back of the yacht.
8. Motioning to the hostages to keep quiet, the divers crept up front to start the ambush while the boats outside kept the hijacker distracted.
9. Unwilling to give in, the hijacker began firing.
10. Trained to fire back when necessary, the coast guard divers shot the hijacker.

Answers to 28–3

POSSIBLE REVISIONS

1. Getting to work from my house by subway takes only about twenty minutes.
2. While riding the subway, you can pass the time quickly if you have something to read.
3. I used to take the bus to work instead of the subway, but the bus is slower.
4. The bus takes nearly twice as long as the subway because of all the traffic.
5. Also, the bus stops at almost every corner.
6. Having taken the bus for years, I had never considered trying the subway.
7. Though rather noisy, the subway is better because I can read without getting a headache.
8. Riding the subway for a year, I haven't gotten a headache even once.
9. Reading on the bus, I found that my head would start throbbing after five minutes.
10. Unable to read, I could only stare out the window.

Answers to 28–4

POSSIBLE REVISIONS

1. While we were painting our living room, our black cat pushed open the door and rubbed up against the wet molding.
2. Looking like a skunk, Lucy was hiding under the bed when we found her.
3. We had painted the molding with oil-based paint, which was now on her fur.
4. After considering our other options, we decided to clean her fur with paint thinner.
5. Now covered with paint thinner, Lucy needed to be washed and rinsed with soap and water.
6. Cleaning our brushes in the basement an hour later, we realized that we had made a terrible mistake.
7. We found Lucy, usually so gentle and affectionate, hissing and arching her back at us.
8. We rushed her to the emergency animal hospital, where the vet told us that you

should never use paint thinner on an animal.

9. During our conversation with the vet, we learned that we should have used just soap and water or a lanolin hand cleaner.

10. Grateful that she was okay, we took Lucy home after she had been sedated and thoroughly bathed.

Answers to 29–1

1. and.   2. but.   3. so.   4. and.   5. for.
6. nor.   7. for.   8. but.   9. or.   10. and.

Answers to 29–2

1. Sports that have historically been considered off-limits to women are changing; women are beginning to participate in professional athletics in areas where they have never competed before.

2. One example is weightlifting; seventeen-year-old Cheryl Haworth has quickly become the most well-known female weightlifter.

3. Haworth is five feet nine inches tall and weighs 300 pounds; she has the ideal build for a weightlifter.

4. She can lift over 300 pounds; this power made her the medal favorite at the 2000 Olympics.

5. She lifts as much as 25 tons in the course of her daily workout; every day she lifts the equivalent of five elephants or one F-15 fighter jet.

6. Haworth is also something of a practical jokester; she has been known to lift her friend's car and move it to a different location.

7. Haworth's thighs measure 32 inches in circumference; she can bench press 500 pounds.

8. She began lifting weights when she was twelve years old and already weighed 240 pounds; she could lift over 110 pounds.

9. She also has the speed and flexibility needed by a great weightlifter; she can run a 40-yard dash in five seconds.

10. Women like Haworth are calling for significant changes now and in the future for women's sports; the inclusion of female weightlifting for the first time in the 2000 Olympics is proof of these changes.

Answers to 29–3

POSSIBLE REVISIONS

1. My friend Simone became pregnant when she was a junior in college; as a result, she could not go back to finish her senior year.

2. She could not afford child care; therefore, she had to stay home after Danny, her son, was born.

3. Danny is five now and is beginning kindergarten next month; as a result, Simone will have five hours free every day.

4. Simone has signed up for two morning classes in nursing at her community college; in addition, she has applied for a part-time job at a nursing home.

5. It won't be easy fitting work and classes into her busy parenting schedule; however, Simone feels that Danny will be better off when they are financially secure.

6. There are things she would like to buy for Danny that she cannot afford; also, Simone wants to show Danny that she can beat the odds.

7. Simone would like to eventually be a nurse; in fact, through caring for Danny, she's already had some practice as one.

8. The three-year course to become a certified nurse is too much for Simone; instead, she could take fewer classes and become a nurse practitioner.

9. Either way, she would be working with patients; in addition, she would be making good use of her naturally caring personality.

10. Simone says she is glad that things turned out as they did with her schooling because she feels more dedicated now than she did five years ago; besides, she has a wonderful son in her life.

Answers to 29–4

POSSIBLE REVISIONS

1. My car started making a funny noise, so I took it to the repair shop down the street.

2. The mechanic told me the car needed a new water pump; he thought it would cost about $300, including labor.

3. My car isn't worth a lot of money; in fact, it's probably not worth much more than $300.

4. It's a 1987 Nissan Sentra hatchback with about 130,000 miles, but up until last week it had been driving just fine.

5. Over the years I've had good luck with this car, and I've grown quite attached to it.

6. My brother thinks I should get the car repaired, but my sister thinks I'd be foolishly throwing good money after bad.

7. My sister is probably right; still, I'm unhappy about abandoning my car.

8. I could buy my neighbor's 1994 Toyota Tercel wagon, or I could go to the used-car dealer my parents recommended.

9. I'm just not sure it makes sense for me to take out a car loan right now; besides, I don't have any money for a down payment.

10. Maybe I should get the car repaired; then I could buy a new car after I've saved some money over the summer.

Answers to 29–5

POSSIBLE REVISIONS

1. On May 21, 1997, Jahmal Haney delivered his first baby, even though he was only eight years old.

2. Although Jahmal's mother, Donna Murray, wasn't due for another month, she started having contractions in the middle of the night.

3. Two hours later she called 911 because she realized she wasn't going to make it to the hospital.

4. When the 911 operator, Sean Stentiford, asked Murray if there was anyone else at home, she handed the phone to her son.

5. After his mother went to lie down in the bedroom, Jahmal listened carefully to Stentiford's instructions.

6. Stentiford told Jahmal to make sure his mother was lying in the middle of the bed since they didn't want the baby to fall on the floor.

7. When Jahmal returned from the bedroom, he told Stentiford he could see the baby's head.

8. Stentiford instructed Jahmal to put his hands under the head as his mother pushed the baby out.

9. Although Jahmal had to run back and forth between his mother in the bedroom and the phone in the living room, he helped deliver his new baby sister, Samantha Elise Murray.

10. The ambulance arrived after the baby had already been born.

Answers to 30–1

POSSIBLE REVISIONS

1. Among college students, halogen lamps have become more popular than traditional incandescent lamps.

2. Halogen lamps are more popular because they are cheaper and brighter.

3. However, there are two problems with halogen lamps: They not only cause fires but also use lots of energy.

4. A 300-watt halogen bulb gets almost three times as hot as a 150-watt incandescent bulb.

5. A Harvard engineering professor discovered that halogen lamps—not toasters, hair dryers, stereos, refrigerators, or computers—were responsible for rising energy consumption in residence halls.

6. Some colleges are considering both banning halogen lamps in dormitories and offering students low-energy fluorescent lamps.

7. The new lamps would be provided either free or at a discount.

8. These energy-efficient lamps cost about four to five times more than halogen lamps.

9. Unfortunately, most consumers would rather save money when buying an item than when using it.

10. To figure out a lamp's lifetime cost, you have to consider the cost of the lamp itself, replacement bulbs, and electricity.

Answers to 30–2

POSSIBLE REVISIONS

1. A migraine is an intense headache characterized by pulsing pain, nausea, dizziness, double vision, and sensitivity to light and sound.
2. Migraines are often triggered by red wine, chocolate, aged cheese, and cured meats.
3. These terrible headaches can also be triggered by certain medicines and food additives.
4. Migraines are three times more common in women than in men.
5. Women's migraines are often hormonal, related to the fluctuation of both estrogen and progesterone during their menstrual cycles.
6. Birth control pills or estrogen replacement therapy can make hormonal migraines much worse.
7. Throughout history, there have been many failed remedies for migraines, such as purging, bleeding, encircling the head with a hangman's noose, and drilling a hole in the skull.
8. In a famous essay entitled "In Bed," the writer Joan Didion argues that people with migraines suffer not only from the headaches themselves but also from the common belief that they are somehow causing their own sickness.
9. Despite what some people think, migraines are caused by neither a bad attitude nor a certain personality trait.
10. An international team of scientists has not only isolated the gene that causes one severe type of migraine but also expects to find genes for more common forms.

Answers to 31–1

POSSIBLE REVISIONS

1. Recently my friend has had problems concentrating on and finishing the projects she starts.
2. Always very thorough, Karen says she has felt distracted since her brother died of cancer last spring.

3. Sadly, this has gotten in her way at work, where she is expected to complete assignments on time.
4. Fortunately, her boss is very understanding and told Karen that she would like to support her through this difficult time.
5. Recently Karen went to a psychologist to see if there was anything that Karen could do about her concentration problems.
6. Gently, the psychologist explained that the overwhelming emotions Karen was experiencing were completely normal after the loss of a loved one.
7. "Luckily, these feelings do not last forever," the psychologist explained, "and the grief will eventually become less consuming."
8. Immediately after talking with the psychologist, Karen began to attend a support group for people who have lost relatives to cancer.
9. Amazingly, Karen said she began to feel a little better very soon after joining the group.
10. Determinedly, she is getting back on her feet.

Answers to 31–2

POSSIBLE REVISIONS

1. Leading the 1996 U.S. Olympics gymnastics team, Kerry Strug didn't let her injured ankle stop her from nailing a perfect landing in her last event.
2. Several of the 1996 women gymnasts have continued training, hoping to be on the 2000 team in Sydney.
3. Wanting to go to Sydney, Dominique Moceanu has had her routines altered to accommodate her nine-inch, forty-pound growth spurt.
4. Containing mostly new athletes, the 2000 women's gymnastics team may not be recognizable to television viewers.
5. Though sometimes criticized for exploiting young children, elite gymnastics coaches turn their protégés into champions.
6. Young girls can lose their childhoods to constant work in the gym, possibly suffering serious injuries as well.

7. Dominating the spotlight this Olympic year is men's gymnastics, which traditionally has held less interest for the public than women's gymnastics.

8. Blaine Wilson appeared to be the one to watch, having won the last five national titles.

9. Wearing three earrings, Blaine also dyes his hair and sports numerous tattoos.

10. Blaine has challenged the stereotypes of the male gymnast, tending to his image both outside and inside the gym.

Answers to 31–3

POSSIBLE REVISIONS

1. Regarded as particularly lucky, the *Essex* was an old whaling ship by the time it sailed its last voyage in 1820.

2. Attacked by a sperm whale, the *Essex* inspired the final scene of Herman Melville's *Moby Dick*.

3. Passed down over the years through town lore, the larger story actually began after the ship was sunk.

4. Considered enlightened and a good place for free blacks to live during the era of slavery, Nantucket, home of the *Essex*, was a prosperous whaling town.

5. Orphaned and desperate for work, many of the sailors on the *Essex* were only fifteen years old.

6. Determined to record what happened during the attack and in the ninety days that followed, Thomas Nickerson was a fourteen-year-old cabin boy.

7. Discovered in 1981, Nickerson's narrative recorded starvation, madness, and desperation.

8. Forced to resort to desperate measures to stay alive, twenty of the crew members were stranded on small boats for ninety days after the *Essex* was sunk.

9. Troubled by his captain's obsession, Melville's narrator, Ishmael, ends his story when the boat sinks.

10. Starved and driven to desperate measures, the crew of the *Essex* may have wished for that fate by the end of their ordeal.

Answers to 31–4

POSSIBLE REVISIONS

1. My brother, a paramedic, has some very interesting stories from his work.

2. Rush hour, a tense and hectic time for ambulance workers, afforded him a particularly good story last week.

3. A pregnant woman, a rush hour victim, called from her car phone.

4. The woman started to go into labor, one of the most intense experiences a person can have.

5. The woman, a first-time mother, hoped that an ambulance could rescue her from a traffic jam.

6. Jake, one of the best ambulance drivers in the area, was working with my brother that day.

7. They found the woman, a model of courage despite her pain and fear, about an eighth of a mile down the highway from where she called.

8. They left her car, a 1997 red Lexus, at the side of the road.

9. They lifted her into the ambulance, a godsend to the woman and her unborn child, and sped away.

10. The woman gave birth to her child, a healthy little girl, seven minutes after arriving at the hospital.

Answers to 31–5

POSSIBLE REVISIONS

1. Alice Waters is a well-known chef who has helped bring attention to organic produce and locally grown foods.

2. Waters has a restaurant named Chez Panisse, which is located in Berkeley, California.

3. Chez Panisse uses only locally grown foods that are pesticide- and chemical-free.

4. In recent years many people who have heard or read about the organic farm movement have become much more aware of the quality of the foods they eat.

5. They have come to realize that the nutritional value of food, which is usually asso-

ciated only with vitamin content, involves many factors.

6. Organic produce, which often has a higher vitamin content, has to be sold more quickly and is therefore fresher.

7. In addition, organic produce is free of pesticides and chemicals, which can be carcinogenic.

8. Chemicals can have other effects that may be less dangerous but are still undesirable.

9. For example, sulfites, which are often added to fruits and vegetables to prevent discoloration, can produce an allergic reaction in many people.

10. Adding sulfites to fruits and vegetables also makes them appear fresher for longer, which allows fruits and vegetables to be sold several weeks after they have been picked.

Answers to 31–6

POSSIBLE REVISIONS

1. Obviously, everyone knows that Disney is the biggest name in children's home entertainment.

2. Probably, unless you have a daughter between the ages of eight and twelve, you don't realize that the second-biggest name is Olsen.

3. Mary-Kate and Ashley Olsen dominate the live-action children's video market, which is incredibly profitable.

4. Entering show business when they were only four months old, the Olsen twins starred for eight seasons in the hit TV sitcom *Full House.*

5. They both played the part of Michelle, the youngest daughter in the Tanner family.

6. Mary-Kate and Ashley, now ten-year-old millionaires, have made three TV movies, a feature film, two home video series, a music video, and two music CDs.

7. Costarring Kirstie Alley and Steve Guttenberg, the movie *It Takes Two* earned a modest $19.5 million at the box office but a whopping $75 million in home video sales.

8. Altogether, the fourteen titles in their two video series, *The Adventures of Mary-Kate*

and Ashley and *You're Invited to Mary-Kate and Ashley's,* have sold more than six million copies.

9. In the *Adventures* videos, the twins play cute detectives who promise to "solve any crime by dinnertime."

10. Aimed at preteen girls, these videos face virtually no competition in the home entertainment market.

Answers to 31–7

POSSIBLE REVISIONS

1. Recently, a group of scientists discovered that babies whose mothers smoked during pregnancy have the same levels of nicotine in their bodies as adult smokers.

2. The results of their study, presented at a meeting of the American College of Cardiology, strongly suggest that these newborns go through withdrawal.

3. Speaking at the conference, Dr. Claude Hanet said that the baby of a smoking mother should be considered an ex-smoker.

4. Conducted by a team of Belgian researchers, the study examined the urine of 273 babies and toddlers.

5. Of these children, 139 were newborns who were one to three days old.

6. Researchers checked the children's urine for cotinine, the substance that remains in the body for several days after nicotine breaks down.

7. Some of the mothers in the study, who had smoked during pregnancy, had newborns with cotinine levels that were about the same as their own.

8. In toddlers with smoking mothers, cotinine levels were significantly higher than in adult nonsmokers who were exposed to secondhand smoke at home.

9. Pregnant women should not only quit smoking but also avoid secondhand smoke, inhaled from other people's cigarettes.

10. A 1996 study found that even nonsmoking pregnant women who have inhaled secondhand smoke can pass cancer-causing chemicals to their fetuses.

Answers to 32–1

POSSIBLE REVISIONS

1. Last Saturday I went to a party at my sociology professor's house.
2. Since I don't own a car, I got a ride to the party with a friend of mine.
3. Professor Zelinsky lives in a big house on a lake, along with his wife (who is an artist) and an enormous dog named McDuff.
4. The dog is a Scottish deerhound, an unusual breed that is almost as big as a pony.
5. The food at the party was delicious: two huge platters of cheese, fruit, raw vegetables, bread, and crackers, plus barbecued chicken, salad, and sesame noodles.
6. A woman who was petting the dog spilled a plate of chicken wings on the living room couch and a glass of wine on a chair.
7. I hope Professor Zelinsky wasn't too upset about the furniture; I thought the woman showed lots of courage in telling him about the spills right away.
8. Professor Zelinsky and his wife had hired a rock and roll band, and the lead singer was a classmate of mine.
9. Everyone danced for hours on a wooden platform that had been set up on the lawn.
10. I went down to the beach to watch the sun set over the lake, and I sat on the sand until the mosquitoes started to bite.

Answers to 32–2

POSSIBLE REVISIONS

1. Because I enjoy working with children, when I graduate from college I hope to get a job as a teacher in a day-care center.
2. I decided to become a day-care teacher because I enjoyed being a nanny last summer.
3. I miss taking care of those two little children, Anna and Ethan; I loved spending time with them.
4. In September I discussed changing my major with my college advisor, and I

began studying early childhood education that semester.
5. **OK**
6. People keep asking me why I would choose to work in such a low-paying profession.
7. I know that childcare jobs do not pay well, but I consider working with children a great privilege and an enormous responsibility.
8. I fail to understand why in this country it costs so much to send a child to day care, yet the teachers get paid so poorly.
9. A beginning day-care teacher can expect to earn about $7 an hour and often cannot hope to receive medical benefits.
10. We as a society need to start treating early childhood education with more respect—and to stop pretending that it requires no special skill or training.

Answers to 32–3

1. of.
2. out.
3. of.
4. in.
5. for.
6. up.
7. about.
8. for.
9. up.
10. about.

Answers to 32–4

POSSIBLE REVISIONS

1. I am writing to let you know that I am very excited about the prospect of working as an assistant teacher in the Preschool 1 classroom at the Kenwood Children's Center.
2. At that age, children are suddenly so aware of the world around them—full of curiosity and eager to try everything they see.
3. When I visited the classroom yesterday, I was impressed by the way all the children were helping out at cleanup time.

4. At circle time I was glad that the teacher called on the girls just as often as the boys.

5. One little girl was so proud of having become a big sister over the weekend that she couldn't wait to share her news.

6. **OK**

7. I have to admit that I couldn't quite understand what one of the younger boys was trying to say, but the teacher didn't give up until she finally understood him.

8. Before nap time, each child chose a book to look at quietly for a few minutes, and then the teacher read *Make Way for Ducklings* to the whole class.

9. After the story, a few of the children couldn't settle down until the teacher turned on some quiet music and pulled down the shades.

10. Some of the kids were so worn out from their busy morning that I don't think they could have stayed awake one second longer.

Answers to 32–5

POSSIBLE REVISIONS

1. **Negative:** I did not come to this country two years ago to attend college.
   Question: Did I come to this country two years ago to attend college?

2. **Negative:** My family does not live in Argentina.
   Question: Does my family live in Argentina?

3. **Negative:** I did not have a job as a camp counselor this summer.
   Question: Did I have a job as a camp counselor this summer?

4. **Negative:** The camp is not located on a lake in New Hampshire.
   Question: Is the camp located on a lake in New Hampshire?

5. **Negative:** It has not been around for thirty years.
   Question: Has it been around for thirty years?

6. **Negative:** I did not teach horseback riding and soccer.
   Question: Did I teach horseback riding and soccer?

7. **Negative:** I also did not direct the camp musical.
   Question: Did I also direct the camp musical?

8. **Negative:** My English has not improved a lot over the summer.
   Question: Has my English improved a lot over the summer?

9. **Negative:** I am not going to work at the camp again next summer.
   Question: Am I going to work at the camp again next summer?

10. **Negative:** It was not a wonderful experience for me.
    Question: Was it a wonderful experience for me?

Answers to 32–6

1. purple nylon.   2. beat-up paper.   3. neat, round.   4. small outer.   5. thick black vinyl.
6. red felt-tipped.   7. cheerful young Italian.
8. old gray marble.   9. enormous new wooden.   10. bright blue cotton.

Answers to 33–1

POSSIBLE REVISIONS

1. I wanted to let you know how much I enjoyed meeting you on Monday.

2. Thank you for taking the time to talk with me about the summer internship in the design department of your advertising agency.

3. Nadler & Lattimore seems like an exciting place to work, and the internship sounds ideal for someone with my background.

4. Having taken two courses in graphic design and one in advertising, I think my qualifications meet your requirements.

5. Based on what you told me about the internship, I know that I could do an outstanding job assisting the graphic designers at Nadler & Lattimore.

6. As I mentioned at the interview, this internship represents a tremendous opportunity for me, since I am planning to pursue a career in advertising design after I graduate from college next spring.
7. I have called my references to let them know that you might be contacting them.
8. Please let me know if you have any other questions.
9. I look forward to hearing from you about the internship.
10. Once again, thank you for taking the time to meet with me.

Answers to 34–1

1. advice; write.   2. it's; piece.   3. except; whose; are; than.   4. past; our; right; advise.
5. there; who's; to.   6. used; then; our; their.
7. principle; have; right; your; are; you're.
8. it's; of.   9. conscience; too; who's.
10. know; have; peace; of; quit; to.   11. it's; quite; used.   12. of; and.   13. conscious; new.   14. buy; to; mind.   15. Then; though; knew.   16. to; an; by; two.   17. accept; lose.
18. have; of; affect; and; too.   19. a; than; right; and; your.   20. suppose; find; sit; and.

Answers to 34–2

1. know; who's; advice; you're.   2. used; and.
3. right; our.   4. then; to.   5. twenty-two; through.   6. conscious; effect; by; have.
7. piece.   8. There; accept.   9. quiet; our.
10. lose; knew; mind.

Answers to 35–1

1. believe.   2. assuming; hurrying.
3. Luckily; corrected.   4. omitted; flipped; *achieve*.   5. used; worried; submitted.
6. saying; sloppiness.   7. portfolios; improvement.   8. tattoos; laziness.   9. conceive; encouraging; hopeful.   10. clapped; cheered; speeches.

Answers to 35–2

1. definitely.   2. convincing.   3. preferred.
4. believe.   5. troublesome.   6. cleaner.

7. happier.   8. offering.   9. neighbor's.
10. argument.

Answers to 35–3

1. stories.   2. their.   3. shelters.
4. making.   5. scheduled.   6. hoping.
7. spotted.   8. happened.   9. friendly.
10. admitted.

Answers to 35–4

1. sophomore.   2. career; definitely; surprise; friends; a lot; arguments.   3. incredibly; disappointed; business; jewelry.   4. probably; secretary; convenience; until; married.
5. intelligence.   6. received; encouragement; perceived; athlete.   7. especially; awful; arithmetic; already; embarrassed; answer.
8. achieve; meant; succeed.   9. analyze; interests; environment.   10. weird; excellent.

Answers to 35–5

1. Until; neither.   2. tried; describe.
3. loneliness.   4. happily; regretted.
5. disappointed.   6. necessary; to.
7. worried; something.   8. already.
9. prettiest.   10. immediately; now.

Answers to 36–1

1. Studies show that newborn babies immediately begin to explore their environment by using their senses of sight, hearing, touch, smell, and taste.
2. Yet, it is difficult to tell what newborns can perceive because they are often sleeping, dozing, or crying.
3. **OK**
4. They film their eye movements and measure changes in their heart rates, sucking, and sweating.
5. **OK**
6. A newborn sees poorly because its brain, eyes, and nerves have not yet fully developed.
7. At first infants can focus only on lines, corners, and the edges of objects.
8. Patterns with large shapes, clear outlines, and high contrast are what they see best.

9. Every parent, grandparent, or babysitter knows that infants love to look at people's faces.
10. **OK**

Answers to 36–2

1. Some people are more motivated to achieve excellence than other people, so psychologists are interested in understanding why.
2. People with high achievement motivation have a strong desire to master tasks, and they experience great satisfaction when they achieve success.
3. In one experiment, researchers gave children a test designed to measure their need for achievement, and then they asked these children to play a ring-toss game.
4. Those children who had scored low on the test stood so close to the target that they always scored, or they stood so far away that they always missed.
5. In other words, they succeeded at an unchallenging task, or they failed at an impossible one.
6. In contrast, the children who had scored well on the test stood far enough away from the target to make the game challenging, but they did not stand so far away as to guarantee their own failure.
7. Psychologists believe that people with high achievement motivation tend to set challenging but realistic goals for themselves, and they are willing to take risks to achieve those goals.
8. They experience intense satisfaction from success, but they are not discouraged by failure if they feel they have tried their best.
9. People with low achievement motivation also prefer success to failure, but they usually experience relief at *not* having failed rather than pleasure or pride at having succeeded.
10. They do not tend to seek out feedback from critics, nor do they struggle with a problem instead of quitting in the face of failure.

Answers to 36–3

1. According to a recent study, children can unlearn violent behavior in less than six months.
2. Published in *The Journal of the American Medical Association,* the study helps disprove the idea that nothing can be done to stop violence among America's youth.
3. For Americans between the ages of fifteen and twenty-four, violence is one of the leading causes of death.
4. Financed by the Centers for Disease Control and Prevention, the study involved 790 second- and third-graders at twelve schools in the state of Washington.
5. Over a period of sixteen to twenty weeks, about half of these students were taught a violence-prevention curriculum.
6. During the study, the behavior of this group of students was compared with the behavior of the students who did not take the course.
7. Six months after the program ended, students who had taken the course engaged in about thirty fewer aggressive acts per day at school than the students in the other group.
8. Significantly, aggressive behavior (such as hitting, kicking, and shoving) increased in those children who did not take the course.
9. Developed in 1986 by a Seattle educator, the Second Step antiviolence program consists of weekly or twice-weekly sessions lasting about half an hour each.
10. Widely used in American and Canadian schools, the program is designed to teach empathy, problem-solving, and anger management to preschool through ninth-grade students.

Answers to 36–4

1. Thousands of "snowballs" from outer space are hitting Earth's atmosphere every day, according to scientists at the 1997 meeting of the American Geophysical Union in Baltimore.

2. Over billions of years, they reported, this bombardment of cosmic slush has added vast amounts of water to Earth's atmosphere and oceans.
3. These extraterrestrial snowballs, made up of ice and cosmic dust, may have played a key role in nurturing life on this planet and perhaps elsewhere in the solar system.
4. They are about forty feet in diameter, the size of a small house.
5. These small, cometlike objects, unlike large comets, are extremely hard to see because they break up into fragments and then vaporize.
6. Astronomers and physicists, however, have speculated about their existence since 1986.
7. Dr. Louis A. Frank, a physicist at the University of Iowa, first theorized about them to explain the dark spots he observed in images of Earth's sunlit atmosphere.
8. Dr. Frank noticed these spots, or atmospheric holes, while analyzing data from NASA's *Dynamics Explorer 1* satellite.
9. NASA's *Polar* satellite, launched in February 1996, produced more detailed images of these atmospheric holes.
10. Many scientists now believe that these snowballs are hitting Earth's outer atmosphere at an incredible rate of five to thirty a minute, or up to 43,000 a day.

Answers to 36–5

1. Bernard Malamud, who was born in Brooklyn in 1914, wrote novels and short stories about Jewish immigrant life.
2. His parents, who were Russian immigrants, owned a struggling neighborhood grocery store.
3. **OK**
4. **OK**
5. *The Natural,* which was made into a movie starring Robert Redford, is considered one of the greatest baseball novels of all time.
6. Malamud's first short-story collection, which won the National Book Award, is called *The Magic Barrel.*
7. **OK**

8. **OK**
9. This novel, which is set in Russia, is about a Jewish handyman who is falsely accused of ritual murder.
10. Malamud, who died in 1986, is considered one of the greatest contemporary American fiction writers.

Answers to 36–6

1. Two years ago, my parents decided to sell their house in St. Paul, Minnesota, and retire to Florida.
2. During a vacation they had stopped in Lake Worth, Florida, to visit my father's cousin Lila, and they decided they liked the area.
3. On December 29, 1995, my mother called to tell me that they had put down a deposit on a house that was going to be built in a new development near Lila's condominium.
4. When I heard the news, I said, "Mom, have you and Dad gone out of your minds? Isn't this kind of sudden?"
5. "Yes, it is," she replied, "but I think your father and I have made a wise decision."
6. Both my parents have always insisted that they would never retire to a place like Florida or Phoenix, Arizona, because they enjoy the winter.
7. My father grew up in Madison, Wisconsin, and moved to St. Paul in 1952.
8. **OK**
9. "Peter, we're putting the Carter Avenue house on the market this May," my mother calmly informed me, "and we expect to be moving to Florida by September or October 1996."
10. On October 3, 1996, my parents moved to a small stucco house at 61 Rosewood Lane, Green Acres, Florida 33463.

Answers to 37–1

1. nation's; schools. 2. students. 3. student's.
4. laws. 5. states; states'. 6. Graham's.
7. Graham's; its. 8. court's; its. 9. Graham's; nation's. 10. Dixon's; her.

Answers to 37–2

1. year's; couldn't. 2. wasn't; students.
3. wouldn't; hour; *A*'s, *B*'s, *C*'s, and *D*'s.
4. hours'. 5. students; 20's; 30's; *Q*'s, *X*'s,
and *Z*'s; 2's; 3's. 6. it's; year's; we'll; week's.
7. I'm; its. 8. I've; 98's. 9. *X*'s; *O*'s; didn't;
it's. 10. It's; months'; teacher's.

Answers to 38–1

1. Darryl called his parents from the hospital emergency room to tell them that he had just been in an accident.
2. "I was riding my bike down New Scotland Avenue," he explained when his mother picked up the phone. "A guy who had just parked his van in front of the Bagel Baron opened his door."
3. **OK**
4. "Luckily, I was wearing a helmet," he said, "or I'd probably be dead."
5. "Are you all right?" interrupted Darryl's mother. "What hospital are you at?"
6. "I hurt my shoulder, but I'm not sure how badly because I haven't seen a doctor yet," replied Darryl. "I'm at St. Peter's."
7. "George," his mother called to his father, "pick up the phone in the kitchen. Darryl hurt his shoulder in a bicycle accident."
8. Darryl said he had to get off the phone because the doctor was ready to examine him.
9. **OK**
10. "Don't let them do anything to you until we get there and talk to the doctor!" insisted Darryl's father.

Answers to 38–2

1. "I think you would enjoy reading some poems by Martín Espada," my English teacher told me during our conference.
2. "I'm going to lend you a book called *City of Coughing and Dead Radiators*," she said.
3. "I'll take a look," I replied, "but I really don't like poetry very much."
4. "I had a student last year who announced, 'I hate poetry,' but he changed his mind after reading this book," replied my teacher.

5. A week later I told Professor Macarrulla that I too had changed my mind about poetry after reading Espada's book.
6. "Which poems did you like the best?" Professor Macarrulla asked me.
7. I told her that my favorites were "Borofels" and "Day of the Dead on Wortman Avenue."
8. I explained that "Borofels" reminded me of my own experience growing up in Brooklyn with Puerto Rican parents who spoke very little English.
9. Professor Macarrulla said that her favorite poem in the book was "Who Burns for the Perfection of Paper."
10. "I like that poem," she explained, "because it reminds me that no matter how much success you achieve in life, you should never forget your working-class roots."

Answers to 39–1

POSSIBLE REVISIONS

1. Scientists at Cornell University have discovered something that seems too good to be true: a strain of bacteria that can break down some of the most toxic chemicals in polluted water.
2. Dr. Stephen H. Zinder and his colleagues have found this pollution-fighting organism in sewage sludge (the solid matter produced during sewage treatment).
3. This strain of bacteria breaks down two of the most common pollutants of groundwater: the chemical compounds trichloroethene and tetrachloroethene.
4. Both chlorinated compounds are solvents that are used in such products as glue; paint remover; and cleaning solutions for clothing, machinery, brakes, engines, and electronic parts.
5. These two water-polluting solvents can damage the human nervous system; they are also suspected carcinogens (cancer-causing substances).
6. They are major groundwater pollutants because for years they were handled carelessly—spilled on the ground, poured

down drains, and dumped into landfills—before their danger was clearly understood.

7. These solvents seep hundreds of feet into the earth and then dissolve gradually as groundwater—the main source of drinking water for half the U.S. population—flows by.

8. Scientists have known for about fifteen years that bacteria can sometimes change these chlorinated compounds into ethylene (the harmless gas that causes fruit to ripen).

9. However, the exact chemical process—as well as the conditions necessary for it to occur—have been poorly understood until now.

10. The Cornell scientists have figured out that these bacteria break down the solvents by using them the way people use oxygen: for the cycle of biochemical reactions known as respiration (breathing).

Answers to 39–2

POSSIBLE REVISIONS

1. The 1993 movie *Schindler's List* (directed by Steven Spielberg) won the Academy Award for Best Picture in 1994.

2. The movie tells the true story of an unlikely hero of the Holocaust: a German factory owner from Czechoslovakia who saved thousands of Jews from almost certain death at the hands of the Nazis.

3. This unlikely hero was Oskar Schindler: drinker, gambler, womanizer, and black-market profiteer.

4. The movie features an extraordinary cast: Liam Neeson as Schindler; Ben Kingsley as Itzhak Stern, Schindler's Jewish business adviser and friend; and Ralph Fiennes as Amon Goeth, the brutal and corrupt commander of a slave-labor camp in Nazi-occupied Poland.

5. This Oscar-winning movie was shown on television in February 1997 without commercial interruption; only a few minutes of the original three-and-a-half-hour film were cut (by Spielberg himself) for the Ford-sponsored broadcast on NBC.

6. The TV broadcast of *Schindler's List* was viewed by sixty-five million people—more than twice the number who saw the big-screen version in movie theaters.

7. Many viewers probably did not realize that the movie was based on a 1982 book (originally published in England as *Schindler's Ark*) by the Australian writer Thomas Keneally.

8. **OK**

9. Keneally's book won England's 1982 Booker Prize for Fiction—the nation's best-known literary award.

10. Keneally's victory generated a huge controversy in England because in the preface the author insists that his book is not a work of fiction; he describes it instead as a "documentary novel" that tells a true story.

Answers to 40–1

1. According to an article in *The New York Times Magazine*, more and more Americans are rejecting their parents' religion.

2. In an article entitled "Choosing My Religion," Stephen J. Dubner analyzes a trend that affects him on a personal level.

3. Dubner, who is an editor at the magazine, grew up in a large Catholic family.

4. His parents, however, both grew up Jewish and converted to Catholicism when they were in their twenties.

5. His mother, Florence Greenglass, and his father, Solomon Dubner, were both born in Brooklyn, the children of Russian and Polish immigrants.

6. When Florence Greenglass was baptized a Roman Catholic, she chose "Veronica" as her baptismal name; Solomon chose the name "Paul."

7. They were married on March 2, 1946, at St. Brigid's Catholic Church in Brooklyn; none of their families attended the wedding.

8. Stephen Dubner, the youngest of eight children, grew up on a farm in upstate New York, near the town of Duanesburg.

9. His family was devoutly Catholic, but by the time Dubner left home for college, he had become uncomfortable with his religion.

10. Under the guidance of his friend Ivan, Dubner began exploring Judaism and learning Hebrew while he was in graduate school.

Answers to 40–2

1. According to Dean Hoge, a sociology professor at Catholic University in Washington, D.C., switching religions is more common in America today than it has ever been in history.

2. In their book *One Nation Under God,* Barry A. Kosmin and Seymour P. Lachman estimate that 30 percent of Americans switch religions or denominations during their lifetimes.

3. Most of these people switch from one Protestant denomination to another, but some changes are more dramatic.

4. Kosmin and Lachman, who surveyed 113,000 people for their book, concluded that the most common reason for switching religions is intermarriage—marrying someone of a different faith.

5. In his *New York Times Magazine* article "Choosing My Religion" (March 31, 1996), Stephen J. Dubner explores his own switch from Catholicism to Judaism, but he also spotlights several other young Americans who have changed religions.

6. Daniel Dunn grew up a Congregationalist but became a Catholic after he almost died in a serious water-skiing accident.

7. Judith Anderson grew up in a Jewish family in Teaneck, New Jersey, but she is now a Buddhist.

8. Like many Jews who practice Buddhism, Anderson has not renounced her Judaism; instead, she feels that she has added another spiritual layer to her life.

9. Fatima Shama is the daughter of a devoutly Catholic Brazilian mother and a Muslim Palestinian father who isn't very religious.

10. She grew up Catholic in the Bronx but began practicing a liberal form of Islam during college.

Chapter Summaries and Quick Review Charts
(*Chapters 21–40*)

Chapter Review: The Basic Sentence

1. A sentence must have three things: _____
   _____ . (See p. 346.)

2. A _____ is the person, place, or thing that the sentence is about. (See p. 346.)

3. A noun is _____. (See p. 346.)

4. A _____ replaces a noun in a sentence. (See p. 347.)

5. A main verb tells _____ or _____ the subject to a word that describes it. (See p. 348.)

6. A _____ is an idea, expressed in a sentence, that makes sense independent of other sentences around it. (See p. 351.)

7. An adjective modifies (gives more information about) a _____
   _____ . (See p. 352.)

8. An adverb modifies _____ . Often, an adverb ends in _____ . (See p. 352.)

9. A phrase is a group of words that (is/is not) a complete sentence because it is missing _____ .
   (See p. 354.)

10. What is the difference between an independent clause and a dependent clause? (See p. 356.) _____
    _____
    _____

11. A _____ is a word that joins words, phrases, or clauses. (See p. 357.)

12. The seven coordinating conjunctions are _____
    _____ . (See p. 357.)

13. The other type of conjunction is a _____ conjunction. Five examples are _____
    _____ . (See p. 357.)

Chapter Review: Fragments

1. A sentence is a group of words that has a _____ ,
   a _____ , and expresses a _____ .
   (See p. 359.)

2. A _____ seems to be a complete sentence but is
   only a piece of one. It lacks a subject, a _____ ,
   or a complete thought. (See p. 359.)

3. What are the five trouble spots that signal possible fragments?
   (See p. 361.)

   A word group that starts with _____

   A word group that starts with _____

   A word group that starts with _____

   A word group that starts with _____

   A word group that starts with _____

4. What are the two basic ways to correct fragments? (See p. 361.)

   _____

   _____

Quick Review Chart: Fragments

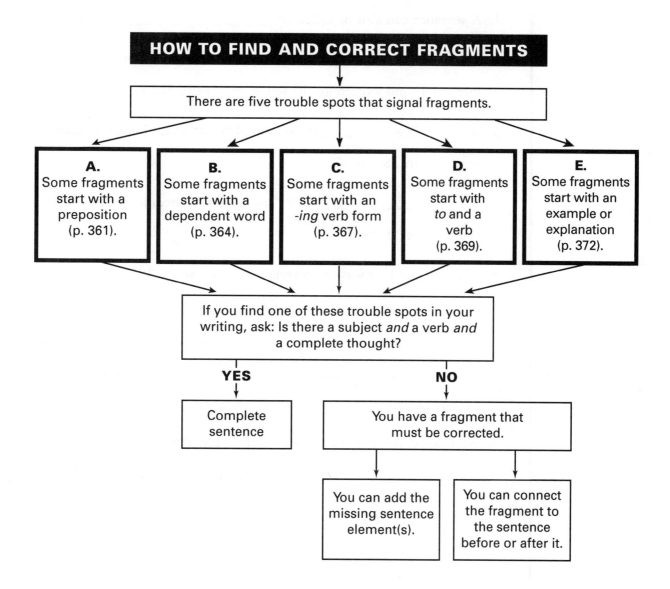

HOW TO FIND AND CORRECT FRAGMENTS

There are five trouble spots that signal fragments.

A.
Some fragments start with a preposition (p. 361).

B.
Some fragments start with a dependent word (p. 364).

C.
Some fragments start with an *-ing* verb form (p. 367).

D.
Some fragments start with *to* and a verb (p. 369).

E.
Some fragments start with an example or explanation (p. 372).

If you find one of these trouble spots in your writing, ask: Is there a subject *and* a verb *and* a complete thought?

YES

Complete sentence

NO

You have a fragment that must be corrected.

You can add the missing sentence element(s).

You can connect the fragment to the sentence before or after it.

Chapter Review: Run-Ons

1. A sentence can also be called an _____ . (See p. 379.)

2. A _____ is two complete sentences that are joined incorrectly and written as one sentence. (See p. 379.)

3. A _____ is two complete sentences joined without any punctuation. (See p. 379.)

4. A _____ is two complete sentences joined by only a comma. (See p. 380.)

5. What are the four ways to correct run-ons? (See p. 381.)

   _____

   _____

   _____

   _____

6. What word in the middle of a sentence may signal a run-on?

   _____ (See p. 390.)

Quick Review Chart: Run-Ons

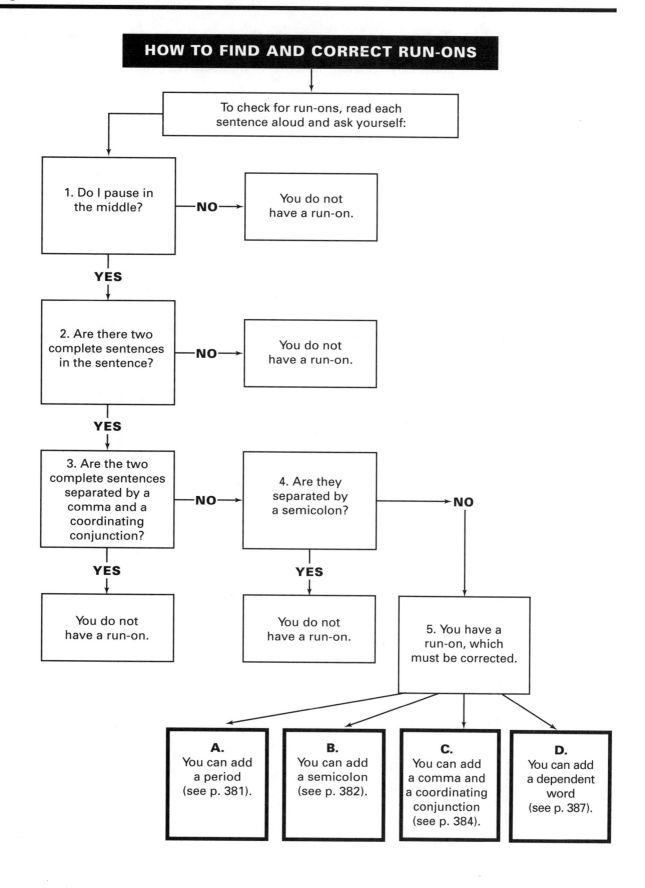

Chapter Review: Problems with Subject–Verb Agreement

1. The _____ and the _____ in a sentence

   must agree (match) in terms of number. They must both be

   _____ or they must both be _____ .

   (See p. 395.)

2. Five trouble spots can cause errors in subject–verb agreement.

   • When the verb is a form of _____ ,

   _____ , or _____ (See p. 397.)

   • When _____ or _____ come between

   the subject and the verb (See p. 401.)

   • When there is a _____ subject joined by *and, or,* or

   nor (See p. 406.)

   • When the subject is an _____ pronoun (See p. 407.)

   • When the _____ comes _____ the

   subject (See p. 410.)

Quick Review Chart: Problems with Subject-Verb Agreement

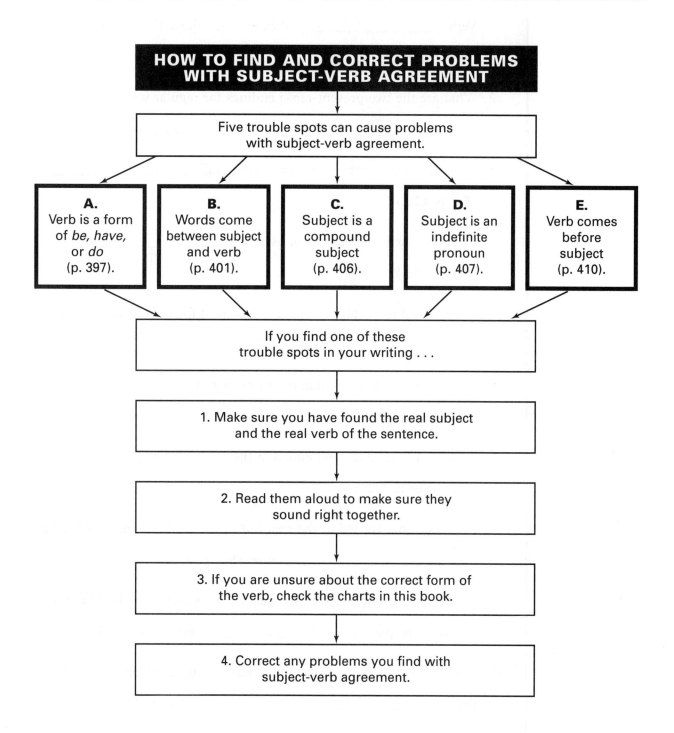

HOW TO FIND AND CORRECT PROBLEMS WITH SUBJECT-VERB AGREEMENT

Five trouble spots can cause problems with subject-verb agreement.

A.
Verb is a form of *be, have,* or *do* (p. 397).

B.
Words come between subject and verb (p. 401).

C.
Subject is a compound subject (p. 406).

D.
Subject is an indefinite pronoun (p. 407).

E.
Verb comes before subject (p. 410).

If you find one of these trouble spots in your writing . . .

1. Make sure you have found the real subject and the real verb of the sentence.

2. Read them aloud to make sure they sound right together.

3. If you are unsure about the correct form of the verb, check the charts in this book.

4. Correct any problems you find with subject-verb agreement.

Chapter Review: Verb Problems

1. Verb _____ indicates when the action in a sentence happens. (See p. 417.)

2. What are the two present-tense endings for regular verbs? _____ _____ (See p. 419.)

3. How do regular verbs in the past tense end? _____ (See p. 420.)

4. The past-participle verb form uses a _____ verb. (See p. 421.)

5. Verbs that do not follow the regular pattern for verb forms are called _____ . (See p. 422.)

6. An action that is happening right now uses the _____ tense. (See p. 419.)

7. An action that began and ended in the past uses the _____ tense. (See p. 420.)

8. An action that started in the past but might continue into the present uses the _____ tense. (See p. 430.)

9. An action that happened in the past before something else that happened in the past uses the _____ tense. (See p. 431.)

10. You should usually avoid using the passive voice, which has a subject that _____ . (See p. 432.)

11. Verb tenses are consistent when actions that happen at the same _____ are in the same _____ . (See p. 434.)

Quick Review Chart: Verb Problems

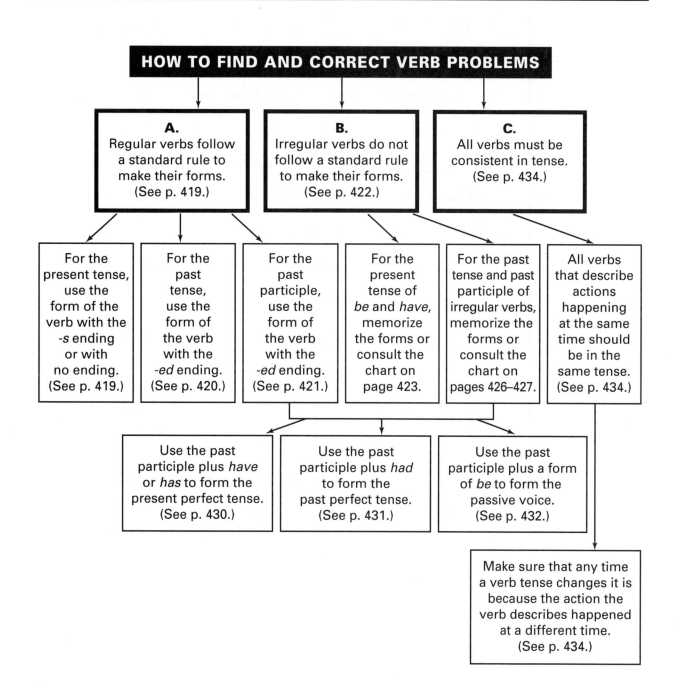

Chapter Review: Pronouns

1. Pronouns replace _____ or _____ in a sentence. (See p. 443.)

2. A pronoun must agree with (match) the noun or pronoun it replaces in _____ and _____. (See p. 444.)

3. An _____ does not refer to a specific person, place, or thing. (See p. 445.) What are three examples of this kind of pronoun? _____

4. A _____ names a group that acts as a single unit. (See p. 446.) What are two examples? _____

5. In an _____ pronoun reference, the pronoun could refer to more than one noun. (See p. 448.)

6. In a _____ pronoun reference, the pronoun does not refer clearly to any particular person or thing. (See p. 449.)

7. In a _____ pronoun reference, the pronoun repeats a reference to a noun rather than replacing it. (See p. 449.)

8. Subject pronouns serve as the subject of a verb. Write a sentence using a subject pronoun. (See p. 452.) _____

_____

9. What are two other types of pronouns? (See p. 453.)

_____

10. What are three trouble spots in pronoun use? (See p. 453.)

_____

_____

_____

11. When you must decide whether to use *who* or *whom,* use the following

    technique: Use *who* when the pronoun is followed by a _____.

    Use *whom* when the pronoun is followed by a _____.

    (See p. 457.)

12. What are examples of first-, second-, and third-person pronouns?

    (See p. 458.)

    First person: _____

    Second person: _____

    Third person: _____

13. Pronouns should be _____ in person. (See p. 458.)

Quick Review Chart: Pronouns

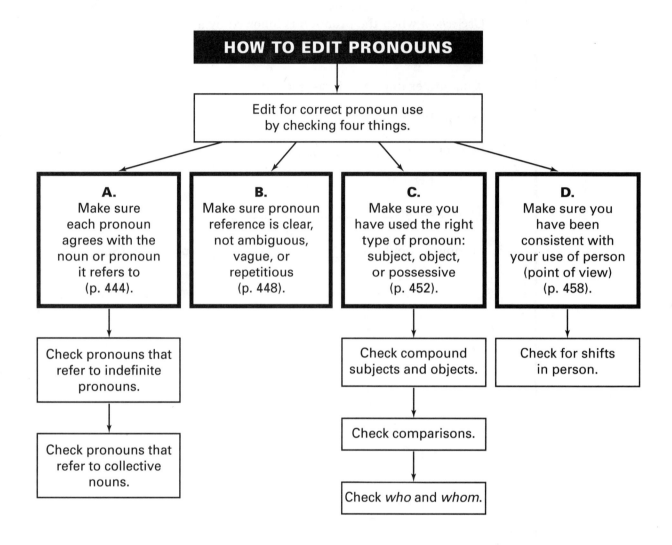

Chapter Review: Adjectives and Adverbs

1. Adjectives and adverbs describe or _____ (give more information about) other words. (See p. 465.)

2. Adjectives modify _____ and _____. (See p. 465.)

3. Adverbs modify _____, _____, or _____. (See p. 465.)

4. Many adverbs are formed by adding an _____ ending to an adjective. (See p. 466.)

5. The comparative form of an adjective or adverb is used to compare how many people, places, or things? _____ It is formed by adding an _____ ending or the word _____. (See p. 467.)

6. The superlative form of an adjective or adverb is used to compare how many people, places, or things? _____ It is formed by adding an _____ ending or the word _____. (See p. 467.)

7. What four words have irregular comparative and superlative forms? (See p. 469.)

   _____

8. *Good* is an (adjective/adverb) and *well* is an (adjective/adverb). (See p. 469.)

Quick Review Chart: Adjectives and Adverbs

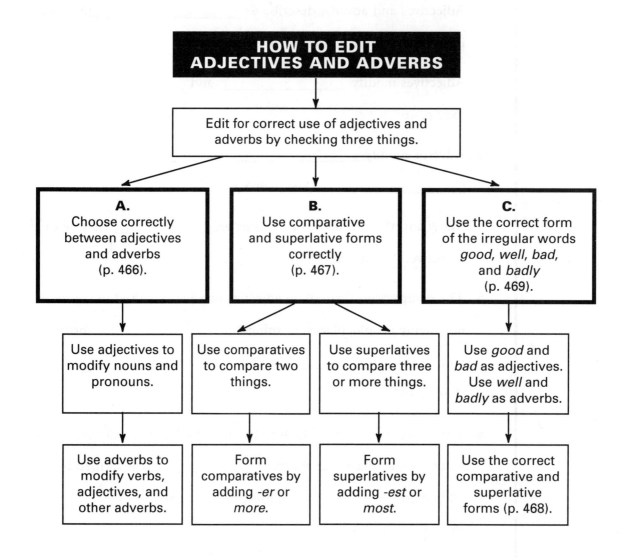

HOW TO EDIT ADJECTIVES AND ADVERBS

Edit for correct use of adjectives and adverbs by checking three things.

A.
Choose correctly between adjectives and adverbs (p. 466).

B.
Use comparative and superlative forms correctly (p. 467).

C.
Use the correct form of the irregular words *good, well, bad,* and *badly* (p. 469).

Use adjectives to modify nouns and pronouns.

Use comparatives to compare two things.

Use superlatives to compare three or more things.

Use *good* and *bad* as adjectives. Use *well* and *badly* as adverbs.

Use adverbs to modify verbs, adjectives, and other adverbs.

Form comparatives by adding *-er* or *more*.

Form superlatives by adding *-est* or *most*.

Use the correct comparative and superlative forms (p. 468).

Chapter Review: Misplaced and Dangling Modifiers

1. _____ are words or word groups that give more information

   about other words in a sentence. (See p. 475.)

2. A _____ describes the wrong sentence element

   because it is incorrectly placed within the sentence. (See p. 475.)

3. When an opening modifier does not modify any word in the sentence,

   it is a _____. (See p. 475.)

4. Edit both misplaced and dangling modifiers by making sure that

   a. the sentence element to be modified is _____ the

      sentence. (See p. 478.)

   b. it is placed as _____ as possible to the modifier.

      (See p. 476.)

Quick Review Chart: Misplaced and Dangling Modifiers

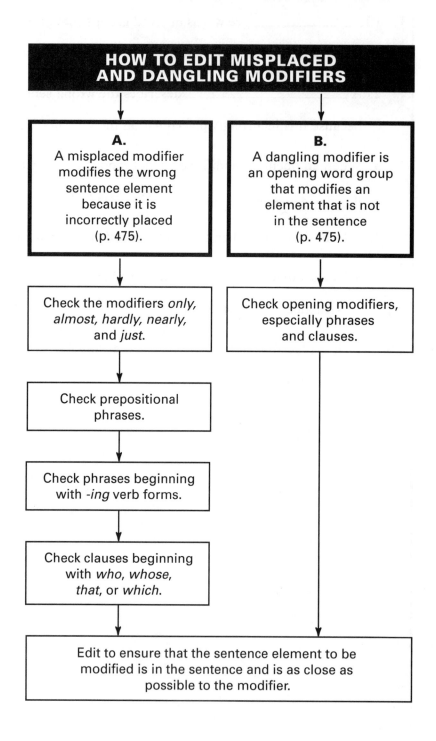

HOW TO EDIT MISPLACED AND DANGLING MODIFIERS

A.
A misplaced modifier modifies the wrong sentence element because it is incorrectly placed (p. 475).

B.
A dangling modifier is an opening word group that modifies an element that is not in the sentence (p. 475).

Check the modifiers *only, almost, hardly, nearly,* and *just.*

Check opening modifiers, especially phrases and clauses.

Check prepositional phrases.

Check phrases beginning with *-ing* verb forms.

Check clauses beginning with *who, whose, that,* or *which.*

Edit to ensure that the sentence element to be modified is in the sentence and is as close as possible to the modifier.

Chapter Review: Coordination and Subordination

1. _____ and _____ can be used to join sentences with related ideas. (See p. 483.)

2. _____ can be used to join two sentences when the ideas in them are equally important. (See p. 483.)

3. Subordination can be used to join two sentences when one idea is

   _____ . (See p. 483.)

4. What are two ways of joining sentences through coordination? (See pp. 484 and 487.)

   _____

   _____

5. List five common coordinating conjunctions. (See p. 484.)

   _____

6. List five common subordinating conjunctions. (See p. 489.)

   _____

Quick Review Chart: Coordination and Subordination

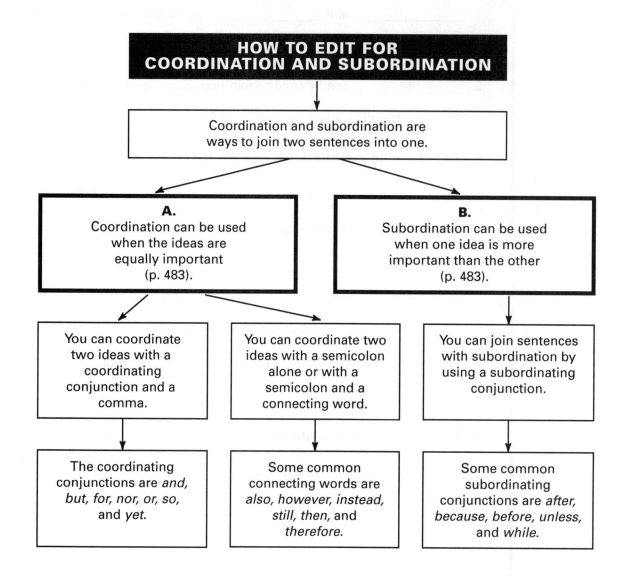

HOW TO EDIT FOR COORDINATION AND SUBORDINATION

Coordination and subordination are ways to join two sentences into one.

A.
Coordination can be used when the ideas are equally important (p. 483).

B.
Subordination can be used when one idea is more important than the other (p. 483).

You can coordinate two ideas with a coordinating conjunction and a comma.

You can coordinate two ideas with a semicolon alone or with a semicolon and a connecting word.

You can join sentences with subordination by using a subordinating conjunction.

The coordinating conjunctions are *and, but, for, nor, or, so,* and *yet.*

Some common connecting words are *also, however, instead, still, then,* and *therefore.*

Some common subordinating conjunctions are *after, because, before, unless,* and *while.*

Chapter Review: Parallelism

1. Parallelism in writing means that _____

_____ (See p. 497.)

2. In what three situations do problems with parallelism most often

occur? (See pp. 498, 499, and 501.)

_____

3. What are three pairs of correlative conjunctions? (See p. 501.)

_____

Quick Review Chart: Parallelism

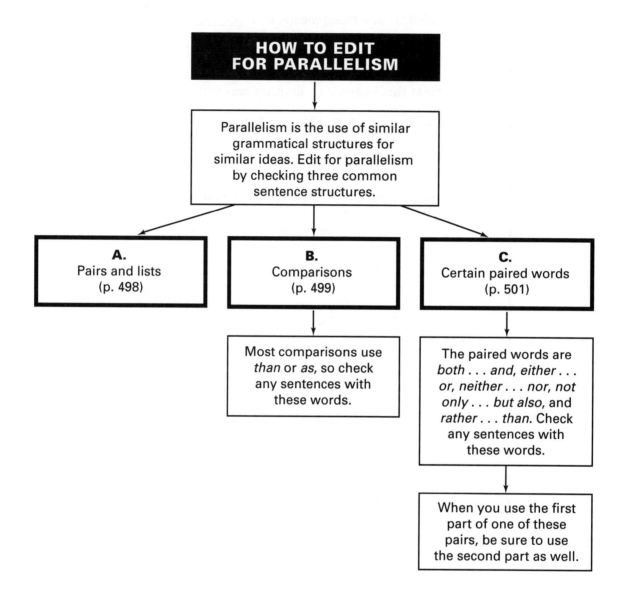

Chapter Review: Sentence Variety

1. Having sentence variety means _____

   _____ . (See p. 507.)

2. If you tend to write short, similar-sounding sentences, what five

   techniques should you try? (See pp. 508, 510, 513, 517, and 519.)

   _____

   _____

   _____

   _____

   _____

3. An _____ is a phrase that renames a noun. (See p. 517.)

4. An _____ clause starts with *who*, _____ ,

   or _____ . It modifies or describes a noun or pronoun.

   (See p. 519.)

5. Use commas around an adjective clause when the information

   in it is (essential/not essential) to the meaning of the sentence.

   (See pp. 520–521.)

Quick Review Chart: Sentence Variety

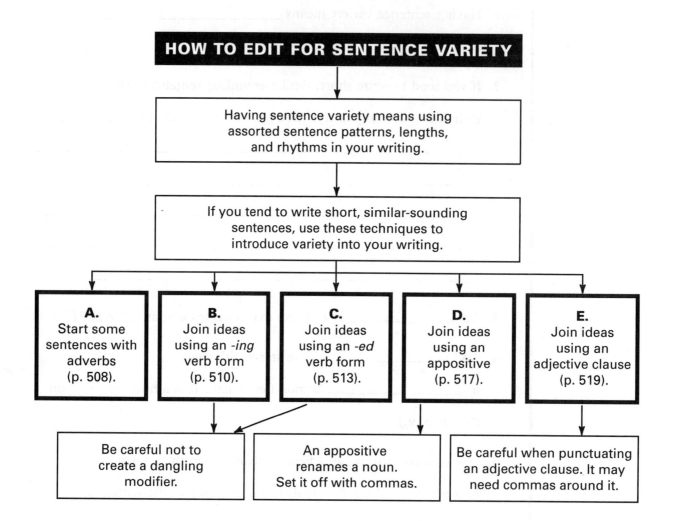

HOW TO EDIT FOR SENTENCE VARIETY

Having sentence variety means using assorted sentence patterns, lengths, and rhythms in your writing.

If you tend to write short, similar-sounding sentences, use these techniques to introduce variety into your writing.

A. Start some sentences with adverbs (p. 508).

B. Join ideas using an *-ing* verb form (p. 510).

C. Join ideas using an *-ed* verb form (p. 513).

D. Join ideas using an appositive (p. 517).

E. Join ideas using an adjective clause (p. 519).

Be careful not to create a dangling modifier.

An appositive renames a noun. Set it off with commas.

Be careful when punctuating an adjective clause. It may need commas around it.

Quick Review: ESL Concerns

1. A noun is _____ . (See p. 528.)

2. A count noun names _____ .

   (See p. 528.)

3. A noncount noun names _____ .

   (See p. 528.)

4. List the three articles used with nouns. _____ (See p. 528.)

5. If the identity of a noun is known, what article do you use?

   _____ (See p. 529.)

6. Use the article _____ for singular count nouns when their

   identity is unknown or not specific. (See p. 529.)

7. Use _____ before words that start with a consonant sound.

   Use _____ before words that start with a vowel sound. (See

   p. 528.)

8. A gerund is _____ .

   (See p. 530.)

9. An infinitive is _____ .

   (See p. 530.)

10. The progressive tense of a verb is used when an action is _____

    _____ . (See p. 532.)

11. List five common phrases in which an adjective is followed by a

    preposition. _____

    _____ (See p. 533.)

12. What are five common verb-plus-preposition phrases? _____

_____ . (See p. 534.)

13. When you are turning a statement into a question, move the

_____ so that it comes before the _____ .

(See p. 536.)

14. In the following sentence, fill in the blanks with adjectives using the

conventional order for adjectives. (See p. 538.)

My _____ , _____ , _____ ,

_____ uncle is visiting for a month.

Chapter Review: Word Choice

1. What two resources will help you choose the best words for your meaning? (See p. 543.) _____

_____

2. What are four common word-choice problems? (See pp. 544, 546, 547, 549.)

_____

_____

3. Replace vague and abstract words with _____ and

_____ words. (See p. 545.)

4. When is it appropriate to use slang in college writing or in writing at work? (See p. 546.)

_____

_____

5. What are three common kinds of wordy language? (See p. 547.)

_____

_____

_____

6. _____ are phrases that are overused. Why should you avoid them in your writing? (See p. 549.)

Quick Review Chart: Word Choice

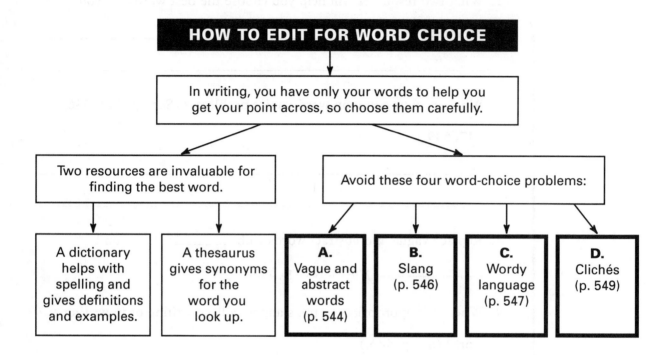

HOW TO EDIT FOR WORD CHOICE

In writing, you have only your words to help you get your point across, so choose them carefully.

Two resources are invaluable for finding the best word.

Avoid these four word-choice problems:

A dictionary helps with spelling and gives definitions and examples.

A thesaurus gives synonyms for the word you look up.

A. Vague and abstract words (p. 544)

B. Slang (p. 546)

C. Wordy language (p. 547)

D. Clichés (p. 549)

Chapter Review: Commonly Confused Words

1. What are four strategies you can use to avoid confusing words that

   sound alike or have similar meanings? (See p. 554.)

   _____

   _____

   _____

   _____

2. What are the top five commonly confused words on your personal list?

   _____

Chapter Review: Spelling

1. What are two important tools for good spelling? (See p. 569.)

   _____

2. What three steps can you use for finding and correcting spelling

   mistakes? (See pp. 570–571.) _____

   _____

3. What four strategies can you use to become a better speller?

   (See pp. 572–573.)

   _____

   _____

   _____

   _____

4. What are the six spelling rules presented in this chapter?

   (See pp. 573–576.)

   _____

   _____

   _____

   _____

   _____

   _____

5. What are five of your own spelling demons?

   _____

   _____

Chapter Review: Commas

1. A comma (**,**) is a _____ that helps readers understand your sentence. (See p. 583.)

2. How do you use commas in these three situations? (See pp. 584, 585, 587.)

   In a series of items, _____

   In a compound sentence, _____

   _____

   _____

   When there is an introductory word group, _____

   _____

3. An appositive comes before or after a noun or pronoun and

   _____ . (See p. 589.)

4. An interrupter is an _____ that interrupts the flow of a sentence. (See p. 589.)

5. Put commas around an adjective clause when it is _____ to the meaning of a sentence. (See p. 591.)

6. How are commas used with quotation marks? _____

   _____ . (See p. 594.)

7. In a date with the month, the day, and the year, a comma goes

   _____ . (See p. 594.)

Chapter Review: Apostrophes

1. An apostrophe (') is a punctuation mark that usually either shows _____ or indicates where a letter or letters have been left out in a _____. (See p. 599.)

2. To show ownership, add _____ to a singular noun, even if the noun already ends in -*s*. For a plural noun, add an _____ alone if the noun ends in -*s*; add _____ if the noun does not end in -*s*. (See pp. 599–600.)

3. Do not use an apostrophe with a _____ pronoun. (See p. 600.)

4. Do not confuse *its* and *it's*. *Its* shows _____; *it's* is a _____ meaning "it is." (See p. 600.)

5. A _____ is formed by joining two words and leaving out one or more of the letters. Use an apostrophe to show where _____ . (See p. 601.)

6. Use -'s to make letters and numbers _____. (See p. 603.)

7. Use an apostrophe or -'s in certain expressions in which _____ are treated as if they possess something. (See p. 603.)

Chapter Review: Quotation Marks

1. Quotation marks look like this: _____ . They always

   appear in (pairs/triples). (See p. 607.)

2. A quotation is the report of _____ . (See p. 607.)

3. A direct quotation is the exact _____ of what someone

   (or some outside source) said or wrote. (Use/Do not use) quotation

   marks around direct quotations. (See p. 607.)

4. An indirect quotation is _____ .

   (Use/Do not use) quotation marks with indirect quotations. (See p. 607.)

5. To set off a quotation within a quotation, use _____ .

   (See p. 609.)

6. Put quotation marks around the titles of short works such as (give four

   examples) _____ . (See p. 611.)

7. For longer works such as magazines, novels, books, newspapers, and

   so on, either _____ or _____ the titles.

   (See p. 611.)

Chapter Review: Other Punctuation

1. Semicolons (;) can be used to _____

   and to _____ .

   (See p. 616.)

2. Colons (:) can be used in what three ways? (See p. 616.)

   _____

   _____

   _____

3. A colon in a sentence must always be used after an _____

   _____ .

   (See p. 617.)

4. Parentheses ( ) set off information that is _____ to a

   sentence. (See p. 617.)

5. _____ also set off information in a sentence,

   usually information that _____ .

   (See p. 617.)

6. Hyphens (-) can be used in what two ways? (See p. 618.) To join two

   or more words that together _____

   and to _____ a word at the end of a line.

Chapter Review: Other Capitalization

1. Capitalize the _____ of every new sentence. (See p. 622.)

2. Capitalize the first letter in names of specific _____,

   _____, _____, _____. (See p. 622.)

3. Capitalize the first letter of _____ in titles.

   (See p. 625.)